NEW WR[...]

New Writing 9 is the ninth volume of an a[...] anthology which promotes the best in contemporary literature. It brings together some of our most formidable talent, placing new names alongside more established ones, and includes poetry, essays, short stories and extracts from novels in progress. Distinctive, innovative and entertaining, it is essential reading for all those interested in British writing today. *New Writing 9* is published by Vintage, in association with the British Council.

John Fowles was born in 1926 and educated at Oxford after which he taught English in France and Greece. Since 1963 he has been a full-time writer. His novels include *The Collector, The Magus, The French Lieutenant's Woman, The Ebony Tower, Daniel Martin, Mantissa* and *A Maggot*. He has also published *The Aristos: a self-portrait in ideas, Islands, The Tree* and *Sleep Holm: a case history in the study of evolution*, and has edited John Aubrey's *Monumenta Brittanica*.

A. L. Kennedy has published three collections of short stories, *Night Geometry and the Garscadden Trains, Now That You're Back* and *Original Bliss*, and three novels, *Looking for the Possible Dance, So I Am Glad* and, most recently, *Everything You Need*, and has won numerous literary awards. She was listed among the *Granta/Sunday Times* Twenty Best of Young British Novelists. Her first full-length film, *Stella Does Tricks*, was released in 1998. She is a Fellow of the Royal Society of Literature.

Also available from Vintage

New Writing 4
ed. A. S. Byatt and Alan Hollinghurst

New Writing 5
ed. Christopher Hope and Peter Porter

New Writing 6
ed. A. S. Byatt and Peter Porter

New Writing 7
ed. Carmen Callil and Craig Raine

New Writing 8
ed. Tibor Fischer and Lawrence Norfolk

NEW
WRITING
9

edited by

JOHN FOWLES
and
A. L. KENNEDY

V

VINTAGE

in association with
The British Council

Published by Vintage 2000

2 4 6 8 10 9 7 5 3 1

Collection copyright © The British Council 2000
Edited by John Fowles and A. L. Kennedy
For copyright of contributors see page viii

The editors and contributors have asserted their rights
under the Copyright, Designs and Patents Act, 1988 to be
identified as the authors of this work

This book is sold subject to the condition that it shall not,
by way of trade or otherwise, be lent, resold, hired out, or
otherwise circulated without the publisher's prior consent in
any form of binding or cover other than that in which it is
published and without a similar condition including this
condition being imposed on the subsequent purchaser

Vintage
Random House, 20 Vauxhall Bridge Road, London SW1V 2SA

Random House Australia (Pty) Limited
20 Alfred Street, Milsons Point, Sydney
New South Wales 2061, Australia

Random House New Zealand Limited
18 Poland Road, Glenfield,
Auckland 10, New Zealand

Random House (Pty) Limited
Endulini, 5A Jubilee Road, Parktown 2193, South Africa

The Random House Group Limited Reg. No. 954009
www.randomhouse.co.uk

A CIP catalogue record for this book
is available from the British Library

ISBN 0 099289946

Papers used by Random House are natural,
recyclable products made from wood grown in
sustainable forests; the manufacturing processes
conform to the environmental regulations of the
country of origin

Typeset by Deltatype Ltd, Birkenhead, Merseyside
Printed and bound in Great Britain by
Cox & Wyman, Reading, Berkshire

A VINTAGE ORIGINAL

CONTENTS

CONTENTS

vi

CONTENTS

Collection copyright © British Council 2000 edited by John Fowles and A. L. Kennedy

Introduction copyright © A. L. Kennedy 2000; *Flypaper* copyright © Simon Armitage 2000; *The Track* copyright © Trezza Azzopardi 2000; *An Afternoon in Murania* copyright © Paul Bailey 2000; *Dominion* copyright © Peter Benson 2000; *Adult Video* copyright © William Boyd 1999; 'Adam and Eve', 'Kestrel' *and* 'The Miracle' copyright © John Burnside 2000; 'The Land Bridge' copyright © Harry Clifton 2000; *The St Andrews Question* copyright © Robert Crawford 2000; *Lennon's Guitar* copyright © Philip Davison 2000; *London Voices* copyright © Louis de Bernières 1999; *Diamond Dust* copyright © Anita Desai 2000; 'The Excuse', 'Reprimands' *and* 'A Sicilian Defence' copyright © Michael Donaghy 2000; 'The Kingdom of Mud' *and* 'Sarkazo' copyright © Vicki Feaver 2000; *Spinach* copyright © Neil Ferguson 2000; *Bad Ju-Ju* copyright © Carlo Gebler 2000; *Big Pockets with Buttoned Flaps* copyright © Alasdair Gray 2000; 'Mephisto' copyright © Lavinia Greenlaw 2000; *The Best Death Ever* copyright © Niall Griffiths 2000; *The Retaining Wall* copyright © Abdulrazak Gurnah 2000; *The Vampires* copyright © Brooke Biaz 2000; *The Children's Day* copyright © Michiel Heyns 2000; *Biography and Death* copyright © Richard Holmes 1998; *Your Novel Needs Indexing* copyright © Robert Irwin 2000; *A Christmas Letter* copyright © Rosie Jackson 2000; 'American Mountain I, II and III' copyright © James Lasdun 2000; *A Small Matter for Your Attention* copyright © Toby Litt 2000; *Tortoises and Bats* copyright © John Logan 2000; 'Paper Boats' *and* 'Scrap Metal' copyright © Michael Longley 2000; 'Virtual Memories' copyright © James McGonigal and Hamish Whyte 2000; 'Harvesting' *and* 'The Belen' copyright © Jamie McKendrick 2000; *I Want Doesn't Get* copyright © Duncan McLean 2000; *Diamond Ella* copyright © David McVey 2000; *The Search for the Lost Condom* copyright © Stuart Marlow 2000; *Garden of Nails* copyright © Adrian Mathews 2000; *Blueprint* copyright © Sarah May 2000; 'The Poet and the Assassin' copyright © Edwin Morgan 2000; 'Moonlighter' *and* 'Clearing a Name' copyright © David Morley 2000; *Being Translated, or the Virgin Mary's Hair* copyright © Lawrence Norfolk 2000; *Morose Delectation* copyright © Julia O'Faolain 2000; 'The Phoenix' copyright © Ruth Padel 2000; *Eros* copyright © Tim Parks 1997; 'Aphorisms' copyright © Don Paterson 2000; *Just Like Him* copyright © Glenn Patterson 2000; 'Northern Lights' *and* 'Orlando's Parrot' copyright © Peter Porter 2000; 'Waking Late' *and* 'Anxiety #101' copyright © Robin Robertson 2000; 'Big in Japan' *and* 'Fruit' copyright © Neil Rollinson 2000; *There's a Lot of Room* copyright © Eva Salzman 2000; 'Dungeness' *and* 'At Chesil' copyright © Derek Sellen 2000; *The People We Want* copyright © Neil Stewart 2000; 'The Attic' *and* 'A Day in Calcutta' copyright © Matthew Sweeney 2000; *Mercenary* copyright © Adam Thorpe 2000; *A Romance Meat* copyright © Jonathan Treitel 2000; *The Stack* copyright © Rose Tremain 1996; *The Spaces in Houses* copyright © Vivienne Vermes 2000; *Let the Worms Carry Us to Heaven* copyright © Alan Warner 2000; *Hate Songs for Emily* copyright © Marc Weinberg 2000; 'Switch on the Waves' copyright © Hamish Whyte 2000; *Mini-Joe* copyright © Jonathan Wilson 2000.

INTRODUCTION

THIS IS THE part of anthologies that I always tend to skip. Readers come to books for the writing, after all, and if that can't speak for itself then it's surely beyond whatever help a few introductory nudges might provide. Still, at the opening of an anthology such as this – a type of annual literary census of British writing – a case could be made for a few words to set a disparate collection into context, to particularly highlight the many strengths of the writing here and to act as a vote of thanks to the contributing authors.

Because editors of *New Writing*, it should be remembered, occupy positions of virtually helpless responsibility. Beyond busying themselves with prayer and begging letters, they spend much of their time simply waiting for work of quality to arrive: work with an unmistakable voice, work with a sense of its own confirmed life. Beyond this rather unhelpful definition, an editor is powerless to describe what it is that she or he expects to find in the next A4 envelope – the whole, worrying point being that good writing will surely declare itself, but only as and when it comes to hand. Fortunately, from a waist-high stack of submissions to *New Writing 9*, a shin-high stack of indispensable inclusions emerged. And, although this would seem to defy logic, the pleasure in discovering a new piece of real quality never diminished, was never blurred away by the kind of homicidal boredom that an unremitting succession of much less happy manuscripts will tend to produce. This introduction would not be complete without a payment of editorial respects to all our contributors – your work has been the making of us.

For the information of those readers intending to cherry-pick through only the names they recognise, I will point out that this year's volume contains startling and enjoyable work from newcomers. We have also been happy to welcome established writers' proof of why they are established, including several excursions into relatively unfamiliar forms. In fact *New Writing 9*, as might be expected from such a large anthology, plays host to a remarkable variety of forms and styles. It is generously supplied with short stories, poetry, essays, reflections and reminiscences. Locations range across most points of possibility and occasionally leave all available maps, world views may be painstaking, playful, sober-sided, paranoid or vigorously demented, vocabularies defend their particular dignities with eloquence and life's two most important horizontals – death and sex – often feature prominently. This is British writing, but like any writing of quality, it deals with the universals of human experience: love, joy, loss, bewilderment, jealousy, anger, pain, fear: the usual emotional alphabet. The desires and necessities of body and soul are international.

This is British writing or – more properly – writing from authors who feel some relationship with Britain and with the English language. The frictions and developing definitions within these two relationships give much of the work its energy. Marginalised experiences are staking out their own territories here and celebrating the voices best suited to their natures. The reality of Britain as an island filled with different experiences, different identities, is plainly displayed. The reality of English as a living, mutating variety of world languages, each capable of enriching and interrogating the others, is celebrated by individuals united in the human desire to communicate, to build something out of nothing, to share a leap of faith.

A. L. Kennedy

Glenn Patterson

JUST LIKE HIM

I AM NOT, I don't think, a bad person. Certainly not in that glamorous 'mad and dangerous to know' way. Nevertheless, I have done many things in my life which I would consider less than good; things of which I am not proud, even ashamed. Several years ago I behaved badly to someone with whom I had been in love. I met someone else and fell in love with her. I returned to Belfast from England, where I had been living for most of the past decade, to look for a place to live with my new love. The circumstances were shoddy, yet in my heart I knew that what I was doing was right. Right for me, right for the person I had come back to Ireland to be with. For a few weeks, while I searched for a flat (my lover had not yet moved from her home in Cork), I stayed with my parents, in the housing estate where I had lived until going across the water to university.

My parents were trying very hard to understand why I had ended my relationship in England. They had been fond of my partner, loved her like the daughter-in-law which in law she was not. They were trying hard to love me as their son the same way they had loved me before they knew I was unfaithful and hurtful.

It was late spring. My parents went out for frequent walks. I spent a lot of time in the back garden, smoking. I was in the house alone one night when there came a knock at the door. Two men stood on the doorstep. I remembered them both from my youth, though I hadn't seen either of them for a

1

good many years. I remembered them as loyalists, hard men. They remembered me.

'Glenda,' one of them said.

Glenda is what some of the people on my estate began calling me when I came home for my first summer vacation from university. I had taken to wearing nail varnish while I was away, dyeing my hair and crimping it. I had taken to wearing tight black leggings and carrying a shoulder bag (handbag, these people preferred to think of it as), sometimes black, sometimes pink. I kept my hairspray in it.

Of course, back then, their ridicule didn't bother me. I invited it. Their ridicule was a measure of the difference between us and I was determined to be as different as I could possibly be from the people I had left behind.

By the time I returned to live with my parents I had published two novels. I had written articles and made television documentaries in many of which I had been critical of the values and beliefs of my Ulster Protestant background. My hair may no longer have been crimped, but I had succeeded in becoming someone completely other than the person I had been when these men and I were teenagers together.

'Glenda. How's it going?'

There were, I noticed, looking out from the hallway, other men at other doors in my parents' street. They all had collecting tins. I had been away from home for a long time, but not so long that I had forgotten what door-to-door collections in spring were for.

'Do you want to give something for the new band uniforms?'

The band was our local flute band. They had the reputation of being loud and aggressive: 'blood and thunder' is the old-fashioned term; 'kick the Pope' they would be called today.

Every year before the Orange marching season began, members of flute bands would go round the doors of their areas collecting money. Uniforms, was what they usually said, though I didn't know too many people who asked to see proof of purchase.

It was part of who I had become that I did not like Orange marches or flute bands. It was part of who I had become that I accused those who turned out to watch them of condoning and perpetuating sectarianism. Mostly, though, I had been proclaiming this all-new me while living away from Belfast.

I was feeling a little vulnerable that spring. The woman I had fallen in love with and who was coming to Belfast to live with me was from south of the border. I was not sure as yet where we would end up having to live. I couldn't guarantee that I wouldn't be seeing a lot more of the local flute band.

So when the men rattled their collecting tin again, I went in to the living room of my parents' house and found my wallet.

'My dad would probably have given you something if he was in,' I said as I dropped a pound coin into the tin.

Of all the things that I did in those weeks, that is the worst, the one I am most ashamed of.

When my parents returned some time later I told them what had happened.

'I wouldn't have given them a penny,' my father said.

As I knew he would.

The night my mother met him, New Year's Eve, 1951, she heard his friends call him the Big Wheel.

She knew he was from the market town of Lisburn, she knew his surname was Patterson. She knew there was a department store in Lisburn, J.C. Patterson's. Lisburn, Patterson, the Big Wheel. It all added up very nicely.

In fact, my father's father worked at Lisburn's linen bleaching greens. It was messy, poorly-paid work. There *had* been 'money', and property, in the family, a generation earlier, but it was drunk and gambled away . . . unusually for the time, by my great-grandmother. My grandfather was born eight years before the end of the last century. He was forty when my father, the second youngest of five children, was born in 1932. Perhaps inevitably, given the reversal in the family fortunes, my grandfather was a deeply religious man, a strict teetotaller. He plucked the name for his second youngest from the Gospel According to St Matthew, Chapter 1, Verse 3:

And Judas begat Phares and Zara of Thamar; and Phares begat Esrom; and Esrom begat Aram.

He called his son, my father, Phares. Pronounced Ferris. As in the fairground wheel.

By the time the pun dawned on my mother, it was too late. She was smitten.

My mother's name is Nessie. Short for Agnes. (She had an aunt called Agnes and the choice, if she was to be distinguished from her in conversation, was between Aggie and Nessie, and Aggie, to the child my mother was, was too old a name.) Like my father's, my mother's is not a name you hear every day. Nessies, I imagine, must dream of a John or a David to absorb a little of their strangeness; Phareses of a Mary or an Anne. But this Nessie and Phares found one another.

They were married in Canada. My mother's parents had emigrated there, six months after she and my father met. My mother had intended to stay at home, but when her younger brother fell sick shortly after arriving in Canada, she went out to join the rest of her family. My father at once gave up his job and followed her.

This was the beginning of the 1950s. For a young man like my father, it must have seemed as though there would always be jobs, wherever he went; but still, giving up the job he had on an impulse was, as they say here, just like him.

When he was fourteen and old enough to leave school, he had been offered a job at the BBC radio transmitter outside Lisburn: a glorified tea boy, but even in those early days of broadcasting, even without hindsight, surely an exciting opportunity, a foot in the door. My father turned down the job and went back to school after the summer vacation in order to be eligible for the Northern Ireland schoolboys' football trials. He had good cause for thinking he might make the squad: an uncle, who played semi-professionally in the Irish League, told me recently my father was the best left-sided player he had ever seen. He made the last-but-one cut.

The final trial, though, did not go well. (The day got off to an inauspicious start. The trialists had been sent the shirts they were to wear in advance. One of the selectors complained about the state of my father's. 'It looks like you slept in it,' he said. Which was exactly what my father had done. Well, he explained to me, he'd never had a proper football shirt before.) He left school immediately on hearing he had not been selected for the schoolboys' squad. The vacancy at the BBC had been filled, of course. Instead, my father was apprenticed as a sheet metal worker to the Ulster Transport Authority, at the bus depot overlooked by Lisburn Central, his old school.

In Canada he worked in a textiles' factory and played amateur football for Galt Celtic, a team made up of recent Irish immigrants. Opposing teams included English immigrants (Hespler Hotspur) and Italian (Internazionale of Guelph). He was known to his team-mates as Pat Patterson. He and my mother had three sons in a little under four years. This being North America, they had, for young married people, a good life. But my father was homesick. His relatives in Lisburn sent him reel-to-reel tapes of family singsongs: sentimental standards, for the most part, 'The Mountains of Mourne', 'That Little Old Mud Cabin on the Hill'.

Possibly against my mother's wishes, my parents came back to Belfast in the final months of the 1950s. They thought they would like to have an Irish girl to go with their three Canadian boys. So they tried for another baby, and they got me. Glenda.

My father was back in work again within days of his return home. He had a spell in the shipyard, where the last of the great Belfast liners, the *Canberra*, was under construction, and then moved to an electronics firm in the east of the city. (These were the days when computers were the size of small houses and were built by sheet metal workers.) A short time after he started in this job, one of his colleagues was sacked for taking time off to get married. The workforce went on strike to get the colleague reinstated. The dispute, dubbed the Honeymoon Strike, made the Belfast papers. My mother told me not long ago that she and my father, with four young sons, were hit so hard by that strike, that for years afterwards they were, financially speaking, running to stand still.

I don't know how the strike ended, but whether or not the colleague got his old job back he was soon in another, better one. I remember visiting him and his wife when I was still quite young in their new bungalow in Belfast's northern suburbs. If I think of the Sixties, in fact, the Sixties as aspired to rather than the Sixties as they were lived by most in our provincial city, the Sixties distinct from the violence which came at the end of them, I most often think of that bungalow and the couple who owned it.

I believe they left Belfast soon after the Troubles began.

My father then was thirty-seven, the age I am today.

My father and I are father and son, which is to say we are close without knowing very much about one another. We talk about events, rather than emotions. We keep from each other certain of our hopes and fears and doubts. I have never, for instance, asked my father whether he has dwelt on the direction his life might have taken if at certain moments he had made certain other choices. (That my being here to want to ask him is dependent upon the choices he did make is not, of course, lost on me.) Whatever, while my father was still in his thirties he found himself, with a million and a half of his fellows, living in what was in all but name a civil war.

As a person who came to full consciousness *in media res*, I try often to imagine what it must be like to be faced with such a situation. What, in the previous course of your life, prepares you for arriving, as my father did, at the scene of a bomb blast close to your brother's place of work and seeing what you suppose, from the colour of the hair, to be your brother lying in the road, only to find that you are cradling the remains of a woman?

I have, in my fiction, returned to this question repeatedly. It has occurred to me recently that I have written a lot about my father.

Some of my father's other friends left Belfast in those early years of the unrest. One friend, Joe, took his family to Boston after his teenage son came under pressure to involve himself in street violence. Joe's family and my own lived a mile apart, in estates, lying at either end of an east-west aligned road, which were mirror images of each other. Joe's estate, like Joe and his family, was, according to the only definition that seemed to matter any more, Catholic; our estate was Protestant.

In both places, at the turn of the Seventies, there sprang up vigilante groups. (At the time I thought the term a Belfast invention.) The fear in those days was of mobile squads of gunmen, touring the night-time streets. My father took his turn with the rest of our adult male neighbours and stood at the entrance of the estate after dark on the lookout for suspicious cars.

Perhaps he only did this for a matter of weeks, perhaps it was many months. (I was, you have to remember, asleep while all of this activity was going on.) What is certain is that he ceased as soon as he realised that the moment for ad-hoc, unarmed vigilante groups was about to be overtaken.

Some time in the summer of 1972, the Ulster Defence Association began drilling on the playing fields of our estate. The U.D.A. originated as an umbrella organisation for vigilante groups, though they appeared to me, a child watching them, composed of a younger element than the original vigilantes. They wore uniforms of denim jackets and bush hats, jeans and Dr Marten boots. Many wore hankies over the lower half of their faces. Undoubtedly, as with the I.R.A., there were still men in the U.D.A.'s ranks who were much like my father. Men who had taken the decision, however, based on what they understood or believed of the circumstances of that time, to go a step further than vigilantism. As with the I.R.A., a good many went a good deal further in the years that followed.

No longer merely 'Protestant', ours became known as a 'U.D.A.' area. Drinking clubs in the locality (and, with night-life in the city centre close to non-existent, all localities had them) were referred to as U.D.A. clubs, since it was generally assumed that takings from the bar and the slot machines went to fund the paramilitaries. There were other ways of funding. Protection money, like vigilantism, was another term I thought we Northern Irish had invented.

It must have been autumn 1972 when the U.D.A. came collecting door to door on our estate. The rumour preceded them: windows were being broken in houses whose occupants refused to donate. Like all the best rumours, this one had the virtue of plausibility. Even a passing acquaintance with the news confirmed that broken windows were the very least that might, at that stage of the 1970s, befall a person not supporting the cause.

As I recall it, the whole family – my mother, my father, my three brothers and I – were in our sitting room (which, with a settee and two armchairs, sat only five) when the knock came at our door. My father went to answer it.

I'm a fiction writer, so perhaps I do not actually remember my mother – when my father returned – her voice troubled, saying,

'Oh, Phares.'

He hadn't made a donation. But neither that night, nor the next, nor any of the nights that followed were our windows smashed.

I am not, as I said, a particularly bad man. My father, by the same token, is perhaps not an exceptionally good one, not a man without shortcomings and contradictions. His refusal to donate was a small act. (And I have no way of knowing how many other households responded in the same way.) Its significance, though, lies in the fact that, even at that time of extreme polarisation, it denied the legitimacy of claims that organisations like the U.D.A. spoke for 'their community'. Without the validation of people like my father, their community could only ever be the community of those who actively or tacitly supported them. It left a space between religion – an accident of birth – and political belief.

The very space I have tried all my adult life to live and work in.

By the way, it would be just like my father not to remember

that I contributed to the flute band, that spring evening in 1994, on the pretence of believing that he would have done so had he been at home.

My father would probably say it is just like me *to* remember and, remembering, to make such a big deal of it: what's past is past, he'd say, and there is no point dwelling on what cannot be changed.

Soon after the night of the flute band's visit, I found a small house for rent in the University area. I got the keys on May Day, the day before Ali, my new partner, the woman whom, in the abstract, my parents were opposed to, was to arrive in Belfast. My father and mother insisted on helping me clean the place from top to bottom. They were still there when I left to meet Ali off the train, but were gone an hour later when the taxi dropped us off at the front door. They had bought flowers, to make the place more welcoming for her.

And that, finally, is so like the two of them.

Alasdair Gray

BIG POCKETS WITH BUTTONED FLAPS

A MILD SEPTEMBER morning. A man no longer young strolls thoughtfully on a narrow footpath along a former railway line. Noises tell of a nearby motorway but brambles, elders and hawthorns on each side hide all but the straight empty path ahead until he sees a small clearing on his right. Two girls sit here at the foot of an old telegraph pole. He pauses, gazing up at the top of the pole, examining its cracked grey timber, cross-pieces with insulators like small white jam pots from which dangle broken wires. He has noticed the girls are in their teens, look surly and depressed, wear clumsy thick-soled boots and baggy military trousers from which rise pleasantly slim bodies. One says crossly, 'What are you staring at?'

'At the wires of that sad sad pole!' says the man without lowering his eyes, 'A few years ago they carried messages from this land of ours to a world-wide commercial empire.'

'A few years? It was yonks ago,' says the girl contemptuously. Without looking straight at her the man glimpses a stud piercing her lower lip and one through the wing of a nostril. He says, 'Yonks? Yes. I suppose this pole was defunct before you were born.'

He continues looking up at it until the other girl stands, stretches her arms, pretends to yawn, says 'I'll better away,' and goes off through the bushes. Her companion still sits as she did before the stroller arrived.

A minute later he takes a folded newspaper from his coat pocket, unfolds it, lays it on the grass where the departed girl sat, then sits carefully down with hands clasped round the knee of a bent leg. Looking sideways at the girl (who still pretends to ignore him) he says quietly, 'I must ask you a difficult question about . . . the eff word. Does it shock or annoy you? I don't mean when used as a swear word, I hate swearing, I mean when used as a word for the thing . . . the act lovers do together. Eh?'

After allowing her a moment to reply he speaks briskly as if they had reached an agreement.

'Now I fully realize that a lovely young woman like you –' (she sneers) '– don't sneer, has no wish to eff with a boring old fart like me in bushes beside a derelict railway line. But I suppose you are unemployed and need money?'

'Fucking right I do!' she cries.

'Don't swear. This is an unfair world but I am no hypocrite, I am glad I have money you need. We should therefore discuss how much I am willing to pay for what you are prepared to do. I promise that a wee chat will probably give all the satisfaction I need. I have never been greatly enamoured with the down-to-earth, flat-out business of effing.'

'Ten pounds!' says the girl, facing him at last. He nods and says, 'That is not unreasonable.'

'Ten pounds now! Nothing without cash up front!' she says, holding out a hand. From a wallet within his coat he gives her bank notes.

'Thanks,' she says, pocketing them and standing up, 'Cheerio.'

He looks up at her wistfully. She says, 'You're too weird for me as well as too old and you're right. This is an unfair world.'

She goes off through the bushes. He sighs and sits there, brooding.

Then hears a rustling of leaves. The other girl emerges and stands watching him. He ignores her until she says, 'I didnae really go away. I was listening all the time behind that bush I don't think you're weird. Not dangerous-weird. You're just . . . funny.'

'Name?' he asks drearily.

'Davida.'

'I thought the Scottish custom of making daughters' names out of fathers' names had died out.'

'It came back. What's your name?'

'I'm giving nothing else away today, Davida. Don't expect it.'

But he is looking at her. She grins cheerily back until he shrugs and pats the grass beside him. She hunkers down slightly further away, hugging her legs with both arms and asking brightly, 'What were you going to say to Sharon?'

'You too want cash from me.'

'Aye, some, but not as much as Sharon. Forget about money. Say what you like, I won't mind.'

He stares at her, opens his mouth, swallows, shuts his eyes tight and mutters 'Bigpocketswithbuttonedflaps.'

'Eh?'

'Big,' he explains deliberately, 'Pockets. With. Buttoned. Flaps. At last I have said it.'

'They turn you on?' says Davida, looking at her pockets in a puzzled way.

'Yes!' he says defiantly, 'Because violence is sexy! These pockets are military pockets with room for ammunition clips and grenades and iron rations. On women they look excitingly . . . deliciously . . . unsuitable.'

'Yes, I suppose that's why they're in fashion, but they're nothing to get excited about.'

'I enjoy being excited about them,' he groans, covering his face with his hands.

'Were you a school teacher?'

'You'll get nothing more out of me, Davida . . . Why do you think I was a teacher?'

'Because you're bossy as well as polite. Yes, and teachers have to pretend to be better than normal folk so they're bound to go a bit daft when they retire. What did you want to do with Sharon's pockets that was worth ten quid?'

He looks obstinately away from her.

'Did you want to stick your hands in them like THIS?' she

12

giggles, putting her hands in her pockets, 'Did you want to fumble about in them like THIS?'

'No more dirty talk!' orders a very tall thin youth emerging from the bushes, 'How dare you molest this young lady with obscene and suggestive insinuations?'

'ME molest HER? Ha!' cries the man and lies back flat on the grass with hands clasped behind head. He thinks it wise to look as relaxed and unchallenging as possible for he is now greatly outnumbered. Beside the tall youth is a small youth who looks more menacing because his face is expressionless, his head completely bald, and beside him stands Sharon saying scornfully, 'Big pockets with buttoned flaps!'

'You should have left us alone a bit longer,' grumbles Davida, 'He was starting to enjoy himself.'

'He was starting to enjoy his antisocial fetishistic propensities with a lassie young enough to be his grand-daughter!' cries the tall youth fiercely.

'Molesting two lassies in fifteen minutes!' says Sharon, 'We've witnesses to prove it. He's got to pay us for that.'

The man says, 'I've paid you already.'

'That . . . is not an attitude . . . I would advocate if you want to stay in one piece,' says the tall boy, slowly taking from a big pocket in his trousers a knife with a long blade. The smaller, more dangerous-looking youth says 'Hullo Mr McCorquodale.'

The man sits up to see him better and asks, 'How's the family Shon?'

'Dad isnae out yet but Sheila's doing well in TV rentals. She went to Australia.'

'Yes, Sheila was the smartest of you. I advised her to leave Scotland.'

'I KNEW he was a teacher,' says Davida smugly.

'You stupid fucking cretin!' the tall boy yells at the shorter one, 'If you'd kept out the way we could have rolled him for all he's got, buggered off and nothing would have happened! We don't live round here, we've no police record, nobody could have found us! But now he knows you we'll have to evade identification by cutting off his head and hands and burying them miles away!'

He saws the air wildly with the knife. The girls' faces express disgust. The smaller youth says mildly 'Don't do that to old Corky, he wasnae one of the worst.'

'Not one of the worst?' cries the ex-teacher jumping lightly to his feet, 'Did I not make my gym a living hell for you and your brothers? I also advise YOU,' he tells the taller youth, 'to put that knife away. You obviously don't know how to handle it.'

'And you do?' says the tall boy sarcastically.

'Yes son, I do. I belong to the generation that did National Service. Your combat training is all from television and video games. When eighteen I was taught armed AND unarmed combat by professional killers in the British army. Davida! Sharon! Shon! Persuade your friend to pocket that bread knife. Tell him he's a fine big fellow but I'm stronger than I look and if he's really interested in dirty fighting I can teach him tricks that'll have the eyes popping out of his head. Tell him I gave Sharon all the money I carry so if he needs more he'll have to come home with me.'

And McCorquodale smiles wistfully at the tall youth's combat trousers.

Michael Donaghy

A SICILIAN DEFENCE

It is another story altogether
by lanternlight, beneath two birches
and the sound of a shallow river
where two men are playing chess
for as long as either will remember,
opening King's pawn on e4 . . .
It's not a question of either/or –

One might be my father, or me at sixty.
The other might as well be me
thinking: his right's my left, my left
his right. I see it now in a different light.
I know it now by another name.

Is it any wonder then this game
runs on through this and every night
forever, lit by lanternlight, two birches
and the sound of a river?

REPRIMANDS

John 20: 24–29

We fell out of love as toddlers fall
glancing down, distracted, at their feet,
as the pianist in the concert hall
betrays her hands to thought and adds an extra beat –
The thought vertiginous. The reprimand.
It fells the bee mid-flight. It made me stall
before a holy water font in Rome

15

half afraid that if I dipped my hand
I'd find the water's surface hard as stone
and – this you'd never understand –
half afraid to leave the thing alone.
For I'd been taught that Jesus walked the sea
and came to Peter three leagues out of port.
Said Peter Bid me to come unto thee
and strode on faith dryfoot until he thought . . .
and thinking, sank. I'd never learnt to swim
but I'd seen insects skim across a pond
and I'd seen glasses filled above the brim.
Some firm conviction keeps a raindrop round.
What kept me rigid as a mannequin?

We fell out of love and nearly drowned.
The very wordlessness all lovers want
to feel beneath their feet like solid ground
dissolved to silences no human shout
could ripple –
              like the surface of that font
when other voices, tourist and devout,
grew still, and someone whispered by my side
O ye of little faith – and shallow doubt –
choose here to wet that hand or stand aside.
No one was there. But I could tell that tone.
I heard his ancient apostolic voice
this evening when I went to lift the phone
to tell you this – and froze. The reprimand.
For once in two minds Thomas made the choice
to bless and wet with blood his faithless hand.

THE EXCUSE

Please hang up . . . I try again.
'My father's sudden death has shocked us all'
Even me, and I've just made it up,
Like the puncture, the cheque in the post,

THE EXCUSE

Or my realistic cough. As I'm believed,
I'm off the hook. But something snags and holds.

My people were magicians. Home from school,
I followed a wire beneath the table to
A doorbell. I rang it. My father looked up.

Son, when your uncle gets me on the phone
He won't let go. I had to rig up something.

Midnight. I pick up and there's no one there,
No one, invoked, beyond that drone. But if
I had to rig up something, and I do,
Let my excuse be this, and this is true:
I fear for him and grieve him more than any,
This most deceiving and deceived of men . . .
Please hang up and try again.

Julia O'Faolain

MOROSE DELECTATION

'THE POLICE RETURNED this.' Madame de Sarre handed me the catalogue. 'Who knows what they made of it!'

It was as soft as unsunned skin and a bit thumbed, looked expensive and must have been done up for owners who had lent canvases. 'Pierre Klovsky' said the deckle-edged cover. The reproductions were the size of postcards.

I looked at them curiously. Klovsky ranks, I'm told, as a painter who just missed being great. His eroticism is odd: pent and disturbing, ogrish yet polite. Viewers cannot be sure that what they see isn't a projection from their own minds. Though never in the mainstream, his pictures fetch high prices.

I often drop into galleries. It is one of the few free pleasures Paris offers on cold days. Before her marriage, I used to go with Claude.

'This catalogue,' Madame de Sarre told me, 'should be useful. The organizers remember asking me to sell my paintings and that I refused. That was three years ago.'

'And now they've been stolen?'

'Two of them.' Her pencil ringed the items.

I read, 'Number 5, *Girl with Apple*, shows a prepubescent model seated with legs slightly apart. A shadow snakes from her dimly visible pudenda to where an apple has rolled to the floor.

Number 17, entitled *Carnality in bud*, shows the same model from behind. She is reaching for a shuttlecock.'

She asked: 'Does this embarrass you?'

'No,' I said, and the fact was that though I had been braced for titillation, there was none. Instead the effect was malevolent. Yvonne de Sarre, as a child, had been the model. 'Unless they upset *you*.' I noticed that scabs on the apple suggested canker.

'Oh, don't worry about me, Father Jean.'

'Jean. Please.'

'Jean. I saw them painted, after all. How old do you think I was?'

I looked from her mouth, laughing at me through wisps of streaked hair, to the painted child with her air of bruised collusion and reflected that I knew Yvonne de Sarre's present age – forty-six – for she had been close to my sister Claude. She lived near Bordeaux, which was why we hadn't met until the memorial service, when she introduced herself and said how moving she had found my sermon which – this seemed to surprise her – was about love. The topic is a common one at funerals, being the obvious antidote to death. Madame de Sarre seemed not to know this. Perhaps she doesn't attend many funerals? Perhaps all her friends are young? Claude *was* young – only thirty-five – and died of cancer brought on, to my mind, by stress. Her last years were spent juggling the demands of marriage to a divorced man with those of a Church which denied her communion. Eric was the innocent party in his divorce, but Rome is holding the line, so Claude suffered. Hence the cancer? Maybe it was a toss-up between losing her flesh or her faith? I thought for a while it would be the faith. But back it came and squeezed her like a vice.

'While I had a lover,' she told me bitterly, 'I could duck and weave. Each time we had a row I'd renounce Gilles and go back to the Church. But now that I'm married to Eric, the welcome mat's gone! They've slammed the door!'

Gilles, a married politician, had kept her on a string. Eric is an honest man.

'*Take* communion,' I advised. 'Can you think God would think the worse of you for receiving His body? Or Eric's?'

'The Church . . .'

'The Church is like a sub-post office. Its staff needs a

simple administrative code. Don't abide by it. Go higher.
Appeal over their heads.'

'How high should I go?'

'All the way. Go to God.'

'Paul says . . .'

'Paul's a tight-assed prig!'

She laughed. Paul – *le Père Paul* – is our baby brother. I
wanted to laugh with her, but felt too angry. Twenty-five
years ago, innocent remarried victims of wrecked marriages
could receive the Eucharist. Then policy hardened and the
Church's top traffic cops lowered the boom. The Congregation for the Doctrine of the Faith! Stop! Yield! No entry! My
heart bled for Claude, and Paul's bullying fired me with the
rage of Cain.

Luckily, his parish is in Savoy. Claude and I lived in Paris,
and Eric intercepted Paul's anathemas when he could.

'I'm a priest too,' I reminded Claude. 'And I say follow
your conscience and forget about Paul's.'

'*He* says I'm following yours and will damn us both. He's
praying for you.'

Now I did laugh. 'Paul,' I said, 'really thinks woman is the
devil's gateway. Like Tertullian! Who, by the way, was more
flexible. *He* accepted divorce.'

'"Be flexible" is Yvonne de Sarre's motto. She claims it's a
better guideline than all the cardinal virtues.'

'A theologian, is she?' Teasing. I was glad someone was
cheering Claude up.

'She's a force of nature!' Claude retorted. 'Volcanic. Rules
in her life never get set in stone because the stone is molten.'

'What about the stones in her château?' Yvonne de Sarre,
having disposed of a limp husband – I was hazy as to how –
had taken over and restored his leaky château, made a film
about this, and now restored similar properties professionally
for high fees. She had a son, presumably by the redundant
husband. I could see why my poor, scruple-ridden Claude
admired her nerve.

'Don't say a word against her.'

'I won't.'

Nor did I. Instead, I was soon keeping her phone number handy when Claude started staying with her for long periods. This arrangement was a relief to us all when the cancer worsened and neither I nor Eric could take time off to be with my sister. Eric's business was new and rocky. He had set up as a printer, just when computers began squeezing his trade, and was now working with some desperation. Come to think of it, the Klovsky catalogue could be his work and Yvonne de Sarre have got him the job. Friendship and business tended to fuse in her life, and Claude had a lot of anecdotes in which this led to her friend's getting herself into and out of what used to be called 'a pickle'.

'She,' these always concluded, 'hates doing things by the book.'

Hearing Claude laugh, I rejoiced at the outrageousness. So when Madame de Sarre rang some months after the funeral with news of her stolen paintings and her quandary, I listened with sympathy. It was, she explained, a moral quandary, and I, as a priest, must help get her head clear. She had come up to Paris from Bordeaux and was at her town flat on the avenue Foch.

'Please,' she wheedled. 'I'm in such a tizz.'

Our school is near the avenue Foch so, as I had no more classes that afternoon, I dropped around and was given tea in what could have been a Klovsky interior. While we talked, great wing armchairs held us in their clasp, while the painter's favoured pinks and yellows bloomed, then withered in the winter dusk. Two of his canvases hung on a wall, and my hostess as a child gazed with precocity from each. Her early selves had a deprived look, as if hungry for the biscuit in my hand.

She asked, 'How old do you think I was?'

Looking at the portraits of that glum little girl, I wondered whether the gloom was the painter's and whether, like the discharged Monsieur de Sarre, he had been made to feel redundant. Perhaps he had wanted this? His stress on the tight, punishing clothes constricting the child's flesh, reminded me of listening to penitents. 'Morose delectation'

21

was the name old confessors gave to the pleasures of revelling in repentance: a mental replay of sin. It was just such revelling which gave these paintings energy. Paedophilia, friskily relished, then renounced, triggered further oscillations, sending the mind bouncing, before returning it to the inedible apple in the stolen painting and to the inviolate little girl. Relinquishment breathed through Klovsky's backgrounds, soft with the same melting, multi-colours as the clouds which Tiepolo liked to use in his ceilings, where dangling bodies seem to dissolve in chromatic light.

What effect must all this have had on her? At the age of ten or eleven? Being dangled in frozen foreplay, exposed to a secret arousal, then dispatched to her nursery concerns, with no more explanation than is due to those statues which, on appointed days, are carried through hushed streets, then returned to their niches until the next festivity?

She had grown up with the paintings. Klovsky had died soon after painting them, leaving six to her in his will. Two had now been stolen. Meanwhile she had lived with them. Had she ever wondered at the bafflement in her child's glance? Perhaps not. Perhaps it was power she saw there and felt bolstered by ever after?

'You look,' I decided, scrutinizing her childish self, 'as though your body were aged about ten and your mind a hundred.'

She shook her head. 'When you hear what has happened, you'll think it's getting to be the other way round. Recently,' she acknowledged, 'I've been a bit imprudent.'

Recently so had I. After Claude's death I quarrelled with Paul. Fearing he might say something to hurt Eric, I refused to let him speak at her memorial service, so we ended by having two, one in Paris, one in his parish. I don't know what was in *his* sermon, but I kept the notes for mine. Reading them gives a false – angry – impression. I was gentle when I actually spoke.

Notes

1. *Say Claude's happiness with Eric proves that their marriage had God's blessing.*
2. *Deplore rigorist legalistic view.*
3. *Point out that in the marriage ceremony the priest is a mere witness to the sacrament whose binding agent is love. If love dies, the marriage, logically, is dissolved. Gospel statements to the contrary need be taken no more literally than the recommendation (Matthew 5:29) that Christians who had seen or done evil should gouge out their own eyes or cut off their hands. In practice Jesus was forbearing. See the woman taken in adultery etc. Obedience to institutional rules is not what sanctifies. Love is. Lovelessness is the true gate of hell.*

   Remind congregation of Claude's goodness, sense of fun, generosity. Read poem? Don't break down. Joke?

My name is Father Jean Duclos. I am thirty-eight and had never, until recently, made love to anyone. I felt relaxed about this and was not the kind of cleric whom people think of as trying to referee a game he doesn't play. I knew about families, having grown up in a big one and am as much at home in kitchens as in drawing rooms or confessionals – more so perhaps for, though it is some years since I did any pastoral work, I am as deft as ever with a paring knife, can clean vegetables by the bucketful, make omelettes for ten people and have, in emergencies, been known to change a nappy. Claude and I were close, and, until our married brother Marc left for Guadaloupe, there were always children and dogs around to enliven holidays and birthdays. No loneliness then. What I do for a living is teach ancient languages in a church-run institute where my colleagues are mostly lay and married and often invite me home for a meal. I am popular and think of myself as a well adjusted and – in a good sense – worldly priest. Or did.

Recently our family has dwindled. Marc hardly comes home any more. He's a journalist and his children are being educated in the States: a hard-headed decision, since American English is so useful. Paul and I are estranged. Cousins take sides, and Claude's death sparked off a series of mishaps: first the row with Paul, then my moment of – what? – moral disarray, which I think of as mirroring the one she herself went through towards the end – her giddy little frenzy when cancer was all through her and she was composing prayers for Eric to print up on coloured paper and post to everyone she knew. Gaudy and random, they fell through our letter-slots in their matching envelopes. Red, purple, yellow, blue. If each recipient read one daily, then . . . Can she really have thought heaven might respond? Probably not, but she had to do something, so she did that. It was a measure of her despair. A plummet. 'Dear Jesus,' the prayers typically began, 'I accept Your will, but beg You to spare Your servant, Claude Regnard, if . . .' Her words so burned the bright paper that I could hardly read. My eyes blurred. I blamed Paul for undermining her nerve – then reflected that it could be my fault that he is the way he is.

He is eight years younger than I, and it was dislike of what he sees as my generation's laxness that turned him into a bigot and scourge of, among others, Claude. He thought me 'wet' and would have hated the way my sermon moved the mourners. By the end of it I doubt if there was a dry eye among them, and I too felt rocked. I had opened myself because of Eric who, to my mind, deserved more thanks than he'd had for his devotion. He had been a childhood friend of ours, and it was like a miracle when he turned up after a long absence and married Claude just as she recovered from her wretched affair with the unspeakable Gilles. To me it seemed like an answer to prayer when this good, likable man came galloping out of our youthful memories to rescue her.

But not to Paul! Never loath to look gift riders in the mouth, he asked Eric, 'Are you married?' Eric said he was divorced.

'Keep away from him,' Paul advised Claude ten minutes into Eric's first visit. This was at our last gathering in Marc's house just before he took his brood to Guadalupe. The

children were teaching the adults clock golf and shrieking at
our lack of skill.

Some of this was deliberate, as when Paul sent his ball
sideways so as to get close to Claude and murmur in her ear.
The day was bright. The new putters were a going-away gift.
A shiny, old soup tin had been used to line a hole in the lawn,
and it was into its dazzle that we, like latter-day sun-
worshippers, were expected to sink our mutinous white balls.
Failures rattled us and there were bumps in the grass. 'You're
vulnerable. He senses it,' Paul warned Claude who was
poised to putt. 'Receptive! He'll move in.'

'Paul's astonishing!' she complained when telling me why
she'd missed her stroke. 'He's as crude as a pimp!'

'Or priest.'

'You're not like that.'

No. But maybe Paul's tyranny reflected a more alert
concern? Later I would wonder what he'd meant was
'vulnerable'? Her affections? Her body cells? Could anybody's antennae be that good?

'I know who stole my portraits.'

'You do?'

Madame de Sarre switched on a lamp and light flowed
around her. Tears refracted it and the gleams reached the wall
above where her young selves seemed startled. Weeping? For
lost property? Wasn't this a bit weak?

'My dear Madame . . .'

'Call me Yvonne. I've been warned not to take him to
court.'

Who? She was looking her age. She hadn't till now, thanks
no doubt to the face lifts which I knew about from Claude.
Embarrassed at knowing about them, I took her hand. She
left it in mine and I said, 'I'm sorry. Is this "him" a relative?
Your son perhaps?' This boy, I knew, had been expelled from
two boarding schools. He had a Catholic name. Ignatius, was
it? Or Xavier? I'd met him years before with Claude: a frail
child who looked at you from under his eyelashes. Sulky. He
had a winning smile though, and Claude said he was

desperate for affection and had, for a while, attached himself to her. By now he'd be sixteen.

Yvonne looked startled. 'You mean Vincent? No. Vincent's upset of course. All this has upset him terribly.' She blew her nose. 'He thought of Livio as a sort of stepfather. Livio's the thief. He was my lover for two years.' The confession came out in a quick spurt. She had it prepared. It was why she had asked me to come. 'Vincent adores Livio. Unfortunately.'

Livio Leopardi! I'd heard about *him*. He had been the Italian consul in Bordeaux. Advised to stay clear of Italy while a misuse of public funds was under investigation, he'd stayed in France two years. Then his friends returned to power and he to Rome though not, it seemed, empty-handed.

'He stole your paintings?' It seemed astounding. Too barefaced surely for his own good? Too private a theft. Claude, speaking with terse tolerance, had described him as not quite house-trained. He had once squeezed her crotch under the table at a dinner party of Yvonne's. 'Used to getting away with things,' had been her opinion, which failed to account for this new development. There is a gulf between reaching for a woman under a table and stealing from friends. 'Actually stole them?' I marvelled.

Yvonne nodded.

'A diplomat? Your lover?'

'Well, you see . . .'

As she talked, I began getting the measure of a way of life where everything was negotiable.

'Do you think of him as a thief?'

Her voice rose. 'What else is he? While I was out of the country – I was in New York on business – he nicked my paintings, sold them in London and pocketed the money. He told the auctioneers he was acting as my agent.'

'And they believed him?'

'So they say. It's my word against his. And theirs.'

'Had you given him power of attorney?'

'No, of course not, but you see . . .'

Their arrangements, she explained, had been informal. Livio, who sometimes got contracts for her to landscape gardens in Italy, had had the keys to her château. Sometimes he took a commission, always in cash. Money, in their world, washed around in funds managed by like-minded souls intent on – well, that depended. Policies could be tinkered with. Friendship was alchemized. The film she'd made when restoring her husband's château and the restoration itself had been funded like this.

'It was a good cause,' she insisted. '*We* were preserving a bit of the national heritage.' Others, she claimed, were less scrupulous. They overstepped.

'Overstepped what?' I asked. Were there limits then? 'Laws?'

'Oh, the *laws*!' Shrugging. Bureaucracy was for little people. 'You have to get round them. In Italy it's worse. Nothing could be done if you went by the book.' Italian workers, she confided, had to be persuaded to build by night. Tear things down. Get others up fast. Once the structure was erected, well . . . 'A bribe here and there and you're sitting pretty.'

Impropriety delighted her. I saw now that Klovsky's portraits suggested this. Modelling for him, while trussed up in ruched velvet, she had played the part of an eleven-year-old Mona Lisa, while the painter, by shaping her short body like a dwarf's, planted a suspicion that childhood was cover for something old and corrupt. Glancing from canvas to woman, I saw guile in three pairs of wide blue eyes.

Tunnelling quick, tense fingers through her hair, she told a cynical Italian joke which must have originated with Livio, then shot me an apologetic smile.

'You mustn't judge me badly.'

'I'm not judging you at all.' This was true. She had been Claude's friend in need, so how could I?

'Ah,' coquettish and despairing, 'but I need a judgement. Let me tell you my dilemma.'

'Dilemma?' That word, though she couldn't know it, does for me what 'swim' might do for a landlocked labrador. It brings back the ideals and tingles of a time in my seminary days when renewal was the rallying cry, barriers to thought seemed as volatile as rust, and a surge of testosterone powered debate, which was the only channel open to it, since none of us chose to look for one in sex. Later, when all debate had been stopped, some did. Some of my friends left to marry; some just left, and I went into hibernation.

'My dilemma . . .'

Memory's potency amazed me, as pulses jumped all over my body. What amazed me more though was the dilemma *she* described, and I prayed it was a joke. Apparently no sooner had she instructed a lawyer to sue Livio than a friend of his phoned, warning her to withdraw her case if she didn't want to have a bad accident.

'An accident?'

'That's what they call it.' The blue eyes blinked combatively. 'Unbelievable? Not with *them*. He says they'll pay compensation for the paintings if I agree not to prosecute. He's sure I can't get them back anyway, as the new owners bought them in good faith.' Flushing pinkly, she said, 'I mean to try, though. They're part of my life, myself, my youth. They're like Samson's hair to me and I can prove I'd never have parted with them willingly. Even last year I had a large offer and refused it.' Then she named Livio's friend. He was a man whom the Italian papers had tipped to be the next prime minister. I nodded. I had read about his ruthlessness. 'He says it will ruin Livio's career if I prosecute. And he, if he forms a government, wants Livio in his cabinet.' She said then that the other horn of her dilemma was worry about her son, Vincent, who would be devastated by a scandal. 'He adores Livio. They used to ride horses together. It's the one thing Vincent does really well. Ride. He's at a crammer's here in Paris. This is an important exam year for him and if he goes off the rails again I'll not be able to get him into any school.'

'I see.' I said, though the mixture of domestic and criminal threats was disorienting.

'Accidents aside,' she told me, 'if I do prosecute, my affair with Livio will be all over the press. They'll drag my name in the mud. They'll drag Vincent into it too.'

'So don't prosecute.' I shrank on her behalf from all this.

'But that's *their* calculation.' She jumped up as if to address a meeting. 'That a woman won't. No Italian one would.' Striking a pose, she looked magnificently reckless and reminded me of why, in my youth, when Rome turned against radicals like myself, I hadn't joined those classmates who left to work in Brazilian slums or, in despair, ran off with girls – playing, as I warned them, into the hands of our opponents. Lie low and wait had been my own tactic, but there was no point in suggesting this to her while she leaned into the lamp so that her streaked hair blazed like a burning bush. She's dangerous, I saw, gets carried away. 'Why,' she demanded, 'should we – I – be muzzled? Claude always told me that you believed in speaking out. That's why I turned to you. It's why I rang you up.'

Oh dear! Claude, I thought! Yes! Poor Claude! Yvonne had been wonderful with my sister when her body let her down. Generous. Devoted. I owed her a debt for that. But my head was in a whirl. What sort of speaking out was involved here? My old words, wrenched out of time and context, were being given unexpected weight and consequence. How unworldly I was, after all! How disgraceful to live in the world and presume to have opinions and yet know so little. How innocent to have supposed that being a lively uncle to Marc's children meant that I knew how people lived.

'Don't you think,' she challenged, 'that a man like that should be punished?'

I couldn't answer without knowing more. *Was* she at risk? What kind of risk? Might Livio's friend actually take out a – what was the term? – contract on her? The notion seemed laughable, belonging as it did to cop films and TV: a compendium of swift-whirring celluloid – but not only. Even I knew that the underworld was real and could touch us all. Maybe shiftiness in a shifty world was the safest course?

While I hesitated she repeated her question: 'Shouldn't he be punished?'

'Why?' An unexpected voice came from the hall behind our backs. My heart jumped and I turned but couldn't see through the gloom.

'Vincent!' His mother called, recognizing him at once. 'How long have you been there? Why aren't you at school? Come in and meet Father Duclos.'

'Why should he be punished?' A boy – Vincent, of course – walked, accusingly, into the light and caught its lustre even more flamboyantly than had his mother. He must have been in the rain, for his glinting hair stuck to his forehead in slick coils. As I had guessed, he looked about sixteen. He was gawky and thin and his raincoat was soaked. 'You're talking about Livio, aren't you? Do you think punishment improves people, Father Duclos?' He had a shocked, round-eyed look and his lips were as pink and puffily tender as raspberries. He evaded the hand I had extended.

I, in turn, evaded his question by reminding him that we had met once with Claude. This obliged him to say how sorry he was about her death, and before he could get back to the other topic, his mother began to worry about his skipping his afternoon classes. Begging me to excuse them, she drew him into another room from whence I heard words like 'your own sake' and 'exam'. Then she said she'd write him a note this once but . . . I didn't want to hear but there was only a door between us. When I heard no more I guessed she was writing the note for his crammer, hoping – a forlorn hope? – to keep him on the long, tedious highroad to university, *grandes écoles* and a solid job. When they came back he did take my hand. He was quite attractive when he smiled. He had fuzz on his upper lip but none of the acne so common at his age.

'Goodbye,' he said, 'father.' Which could have been meant as insolence.

When he left his mother moved to the window to make sure he wasn't still lurking on our floor but had gone down to the street. After a minute he must have appeared there, for she turned back to the room. 'I need a drink,' she said, 'Uff!' And released a great pent puff of breath. 'Do you like whisky? I have Scottish cousins who sometimes send some which they say is very good.'

I let her pour me a mouth-puckering sample which tasted of smoke and made me think of films about the north. I imagined herrings hanging from rafters and draughts leaking through cracks.

Her mother, she told me, had been a Bluebell, one of those well-chaperoned, long-legged English chorus girls who so often married and settled here in France. From time to time, while the Bluebells were on tour, the small Yvonne had been boarded out with a family who lived near Klovsky. That was how he came to paint her.

'There was no paedophilia, you know. He behaved impeccably.'

I said I had guessed that because restraint was what gave his work its tension and power.

This pleased her. 'Especially coming from a priest! You'd recognize the feeling! Oh dear, am I being awful? Like Vincent.'

Her mind swung back to him. 'He came to argue with me about suing Livio.' She crossed her legs with a stoical sigh. 'I doubt if he's gone to his class. The maddening thing is that he's clever if he'd only work. But this could tip him back into taking drugs.'

I thought it was time I gave some sound pastoral advice. 'Perhaps he's right,' I suggested, 'about your dropping the case.' Why, I asked, didn't she? In the circumstances.

'Why,' her chin rose pugnaciously, 'let Livio get away with giving me a slap in the face? I never thought he'd expect payment for his favours. Have I quite lost my looks?' This was meant as a joke, but the jokiness faltered. She was in disarray.

I said, meaning it, that she was a truly beautiful woman. She shook her head impatiently. 'Surely,' I tried another tack, '*he* doesn't see it like that?'

'How else can he see it? Either he's a gigolo or a common thief.' Her voice cracked; her mouth gaped in surprise and I thought of those lush, split pomegranates in still-life paintings: the rough rind, the red, luminous pith. She mentioned principle again and women standing up for themselves, but I saw that her anger had little to do with feminism. Klovsky's gift of paintings had been an affirmation of her power. The theft by a lover stripped her of it. She was forty-six.

Meanwhile I was smarting over my own inadequacies. Swallowing some more mouth-burning whisky, I blurted, 'Will you let me make love to you?'

'Do you want to?'

'Very much.'

She stood up, went into the hall where she bolted the main front door then, returning, beckoned me into her bedroom, took off her clothes, lay on the bed and, teasingly, struck a pose. 'A Titian?' she suggested. 'Or would you rather a Klovsky?'

'Don't intimidate me,' I begged. My mouth was dry. I took off my shirt, trousers and underpants and moved close. I didn't tell her I hadn't done this before. I knew the theory after all. I'd read novels, heard confessions, seen erotica.

She put a hand on my penis. '*This* isn't intimidated!'

We both laughed and when I lay down beside her she guided it into herself without difficulty. The heat of her vagina was what surprised me. I felt no guilt at all.

Afterwards she said, 'You're too quick.'

More inadequacies! I decided to face up to them. 'Tell me what to do,' I said. 'I'll do whatever you want.'

'Let me wash you,' she said. So she led me into her bathroom, which was amazingly luxurious by my standards, and smeared bath gel on her hands then ran them all over my body. It struck me that perhaps I didn't wash as much as I ought to. Celibates probably don't and my smells may have been unpleasant. I was embarrassed, but saw no point in letting her know this. She seemed very beautiful to me in a way which reminded me of Colette's Léa, who must have been about her age with ripe, well-kept, scented flesh. She joined me in the bath and, right away – but this *is* morose delectation and better halted now. My fever and addiction started then and I mustn't feed it.

Afterwards I made us an omelette which we ate with chunks of *pain poilane*, comté cheese and several glasses of Bordeaux. Then I went home by foot, striding excitedly up the damp oily avenue at about three in the morning. I had an early class.

That night I had a nightmare featuring a bus which kept falling into a ravine. A woman who was both Claude and Yvonne kept being thrown from it, and I kept having to rewind my mental film at top speed to stop her body landing on jagged rocks. It was one of those dreams where you think you can control what happens. In the end I woke up, went back to sleep, then was woken by a call from Yvonne, who had heard again from Livio's friend and needed moral support.

'He's to ring back. I told him I needed to think.'

'Don't sue,' I told her.

'Why not?'

'Unwinnable battles shouldn't be fought. The cost is unjustified. Think of Vincent. You have four other paintings. You've turned the lost ones into an omen. But they're only bits of pigment on canvas.'

'Come and persuade me.'

Rain was raking my window but she, who goes everywhere by car, didn't think of that. Again I had no afternoon classes – it was a Saturday – so I took an umbrella, which promptly broke in the wind, and tramped gamely up the avenue, holding its bent, slack, black cotton shield in front of my face. When I reached her door I was soaked and accepted a small whisky to warm me. I was sitting soggily steaming by her radiator when the telephone rang. It was a spokesman for Livio and she spoke coolly into it, promising not to sue.

On putting down the receiver, she said, 'Now I'm really worried. After all, once I accept their money, they'll have no need to fear me, but they'll go on being dangerous. Maybe I'd be safer if there were a scandal? What do you think? Mightn't it be protection?'

She was tremulous and, to my surprise, so was I. I remembered a twitching virus I'd had once which puzzled my doctors until, as suddenly as it had come, it went. Centuries ago they might have called it a demon.

I will not let myself dwell on our love-making. At first I was able to persuade myself that I was doing it from a mixture of gratitude and pastoral concern. There were immediate pre-texts too, as when she said, on that second day, 'You're wet through. Let me disrobe you.' She did this ceremoniously, and as I slid into her, whispered, 'This is my reward.'

'For what?'

'For refraining from taking revenge on Livio.'

We now had a sort of bargain: she wasn't to sue. I was to find a place for Vincent in one of our schools and, meanwhile, we would comfort each other. The truth was that she had taken me over like a fever and I thought of her constantly. She was a radiance in my mind's eye, a warmth, a haven and an unattainable home: attainable, that is, only at furtive, thrilling moments and offering none of the constancy of a home. Yet that was the word I thought of when I thought of her. It was as if I'd found the place where I fitted but mustn't stay. I felt unbalanced, guilty, unable to work, frighteningly out of control, and I promised myself that I'd see her through the crisis over Livio and Vincent, then break off.

Instead, one night some weeks after we became lovers, as we lay in her bed at about 1:00 a.m., her door bell rang and someone started trying to unlock the door. She whispered, 'It's either Livio or Vincent.'

'Have they got keys?'

'Old ones. I had the locks changed.'

It rang again and a key scraped at the lock. 'Maman,' called Vincent. 'Your car's in the garage, so I know you're there. If you're with Livio, let me in.'

She put a finger to her lip and we lay quiet until, after some more rattling, he gave up and left.

I wanted to leave too but she wouldn't let me.

'He may come back.'

'No. Please stay. Don't you want to?'

'Of course I do, only . . .'

'Please.'

My motives after that became painfully confused. There

was concern, even charity in my acquiescence. I loved making love to her, yes, but I also felt an obligation to love it since there was an increasingly reproachful desperation in her eagerness to please. This upset me. Had I made her anxious? How? Was I a bad lover?

'Would you rather,' she'd ask, 'that we did this some other way?'

'No, no, it's lovely.'

'Are you sure? You must say what you prefer.'

'I like it every way.'

It seemed I lacked ardour. How could I know? I had no standard of comparison. I feared my lack could set up stress in this wounded woman and bring on a cancer or worse. She asked me to spend more time with her. I did and grew even more addicted, wallowed with her, dreamed of her, smelled her on my fingers while sitting in a bus or teaching, imagined I smelled her even when I had scrubbed my hands, found myself moving in a constant fever of mounting need, worried about this, wondered how to break off without damaging Yvonne, then found that the cost of not breaking off had mounted.

She asked me to provide Vincent with a false alibi. The boy had gone to a party where drugs had been taken and a girl raped. There was to be a court case. The law which Yvonne so despised was wreaking its revenge. The crammers had decided to expel all pupils who had attended the party.

'Just say you and he were dining here with me. It's almost true. The thing happened the night he knocked and we wouldn't let him in. So we know he was here.'

'We could tell the truth.' I felt I had to make the offer.

'It wouldn't work.'

'Why?'

'The time's wrong. The party went on into the small hours. 4:00 a.m. is when the trouble took place. Just stretch the truth for once, Jean. I'm sure poor Vincent had nothing to do with the rape. Anyway, they're expelling pupils for just being at the party. We'd have to say he dined here and stayed the

35

night. They won't believe me if you don't back me up. I've covered for him too often.'

'I'm sorry, Yvonne.' I imagined a maze of scandal unravelling if I gave in to her request. Other people must have seen Vincent at the party and might challenge my testimony. The lie would then do him no good, and publicity would follow. The institution where I teach would suffer and so would my order. Though they allow me leeway and autonomy, they could not fail to be tarred by any black marks I might incur. My first duty was to them. Besides – quailing, I imagined the journalistic opportunities: '*Sleazy Priest Lies to Save Teen-age Rapist. Bent Cleric Vouches for* . . .' I shook my head helplessly.

'You mean you won't do it? Jean? You're not serious?'

'I'm afraid I am.'

She couldn't believe this. 'You're saying "no" '? You refuse to help! God, what a prick! You're no better than the others! And you pretended to be so concerned!' Indignantly and wonderingly – the process was mesmerisingly slow – her cheeks began to flush and swell and her eyes to burn with the cold blue of gas jets. Her code – friendship – and mine had collided. She saw now, she exclaimed, that she had been as wrong to trust me as she was to worry about Vincent – 'He'll be as bad as the rest of you!' – or to bargain with Livio. 'I'm going to sue him,' she cried. 'There's safety in publicity! He won't dare touch me then. I'll rely on myself! All men let women down one way or another. Look how the lot of you destroyed Claude! You're a hypocrite, Jean.' Again I apologized. Her lip curled. She was badly hurt but I couldn't comfort her. She threw me out.

Was this the end then? Just like that? Outside her door, I stood where Vincent had stood that night, pleading and rattling his obsolete keys. Like him I kept expecting it to open and that she'd say all this had been a joke, a test, a bit of sexual play which I had misunderstood. I thought of knocking – then saw that there would be no point. I had been serious just now and so was she.

So down her stairs I slunk, out and across the cold

macadam, past the sign named for that fervently hawkish Catholic hero, Marshal Foch. Some days earlier, a German tourist, perhaps innocently mispronouncing it, had asked me the way to Avenue Fuck. Now, as I retreated ingloriously down its slick, broad expanse, I echoed his words in sorrow while heading for my bachelor home which is no home at all.

Our paths don't cross, and I don't suppose I'll see her again in the flesh, but for months we've been meeting in unconsenting corners of my mind. 'Try *not* to think of redness,' Claude and I used to challenge each other when we were small. 'Or sweetness.' Then our mouths would flood with the imagined taste of blood oranges.

Try not to . . . Shamingly I think of her more now than I do of Claude, whom I always loved. Three years younger than I, with just a few smears of shiny, sugar-stick-yellow hair on her delicate infant's skull, Cloclo, as we called her, arrived in our family like an exotic new pet, and I felt no sibling jealousy at all. It was different with Paul who came later and became *her* pet. He and I pulled her different ways, and one of us should have let go. That must be what Yvonne meant about our destroying Claude. Yvonne – how persistently her name and memory crop up!

Might an accurate confrontation exorcise them? Here is what happened after we broke up.

Plans to get Vincent into one of our schools had of course to be dropped, but some powerful string must have been pulled, for the business of the party was hushed up and his crammer was persuaded to keep him on. What did go forward was Yvonne's case against Livio. Months later a packet of cuttings about it reached me through the post. '*Art Collector*,' ran the headline, '*Accuses Former Lover of Theft. Italian Politico Embroiled in Shady Deals.* "I Couldn't Believe Livio Would Do such a Thing" says fashionable French hostess, Yvonne de Sarre. "How, if we have to frisk our friends' pockets, can we have social relations at all"?' She looks young in the newspaper photographs and glows with a triumphant candour. The Italian press, eager to nail Livio and his friends – public opinion had again swung against them –

chose to present images of her as a wronged, frank-eyed, bravely-smiling victim. Even its reproductions of the stolen paintings received luminous baptisms which blotted out Klovsky's louche fancies, while the shadowy pudenda described as 'dimly visible' in the old exhibition catalogue were now not visible at all. The papers, it strikes me, have done for her what I failed to do – and maybe this is why she ensured that the cuttings reached me. Like a mediaeval ordeal, they have washed away her blemishes, appeased her fury, and restored her pride.

My own spiritual well-being is not so easily recovered. I am tormented, as Klovsky must have been, by an impossible yearning. Our affair was interrupted before I was ready to relinquish it. We ended on bad terms. I daren't telephone her, and indeed don't want to, but neither can I stop remembering. For a while I kept the newspaper prints of Klovsky's paintings of her and even had them blown up and framed. I persuaded myself that their new wholesome, even dewy purity must be beneficial to me. Then one day it struck me that a paedophile might reason like that, and I burned them all. Morose delectation tempts me constantly – I suppose I'm indulging in it now – and I am seriously thinking of putting my pride in my pocket and travelling to Savoy so as to go to confession to my brother, Paul. The shame involved in that would be powerful surgery: it could cut her out of my head.

To be sure, a sober meeting with Madame de Sarre, who is now forty-seven, might have the same effect, but begging for one would also involve putting my pride in my pocket. Maybe I should do just this.

Stuart Marlow

THE SEARCH FOR THE LOST CONDOM

GILBERT AND NANCY LOU were only minutes away from reaching unscaled heights of mutual passion when *it* happened, or to put it another way; when *it* didn't happen.

MUTUAL MONITORING

After years of staring at each other across the grey-cased computer screens of the *Third City Eurobank Incorporated*, Dutch American fast tracker Nancy Lou and Gilbert the French financier with the Italian Connection finally get it together (well almost). After months of: croissant and espresso lunches discussing inadequate marriage partners, of reaching mutual desire's critical mass at their regular working dinners in *Dal Passatore*, of seriously speculating on the idea of having sex together, of making promises but stopping just short of a binding agreement; this is it. Tonight is the big night. A coded fax confirms it. Gilbert and Nancy Lou have decided that both of their partners have become sufficiently difficult to push infidelity beyond the guilt threshold. This is to be their first real as opposed to imagined adventure together. Of course it will be a celebration of a deeper mutual understanding as they've repeated on countless occasions.

THE FINAL JUSTIFICATION

Of course as a European property dealer in a competitive open border market, Nancy Lou's husband Wim has to go wherever his business takes him. She had of course taken this into account when she married him, but not to have had one single weekend together for over four months is the limit. She doesn't doubt his fidelity, but such long and frequent conjugal absences make the whole marriage lonely, frustrating, and above all play havoc with their social calendar. Financially of course they're trapped. If Nancy Lou were to split up with her husband, neither of them would be able to afford a mortgage on their own. The apartment is the envy of all Nancy Lou's friends, which of course makes her skeleton marriage a mortgage prison. Gilbert's problems are of a different nature, but equally demoralising. His English wife has turned completely frigid on him in the two years since the birth of their second child Oliver-Marie. Gilbert is at a complete loss. He finds his wife clinging to the children and refusing even to talk to him let alone sleep with him.

THE TIMING WAS RIGHT

This weekend after promising faithfully not to let business wreck their partnership, Nancy Lou's Wim has flown off to yet another international estate agents' congress. This time in Madeira, and he won't be back for three days!

SATURDAY AFTERNOON

sees Gilbert standing nervously outside Nancy Lou's fashionable studio apartment building on the *Westside Canal Boulevard*. He is carrying a small bunch of genetically-engineered black roses. He adjusts his tie nervously as he presses the bell. The door is soon opened and he rapidly slips inside. Were this a bygone age, people may well have thought he was attending an illegal political gathering. Whereas in fact, the limits of Gilbert's 1990s political awareness amount to such things as the political correctness of presenting a woman with flowers at all.

INSIDE OR ON THE SIDE?

Once inside of course bottles of wine are opened. The lovers giggle about the political correctness of black roses and wonder how politically incorrect it is to refer to each other as: *bits on the side (English), sideways jumps (German), little side skids (Dutch)* before deciding on the highly unoriginal term of *lovers (international)*. The problem of terminology settled, embraces tentative at first become more intimate, sticking of course to the standard conventions of progressive barrier dropping. Problems with partners are once more briefly discussed. Both are nervous about the other perhaps not wanting to. Ah, but judging by the intensity of the subsequent embraces, now erupting into gropes, these fears are quite obviously unfounded. Nevertheless, polite rituals are rituals which must be observed.

IN BED

at last, where they have wanted to be for so long. (The undressing aria was a bit clumsy, but there may well be many future occasions when they'll be able to improve on this.) As tenderness is brushed aside by the power of passion's thrust, Nancy Lou yearning begs the likewise yearning Gilbert to get out the condoms. There's a slight lull in the proceedings. Gilbert didn't want to appear too presumptuous by bringing condoms with him. Never mind, Nancy Lou's husband Wim always kept a supply in the bedside cabinet. Loss of erotic tension Gilbert's fault? Nancy Lou is torn between admiring his discretion and resenting his lack of foresight. She reassures him, stressing that putting the things on always does cause a bit of a flat spot in the rhythm of love-making anyway. Such interruptions are an essential feature of the cautious generation of post-1990 lovers.

AND NOW?

Gilbert and Nancy Lou start building up again, all Nancy Lou has to do is fumble in her bedside table with her left hand whilst priming Gilbert; priming and split-second timing. But, oh dear, she can't find the things! Oblivious to the reality of the empty drawer Gilbert writhes in anticipation. *Damn*! Nancy Lou has to get out of bed. They are definitely not in the drawer. She dons her dressing gown and goes to look in the bathroom cupboard.

MEANWHILE

Gilbert tries to think erotically and keep up his erection However, he feels doubt, like an unwanted messenger running towards him along the canal. Is his wife Moira frigid because she suspects he's having an affair? Why had she become obsessively close to the children? Could it be that she was missing Britain and her family, feeling culturally dislocated or something?

Nancy Lou also finds a doubt-mail deliverer knocking at her mental door. The condoms are not in the bathroom cupboard either! Her husband must have taken them to his conference, *Wim! The unfaithful bastard! How dare he! Right!* She would make love to Gilbert now, with a passionate sense of justified retribution and become unspeakably intimate with him!

MEANWHILE

Gilbert has decided to blot Moira's provincial island mentality out of his French cosmopolitan mind. He struggles to keep up the good work of intermittent self-arousal, but is further inhibited by feelings of incompetence about not bringing the condoms.

THE SEARCH CONTINUES

Nancy Lou goes into the living room to find the secret supplies she always kept in her locked-up box of holiday snaps and souvenirs. She fumbles with the lock and all the photos and bits of jewellery fall onto the floor. She curses! She curses again as she realises that she used them up the last time. There was of course no last time. Last time was a secret that she had not even told herself about.

MEANWHILE

back under the thin Laura Ashley sheet, Gilbert now feels the odd tension of being involved in a deception. How can he be sure that the conference hasn't been cancelled at the last minute . . . and anyway the guy might be a jealous maniac? But no, Dutchmen are supposedly much less passionate than the French. Wim would probably assess the situation of any interrupted transgression with boring protestant logic, and insist on seriously talking to his wife later. But can Gilbert rely on national stereotypes to soothe his nerves ???

???

This is the first time this evening that Nancy Lou wonders if it is worth it. *But, of course if Wim thinks he can bonk his way through a few travel agents . . . or maybe the whole conference was just a front . . . a hastily constructed facade . . . Well he can't have his Madeira cake and eat it can he! . . . Of course Gilbert shall be bonked and that's that . . . but how? Ow!*

OW!

Nancy Lou treads on the sharp end of one of her trinket-souvenirs that had fallen out of the box.

MEANWHILE

Gilbert has just enough time to relieve the pressure of one of his all too frequent build-ups of flatulence, before Nancy Lou's return.

NANCY RESOLUTE!

It's no good, Gilbert will just have to get dressed and go to the WC in the corner Bistro. Looking strangely preoccupied, she returns to the bedroom to find him waving his hands around as if trying to shoo away an evil spirit. Nancy Lou coolly opens the window and gives Gilbert precise instructions and the correct small change. So much for French lovers! Gilbert shuffles off towards the Bistro, irritated by the incomprehensible coolness of both Dutch and English women, and suffering a strange pang of nostalgia for good old French family values.

THE GOODS HAVING BEEN ACQUIRED

Gilbert rings the doorbell twice as planned, and dressing-gowned Nancy Lou has made a night cap and rolled two cigarettes. In one of those embarrassing moments of interpersonal tension and doubt, he reads the instructions on the condom packet. He discovers to his horror that *this protective device must at all times be held in place at the base of the member at all times, as violent movements could mean rupture or sudden loss with potentially ruinous consequences*. In Gilbert, attacks of nervous anxiety induced by constant worries over the financial markets can be triggered by the slightest linguistic association. The condom packet is full of unfortunate phrases. His mind is catapulted back into his renewed anxieties about the Italian accounts. Unfortunately such attacks of anxiety usually exacerbate his already embarrassing problems of flatulence.

IN THE MEANTIME

Nancy Lou is scouring Wim's papers looking for any concrete reference to a conference in Madeira. Has he left a telephone number? If not, why not? She'd been so busy dreaming up this scheme of infidelity with Gilbert, that she'd virtually ignored Wim. Actually if Gilbert hadn't spent so much time seducing her across the computer screens with his pathetically-appealing hungry eyes, she would not have been subtly blackmailed into planning an affair, and would have paid more attention to her husband's possible games of deception! She hurries into the hall and looks frantically through the memo pads for a Portuguese-looking phone number.

BURSTING POINT

The sight of Gilbert reading the condom packet instructions and trying to hold vast volumes of gas within the confines of his lower abdomen hardly registers in Nancy Lou's mind. She wants him out of the way, so that she can scour the flat like a determined detective looking for evidence to throw light on the Madeira case. Under threat, the flat suddenly looks so wonderfully attractive, so exclusive, only a fool would risk giving all this up!

SANCTUARY

Gilbert manages to reach the loo without letting rip. Despite remote risk of husband returning, the temporary sanctuary of this apartment becomes more welcome the more he contemplates his alternatives. What with the Italian accounts looking far less certain than last week and throwing atmospherical wobblies across his desk, and his wife Moira making his home hearth like a fridge, he needs an emotional refuge. Of course Nancy Lou will settle for a cosy evening meal and a warm deeply sympathetic chat. The thought of such imminent cosiness leads him to breathe a great sigh of relief. What a positive shift of mood from anxiety to harmonious calm. A womb embraces him and peace returns to his abdomen. Nancy Lou is so well organised that of course there's no chance of her husband returning early. Even if he did, any reasonable likelihood of this is two days away at least, what bliss!

AN EPITAPH

Nancy Lou restlessly picks up the discarded condom packet so faithfully delivered by the machine and reads *This refined product is the most reliable known method of birth control and prevents exposure to sexually transmitted diseases.* Whoever wrote this must have been a prophet! whispers Nancy Lou, hoping that Wim has at least the sense to use them in Madeira, hoping that he will keep whatever he did to himself, praying that her suspicions are unfounded, and that he might come home early. How she loves the sanctity of her own four walls! Maybe they could afford the mortgage and a child after all. How foolish of her to think that things at the centre of her world had all been yawned out. Putting on the CD player, and nervously looking at her watch she is sure that Gilbert, now a total irrelevance, will get the message and get the hell out of the apartment as soon as he leaves the loo, her sacred territory. Their coded fax only confirmed a rendezvous in the afternoon. Any reference to the evening was optional and not obligatory, and cannot possibly be seen as a verbal agreement. Of course Gilbert will understand this. The thought of an evening on her own in her own space, what bliss!

Duncan McLean

I WANT DOESN'T GET

I WENT INTO town, up to the infirmary, asked if I could open an account at the sperm bank. Took a while for them to get their act together, like, but eventually they sent me along a special building, the genital-urinary department it was called, though don't ask me why: where else is your urine going to come from but your genitals, eh?

I sat down in the waiting-room and waited. There was a few other folk sitting there too, looking a bit sheepish, ken. But not me: no way. I was loud and proud, I was. On a mission to posterity, me. I nudged the guy next along.

Listen mate, I said. Just in case you're wondering: I do *not* have the pox.

He looked at me. Neither do I, he said, starting to take a redder.

Aye, fine, I went. Whatever you say. But listen: not being funny, I just want to be quite clear. I might be sitting here in the genitals, but I DO *NOT* HAVE THE POX.

Ken what the radge ups and does? Moves to another seat across the room! I ask you.

Just then my name got called. A blonde nurse in a white coat took me ben her office. It wasn't like a ward, there were no beds or nothing, it was just filing cabinets and potplants and a computer. And framed certificates on the walls saying she was a doctor, not a nurse.

Sorry about that assumption there! I said. Didn't mean anything by it, not at all! I looked her up and down. You got anything on the night, by the way? Fancy a date?

She paused, turned to face me, frowning slightly. Did you say something Mr Doig?

I smiled back. You tell me! You're the doctor!

Yes, she said, I am, and sat down at one side of the desk, pointing me into a plastic chair on the other side.

I'd like to leave a long-term deposit, I said, once we were all sitting comfortably. Ken what I mean? I'm not wanting it thawed out the morn's morn or next week and used to impregnate some bat-faced lesbian. I'm needing it saved long term, down in the freezer vaults, ken, kept till the twenty-first century.

She gave me a smile. That's less than two years now, she said.

Eh? Oh aye . . .

Legislation allows us to keep donations for up to five years, so it's quite possible that . . .

No, listen, I said. Scrub that, I've changed my mind. I want it kept longer: till the twenty-second century at least. The distant future, ken, when they're putting the super-race together. They'll have the super-chick, right, the super-babe, and they'll be looking around for some male super-genes . . . but the twenty-second century men'll no do, cause they're too fucking wimpy, life's too soft up there in the future. Shit, goes the speccy guy in the white coat. I wish we had some of that late twentieth-century spunk, that was the last time men were really men. Hold on a minute, says the second speccy cunt. There was that one test-tube stuck in the ice way at the back of the freezer . . . The spunk of Billy Doig! goes the first guy. That's the gadge, goes the second guy. 1998 vintage I think, a damn good year! So they dig out my donation and . . .

EXCUSE ME! shouted the doc lass.

I stopped.

Mr Doig, she said. Even if your donations turn out to be suitable, we can't possibly keep them as long as you're suggesting. We just don't have the technology.

Shit! I said. Cause it was cheering me up, that thought. I've been a bit depressed lately, ken. Well, not depressed. A bit down, just, a bit low. Kind of how-low-can-you-go, Mr

Misery-guts, *suicidally* low, ken. Walk-the-streets-all-night-looking-for-a-bus-to-chuck-myself-under low. Ha! Lucky I live on the 14 route, eh?

She frowned. Maybe I could refer you to another department . . .

No no, I said. I've been through all the departments. This is the place right enough. This is what's keeping me from jumping off the top of the multis: the thought that you might take some of my spunk and freeze it till the twenty-second century. Aye, that's what's cheering me up. I sat back. Well, that and the lithium.

She tapped her pen on the notepad in front of her. Why does the idea *appeal* to you so much, Mr Doig? I mean, what's your motivation for . . .

Well, it's obvious, isn't it, eh? I gave her a wink. It's unlikely I'll get shagging Naomi Campbell in this life, but it's a consolation thinking my, eh, my *donation* might get squirted up her great-grand-daughter in a hundred years or so.

Mr Doig, may I suggest . . .

I jumped up. Shagging supermodels in the afterlife! Just the thought of it! If I kent that was arranged, I *could* jump off the multi-storey: and I'd be smiling all the way to the ground, I tell you!

She stood up too. We're wasting our time here, she said. I really think . . .

I agree completely, I said. To hell with you: I'll do it myself. As per bloody always.

I made it back to the flat about seven. Walked into all dim lights, air freshener, and Barry White on the CD. I hope this lot isn't for me, I called out.

No, said Bog from the kitchen. There's this girl I was talking to last night at the line-dancing. Tanya's her name, pretty fucking tasty, so I asked her round. Thought I could . . .

HOLD ON! I yelled.

He stuck his head round the door, a bottle of Bud in his hand. What's up?

Where did you meet the girl?

At my evening class. He took a drink, swallowed. Education's a wonderful thing, man.

Aye, maybe. But what are you studying?

He took another long drink.

Come on! I said.

He ducked back into the kitchen again, muttering. Line-dancing . . .

I thought for a second, running through all the possibilities for what he must've really been saying when I thought he said line-dancing. There weren't any possibilities. I gave a wee sob. Jesus!

Sixteen weeks, he said, and I heard him drop his empty bottle into the bin. Two-fifty a week.

I rested my forehead on the woodchip by the kitchen door. I don't believe it, I said.

Aye, and that includes a cup of coffee and a Wagon Wheel half way through. Good value, eh?

I laughed, banged my forehead against the wall a couple times to calm myself, then walked into the kitchen. Bog was bent over the sink. You're off *your* fucking wagon, man, I said.

He grinned, Every one says that. But I don't give a monkey's wank. Ken how? Cause that means they won't come down the class, and I'll get the pick of the women. Hot to trot, Billy, I swear to god.

I had a look in the fridge. His shelf was full of long brown bottles, but all I had left was a couple totie Royal Dutches. Weak as pish. Not much wonder they sold them in packs of twelve: it takes that many to get you half-stooshed. I shut the fridge again.

Twenty-four women and just two men at the class, he was saying. And the other guy's a sad wee fuck with bad breath and his neck in a brace, he's no competition. Figure it out: sixteen classes, twenty-four women. That's a different shag every week for the whole course.

And eight over? I wrinkled my nose at him. They'll be cover for the Christmas holidays, I suppose?

You can laugh, you bastard, but even if a couple of them aren't up for it, that's still more fanny than you've had in all the time I've kent you. Now *that's* what I call therapy!

Ha! I snorted. Don't worry about me. I'm shagging Naomi Campbell's great-grand-daughter!

What?

Nothing, I said. Forget it.

Listen Billy, I've work to do, he said, hunching over the sink with a knife in one hand and a lump of pink stuff in the other. Out of my light, will you?

I went to the fridge again, looked in at my pathetic shelf, then opened the freezer compartment. Empty. There wasn't even any ice in the ice-cube tray. I let the door snap shut, and grabbed one of my wee green beers.

I opened it, took a swig (careful not to finish the fucking thing in a oner) then looked across at him.

What in hell's bells are you doing? I said after a minute.

Is it not obvious? he said. I'm scraping Bernadette off a Lourdes candle.

I sipped. Losing your religion, are you?

Nah, wise up. I'm needing some intimate lighting, ken, for when Tanya comes round, and this was all I could find in the house.

Terrible, I said. Using holy relics to get into the pants of country and western fans! I'm sure there's something about that in the bible.

Well, he said, I *am* feeling guilty, if it's any consolation.

We're all feeling guilty, I said. Nothing special there. It's quality guilt that counts these days, *quality*. Let's see . . . I thought for a minute. What're you giving her to drink? Is it communion wine?

He whittled away a bit more, shaving flakes of transfer and pink wax onto the draining board. Nah, he said at last.

Shame. That would've been worth feeling guilty about.

Nah, he said again. Budweiser. American, see? Attention to detail is what it's all about. I even got some of that microwave popcorn. Bowfing, so it is, but if that's what it takes, ken?

I laughed. You're putting a big investment into this, Bog.

That's not the half of it, he went. I had to get the bait to get her round here in the first place. Sixteen quid for a fucking Garth Brooks video!

I gave a hoot. Jesus, I said, You've really sunk low this time ya bas. Garth fucking Brooks. You ken why he wears that big black hat all the time?

Bog held up the candle and inspected it, twirling it round in his fingers. Cause he's a cowboy, right?

Nah, cause he's got no head underneath.

He squinted at me.

It's true, I said. See just above his eyebrows, he always keeps his hat pulled right down to there. It's cause his head goes straight back after that: like the top chopped off an egg. Total fucking lobotomy job.

Shite, said Bog.

I laughed. It's true. Soon as anyone shows an interest in country music, a special team of lassies in blonde wigs and white coats come out of Nashville – K-CHUNK! SOOK! – say goodbye to your brain!

Fuck, he said, then, Give us another Bud, will you?

Bog, I said. Have you ever thought about having kids?

He rolled his eyes. I like you fine, Billy, but not *that* much.

We both laughed. Bog tipped the last of his bottle down his throat, but his timing was bad: the last laugh was still coming up. Beer sprayed everywhere, spirking over his breeks and the carpet. He spluttered and clamped his lips shut, but that just meant the beer came snorkelling out his nostrils instead. I almost ended myself laughing.

He ran off to the kitchen. I heard the tap running, Bog splashing about, then bottles clinking and the rasp of a match being struck.

Put out the lights, Bog shouted. I'm coming through.

I leant over and unplugged the lava lamp. Okay, I said. Blackout.

Through in the kitchen Bog started singing:

> *Jambalay, cod fish pie*
> *Mumbo jumbo*

His voice was strange and nasal. I couldn't tell if he was sounding like that on purpose, or if it was a side-effect of the Bud sloshing up his cavities.

> *For tonight I'm going to see*
> *Hawaii 5–0*

He came pacing into the living room, a full bottle of Bud in one hand, an empty one in the other with the Lourdes candle stuck in top. He'd scraped off Bernadette so thoroughly that the candle was no thicker than a pencil, and only an inch long.

> *Old foot jar, boot the car*
> *Feely two tit*

He bowed towards the telly, set the candle on top of it, then hunkered down and pressed the play button on the video.

> *Son of a gun we'll have big fun*
> *If we do it*

The screen fizzed into life: comedy music and zaps, and a cartoon of a fat grumpy-looking ginger cat.

Bog rocked back on his heels. What the hell's this?

I watched for a few seconds, then started laughing. Great! I said. It's Garfield!

Flix bastards! He's not even *wearing* a hat!

He pressed fast forward, and the cat leapt about the screen at great speed, like it was trying to escape. Various humans walked in and out of the room. The cat scowled at them, spent a lot of time on his back. Bog grabbed his Bud from the top of the telly and downed it in one. More leaping about, like the beast was wired to the mains, more scowling. Then the tape clicked to a stop.

Jesus, he said. What am I going to tell Tanya?

Tell her you love her, I said. Tell her you want to have her babies.

ABOUT THE FUCKING TAPE! he screamed.

Eh . . . tell her you're an incompetent paranoid depressive with alcoholic tendencies and if it wasn't for your slightly better adjusted flat mate you'd be in a right state.

But I *am* in a right state! he shouted.

I shrugged. Tell her you fucked up.

He looked at me. Be honest you mean?

Aye, I said. You be honest, I'll tell lies, let's see which works best. Next week we'll swap.

What time is it? he said.

I checked my watch. Just gone eight. When's she due?

Eight, he whispered, looking up with a shitting-it expression on his ravaged puss.

Right, I said. You drink as many of those Buds as you can before she gets here. Remember: women are always impressed by a pished man.

Is that right? he said.

No, I'm the one doing the lies thenight, mind?

He got to his feet. I think I'll try it anyway, he said.

Good idea, I said. It can't make you any *less* attractive.

An hour and a half later the doorbell rang.

Does Kevin Marsh live here? said the woman in the fringed white-leather jacket.

Sure, I said. He's in the lounge. A regular lounge lizard, old Kev.

Sorry I'm so late, she said as she walked past me. There's a bullock loose in the street.

A bullock? I said.

Aye! Roadblocks everywhere!

She paused at the living-room door, looked down at Bog sprawled along the settee.

Hiya Kevin, she said.

Howdy, he replied, raising his bottle of Bud in salute.

Let me take your jacket, I said, and stepped up close behind her.

You should've seen it, she said, shrugging out of the jacket as I fingered the collar. Police marksmen all over the place: never seen so many out at one time. What a laugh! All firing away trying to shoot this bloody bull.

Could you not have lassoed it? said Bog.

The thing was, said Tanya, It'd run over a wee girl. One minute she's playing with her Game Boy in the gutter, next she's being trampled into the ground by a bullock.

That's terrible, I said.

Bog opened another bottle of Bud, tipped it down his throat. Halfway through he stopped, burped, and said, Raging bull-ock.

Tanya frowned, turned to me as I sat myself on the settee next to her. Ken what happened then? The father of the girl – he'd seen it all – came running out of the closemouth, bellowing, and – BANG! – the police marksmen shot him! Thought he was the bloody cow!

Terrible, I said. Tragic.

Meanwhile the beast's run through into the backgreen, and it's charging about amongst the washing lines, all these sheets and knickers sticking to its horns!

Laundry carnage, I said.

Bog tossed his empty bottle into the coalbucket and opened another.

That's nothing, said Tanya. Ken what next? The cub scouts from the hall were camping in the middle of the green: they'd set up their wee tents in a circle and were all lying inside, practising sleeping in the wilderness for when they go to Burntisland next holidays. Picture it: six wee tents, six cubs in each, head to toe to head like little sardines in neckerchiefs – and this big crazed bullock and all these big crazed police marksmen, pawing the ground and firing off potshots, all of them charging down on top of the camp!

Jesus, I said. Terrible. What happened?

Tanya shrugged. I don't ken: didn't hang about. Couldn't wait to see Garth!

I looked across at Bog, waiting for his honesty. He was lying flat out on the settee now, two bottles of Bud held against his forehead like bullhorns. WHAAAOOO! he trumpeted, then sat up, grinning and snarling. Beer out of the open Bud-horn scooshed over the carpet, our settee, and onto Tanya's tight jeaned lap.

God's sake! she yelled, bouncing sideways on her seat out of the damp patch and towards me.

See that blonde hair of yours, country girl? growled Bog.

Tanya patted it above her lug, where the roots were most visible. What about it?

Is it a wig?

It is not!

I leant in towards her. Don't mind him, I said quietly. He's had one too many buddy buddy and the buddy bud buds.

Bog drained his bottle, chucked it across the room, glared at Tanya. I know why you're here country girl, he said. You've come to suck my brains out!

You should be so lucky, said Tanya. I've come to see Garth Brooks fly through the air and smash guitars, that's *it*. Well, maybe a wee drink or a smoke, I don't ken what youse guys are into. But that's *it*.

How about something to eat? I said.

Popcorn! yelled Bog.

I wouldn't mind a box of chinky-ribs from the carry-out, said Tanya. But that's *it*. I bloody *hate* popcorn!

How about sex? I said.

With you, not him, she said. Nothing weird, you wear a rubber, fuck me senseless. That's *it*.

After I'd come we just lay there for a minute. Then I heaved myself up, held the doob onto my cock with one hand, and rolled off her. She breathed out a big sigh. I got up into a kneel, then reached forward and stroked the side of her head till my fingers touched a kirby grip. I took hold, yanked it clear of her hair.

Ouch! she said. What are you doing?

Nothing, I said, sliding the condom off, giving it a wee shake, and sealing the open end with the kirby.

What is this, some kind of budget S&M? Kirby grips instead of nipple clamps?

You couldn't tie a knot in it, I said. Stuff would come squirting out when you pulled it tight.

She was sitting up in the bed now, relighting the end of her joint. *What*? she said.

Plus you have the problem of what to do when you want to get it out.

Get what out? she said.

What do you do: untie the knot? Slit the rubber with a knife? Tricky.

She held out the joint, and I leant towards it, opening my lips. She moved her head, kissed me briefly, holding the drugs out of the way up by my lug somewhere. Then she lay down, took another big drag.

Oh, I went.

What?

I shook my head, leant back again. You could staple it, I suppose, I said. But that wouldn't be a proper seal, would it. Precious stuff: wouldn't want to waste any of it!

She reached under the covers to scratch herself, and I took the opportunity to get off the bed. I'm just going through the eh . . .

She looked up, frowning. I hope you're not going into the bathroom, she said. Not dressed like that with nothing on. Cause Kevin's still in the bath.

Is he?

I haven't heard him come out, have you?

The water'll be freezing!

Nah. He went in there just when you went in me. He tried to cover it up by playing Garfield really loud, but I heard him. And water doesn't go cold in thirty seconds, you ken.

Don't hassle me, I said, then made for the door, the glistening doob swinging in front of me. I turned the knob, left-handed. I'm not going there anyway, I said: I'm for the kitchen.

I stepped out of the bedroom and headed down the hall, pausing for a second outside the bathroom door. From inside came faint splashings, the occasional low moan, and the smell of fresh porridge. Bog always put a handful of oats in the bathwater, to help with his skin condition. It meant that the plughole would be clogged again when he got out, but at least he wouldn't be slitting his wrists. I mean, who worries about treating their eczema if they're going to be dead in five minutes?

No need for the kitchen fluorescent: when I opened the fridge the little bulb in its plastic cage plinked on, and I could see everything very clearly. Everything. I slid the ice-cube tray out of the freezer compartment, laid it on the draining board next to Bog's pink candle shavings, and shut the fridge door with my arse.

There was a footslap on the lino behind me. What next? said Tanya.

I glanced over my shoulder at her. I've never told anyone about my scheme before, I said.

She shrugged, her nipples bobbing up like corks. I've never told anyone about my bullock before, she said.

Your bullock? I said. You mean all that stuff about why you were late . . .

Aye, she said, and giggled.

That bullock *belonged* to you?

Eh . . .

You really are a cowgirl then? All is forgiven!

What's to forgive? she said.

I looked at her. It's to let somebody off when they've done something bad. So they don't have to feel guilty.

Eh . . . aye. About the bullock . . .

Shoosh, I went. Let's send our little present to posterity.

Are you serious? she said.

Aye, I said. Have you never thought of having kids?

I've got two already, she said. That's how I was late. All that stuff about the bullock, it's just . . . just . . . my fantasy.

She dropped a hand down to her belly and started scratching again.

I turned away, concentrated on adjusting the position of the ice-tray. My kids all live in the twenty-second century, I said. Life's much better in the future.

I hope to Christ you're right, she said.

I unclipped the kirby from the end of the condom and couped it.

Gloop gloop, I said.

Dribble, dribble, she said.

My donation ran out of the doob and into the first cube in the tray. I gave it a little shake, and one last drop ran out: still the cube was less than half full.

Here . . . All of a sudden Tanya was looking worried. Listen, she said. When you gave me that Hooch on the rocks, I hope . . .

What do you think I am? I cried. Some kind of nut? It was frozen water and nothing else. I scraped it off the sides of the freezer box with my own fair hands. Christ, I even washed them first!

Someone switched the light on – Bog – me and Tanya standing stark naked in the middle of the kitchen floor, him at the doorway, starkers too except for the little white flecks of oatmeal stuck all over his body, and a pair of bright red gloves.

I'm homesick, he said.

But this is your home, said Tanya.

He blinked. Aye, and I'm sick of it.

They weren't gloves.

What have you done to your hands? I said.

He looked down at them, just as the blood started dripping off his fingers onto the floor.

Robert Irwin

YOUR NOVEL NEEDS INDEXING

AMONG THE MANY issues currently dividing theorists in literary critical discourse, it is probable that the most hotly-contested ones concern the indexing or not of works of fiction. Academic partisans for the indexed novel have presented it as a transgressive act and as something that can provide the work of fiction with an additional metatextual level. Moreover, it has been argued that an index can set the reader-victim free from the tyranny of the author's intentions, as it provides the reader a liberty to roam around the text. Partisans of this viewpoint mock the old notion that the reading of a novel should be a linear progression from the beginning to the end, as if the joys of fiction should be reduced to a compulsory one-way journey down a single-track railway line.

Opponents of the indexing procedure on the other hand might argue that providing a novel with an index is a distasteful kind of 'convenience packaging'. The capricious 17th-century historian Thomas Fuller anticipated its coming: 'I confess there is a lazy kind of learning which is *only Indical*; when scholars (like adders which only bite the horse's heels) nibble but at the tables, which are the *calces librorum*, neglecting the body of the book. But though the idle deserve no crutches (let not a staff be used by them, but on them), pity it is the weary should be denied the benefit thereof, and industrious scholars prohibited the accommodation of an index, most used by those who pretend to contemn it'. Other critics maintain that the index, by providing a kind of school

Misery-guts, *suicidally* low, ken. Walk-the-streets-all-night-looking-for-a-bus-to-chuck-myself-under low. Ha! Lucky I live on the 14 route, eh?

She frowned. Maybe I could refer you to another department . . .

No no, I said. I've been through all the departments. This is the place right enough. This is what's keeping me from jumping off the top of the multis: the thought that you might take some of my spunk and freeze it till the twenty-second century. Aye, that's what's cheering me up. I sat back. Well, that and the lithium.

She tapped her pen on the notepad in front of her. Why does the idea *appeal* to you so much, Mr Doig? I mean, what's your motivation for . . .

Well, it's obvious, isn't it, eh? I gave her a wink. It's unlikely I'll get shagging Naomi Campbell in this life, but it's a consolation thinking my, eh, my *donation* might get squirted up her great-grand-daughter in a hundred years or so.

Mr Doig, may I suggest . . .

I jumped up. Shagging supermodels in the afterlife! Just the thought of it! If I kent that was arranged, I *could* jump off the multi-storey: and I'd be smiling all the way to the ground, I tell you!

She stood up too. We're wasting our time here, she said. I really think . . .

I agree completely, I said. To hell with you: I'll do it myself. As per bloody always.

I made it back to the flat about seven. Walked into all dim lights, air freshener, and Barry White on the CD. I hope this lot isn't for me, I called out.

No, said Bog from the kitchen. There's this girl I was talking to last night at the line-dancing. Tanya's her name, pretty fucking tasty, so I asked her round. Thought I could . . .

HOLD ON! I yelled.

He stuck his head round the door, a bottle of Bud in his hand. What's up?

Where did you meet the girl?

At my evening class. He took a drink, swallowed. Education's a wonderful thing, man.

Aye, maybe. But what are you studying?

He took another long drink.

Come on! I said.

He ducked back into the kitchen again, muttering. Line-dancing . . .

I thought for a second, running through all the possibilities for what he must've really been saying when I thought he said line-dancing. There weren't any possibilities. I gave a wee sob. Jesus!

Sixteen weeks, he said, and I heard him drop his empty bottle into the bin. Two-fifty a week.

I rested my forehead on the woodchip by the kitchen door. I don't believe it, I said.

Aye, and that includes a cup of coffee and a Wagon Wheel half way through. Good value, eh?

I laughed, banged my forehead against the wall a couple times to calm myself, then walked into the kitchen. Bog was bent over the sink. You're off *your* fucking wagon, man, I said.

He grinned, Every one says that. But I don't give a monkey's wank. Ken how? Cause that means they won't come down the class, and I'll get the pick of the women. Hot to trot, Billy, I swear to god.

I had a look in the fridge. His shelf was full of long brown bottles, but all I had left was a couple totie Royal Dutches. Weak as pish. Not much wonder they sold them in packs of twelve: it takes that many to get you half-stooshed. I shut the fridge again.

Twenty-four women and just two men at the class, he was saying. And the other guy's a sad wee fuck with bad breath and his neck in a brace, he's no competition. Figure it out: sixteen classes, twenty-four women. That's a different shag every week for the whole course.

crib to the novel's themes, tends to foster reductionist readings of that novel. It is also often argued that an index can provide an unmerited and misleading academic gloss to novels which have nothing to do with academic concerns (except of course for campus novels, which are hardly concerned with anything else).

I do not feel qualified to judge on the merits of the theoretical positions outlined above and I feel hesitant about adding to the vast quantity of critical debate regarding the indexed novel. However, as a practising writer myself, I find that I am always being asked by would-be novelists, 'Should I index my novel and, if so, how do I set about it?' This sort of question comes ahead even of, 'Does the novel I am planning to write have to be typed on one side of the paper only?' and 'Do I need an agent?' I have even been asked on one occasion whether it was desirable to do the index before writing the novel. This is not as stupid a question as might appear at first sight, since the preparation of the outlines of an index, with its headings and dependent subheadings, may well clarify the structure of the novel which has yet to be written: the deeps and shallows of character drawing, the patterns and rhythms of the sub-plots, the shadings of mood, the climactic moments and the various necessary props (cars, gloves, antimacassars, guns, ear-trumpet), as well as the grand diapason of the story as a whole. On second thoughts it is as stupid as it seemed at first sight.

If the novel is not very good in the first place, even the best sort of index will not rescue the book from mediocrity or worse. Take George Gissing's *The Private Papers of Henry Ryecroft* (1903). This is one of those classics which everyone has heard of, but which nobody should read. It is so tedious that many readers must have put it down long before reaching the end and consequently never discovered that the tedium has been broken down and categorised in Gissing's index.

Sainte-Beuve, 171
Science, 267

Seaside, 79, 117
Shakespeare, 61, 89, 150
Silence, 71
Sixpence, the lost, 11
Snob, the English, 137
Social characteristics of English, 124
Somerset, 81
Spinoza, 182
Spring, thoughts of 16, 18, 46, 74
Steamboats, advertisement of, 118
St. Neots, 285
Stoicism, 184–91
Stratford on-Avon, 129
Suffolk, 105, 283
Sunday, the English, 85
    books for, 89
Sunrise, 107
Sunshine, 97
Swallows, 221

A glance at the index suffices to show the novel to be bookmanly, tweedy, insular, complacent stuff. Its protagonist ruminates purposelessly, unless the purpose be to flaunt the breadth of his culture. There ought to a heading for 'Plot, total absence of'. The only character in the book to feature in the index is the self-regarding Henry Ryecroft. Under the heading 'Ryecroft, his life and character', we find such subheadings as 'apology for his comfort', democratic temper', 'delight in giving' and 'desire of knowledge'. Nothing happens in the book, except that Ryecroft who, after years of hack-work as a writer, has retired to the countryside, repetitively and monotonously congratulates himself on having done so. Oh yes – and he lost that sixpence, and this furnishes a pretext for more would-be humorous meditations on the small things in life. Since this was what George Gissing himself did (retire to the countryside, that is – we cannot be sure about the sixpence), the book is much too close to autobiography (of a rather dull kind) to be satisfactory as a story. The index of Gissing's novel is boring, but it is no more so than the text it is appended to.

Yet some novels deserve more from their indexes. Consider this extract from Ethel Mannin's all but forgotten romantic novel, *Women Also Dream* (1937):

Fascism, 181, 226, 252
Finland, 139
Finmark, 134
Fleming, Peter, 141, 219
Forbes, Rosita, 17
France, Anatole, 240
Freedom, 140, 192, 226, 251
Freud, Sigmund, 183, 195

Essentially this is a non-fiction index inappropriately tagged on to a work of fiction. Fleming, Forbes and Freud are real people and consequently they feature in the index. However (and this is really rather shocking) there are no entries for Janet Forrest, the bold aviatrix, or for Peter Dain, the builder of luxury flats whom she marries, or for Addison Maitland, the pilot with whom Janet eventually escapes, heading towards adventure and, it may be, death. These sins of omission and commission amount to a cowardly strategy which pulls apart the fabric of the novel, as the student of the index is effectively being instructed as to which parts of the book are research and, as such, listed in the index and which parts of the novel are made up and therefore are not. There are no entries in the index for adventure, death, fate, boredom or sexual desire, even though these are the engines which drive the story along. Only it must be conceded that 'Freedom' is an uncharacteristically bold index entry by Mannin. It unambiguously signposts the leading theme of *Women Also Dream* – the superior place of the lust for freedom and adventure in the heart of Janet Forrest. (For the sort of woman represented by Janet, see index-headings, 'Bell, Gertrude', 'Maillart, Ella' and 'Stark, Freya'.)

Large matters apart, Mannin's plonking provision of page-references to places and pundits, retrospectively elides the sentimental charm of the story she has written. Why did she not index 'Drumbeats, in the heart of Peter Dain', or 'Honeysuckle, smell of associated with the lure of domesticity'? The period charm of the book could be brought out by headings for 'Right Thing, doing the', 'Dinner, dressing for', 'Logic, feminine'. Mannin could have advertised her sensitivity and descriptive powers by indexing such matters as 'slither, cold, of rain' and 'nettles, smell of, in paddock'.

American compilers of indexes to novels are more alert to the ludic possibilities of the practice, though consequently they often disdain to engage fully and directly with the fictions they are attaching the indexes to. John Updike's *The Centaur* (1963) purports to tell the story of the evolution of a father's relationship with his son in a small town in modern Pennsylvania. At least this is how the averagely dopey reader would understand the story, until, that is, after some 222 pages, he is confronted with an index which begins with 'Achilles 16, 75–6, 167. Adonis, 24, 27, 36, 39, 203. Aphrodite (Venus), 11, 13, 16–17 . . .' And the index continues in the same vein, listing and placing the gods and heroes of antiquity in the small town of Olinger, Pennsylvania. Caldwell, the father and protagonist of the novel, does not feature in the index under his own name. Neither does he appear under the name of his Greek avatar, Chiron, for Chiron, the wounded centaur and teacher, is disguised *passim* throughout the novel under the name of Caldwell. The fuming reader, having belatedly realised that the modern-dress story is a retelling of the legends of classical Greece, has to go right back to the beginning of the novel and start again.

At the heart of Vladimir Nabokov's *Pale Fire* (1992) is a poem by a New England academic, John Shade. The poem is 992 lines long and somewhat in the manner of Robert Frost. Shade's poem is, among other things, a lament for his shy, plain daughter, Hazel, who has committed suicide. Shade himself dies violently, having been mistaken for someone else by a Zemblan assassin called Gradus. However, Nabokov's novel is swelled out by an introduction and commentary provided by Charles Kinbote, an eccentric academic friend of Shade's. Kinbote implausibly relates the contents of the poem to events in the imaginary kingdom of Zembla. Here an alert reader might point out that Shade and his poem are also imaginary, for they are in a novel and Nabokov has invented them, but Zembla is even more imaginary, being the solitary delusion of an imaginary man, invented by Nabokov. The imaginary man, Kinbote imagines that he is King Charles Xavier the Beloved in exile from his throne in Zembla. If the introduction and notes are eccentric, the index is of a similar quality, as the opening entries may serve to indicate:

A. Baron, Oswin Affenpin, the last Baron of Aff, a puny traitor, 286.

Acht. Iris, celebrated actress, d. 1888, a passionate and powerful woman, favourite of Thurgus the Third (*q.v.*), 130, she died officially by her own hand: unofficially strangled in her dressing room by a fellow actor, a jealous young Gothlander, now at ninety, the oldest and least important of the members of the Shadows (*q.v.*) group.

Alfin, King, surnamed The Vague 1872–1918, reigned from 1900; K.'s father; a kind, gentle, absent-minded monarch, mainly interested in automobiles, flying machines, motorboats and, at one time, seashells; killed in an airplane accident, 71.

Andronikov and Niagarin, two Soviet experts in quest of a buried treasure, 130, 681, 741; see Crown jewels.

As can be seen from a quick glance at its opening entries, the index to *Pale Fire* is not entirely satisfactory, as it appears to have been compiled, as it were, from within the novel, for what we have here is Kinbote's index, and while his laboriously cross-referenced index is a rich source on the history and culture of Zembla, he seems to have missed the point of the poem to which the index is at least nominally ancillary. At this point the alert reader, who has been quietly musing over what I have written above, may belatedly object that if Zembla is indeed a more imaginary place than the American college which John Shade taught in, how come Shade actually dies at the hand of a Zemblan assassin? That is such a stupid question that I am not going to bother to answer it here. Surely the main point is that Kinbote's index is a symptom of his insanity. It is also, for my taste, somewhat prosy.

There are also, at first sight, some serious lapses in basic indexing practice, for if one follows up the cross-reference given under '*Andronikov and Niagarin*' to '*Crown Jewels*', one is directed on to '*Hiding Place*', but '*Hiding Place*' only gives us '*potaynik (q.v.)*', '*potaynik*' refers us on to '*taynik (q.v.)*', and '*Taynik Russ*, secret place' takes us all the way back to '*Crown Jewels*'. Yet it is precisely such lapses which provide us with clues to the underlying literariness of the text. Roland Barthes has taught us that novels are not about anything except themselves. The signs on the page refer only to each other and not to anything outside the text. The meaning of any novel can be nothing other than its circular transcribability. This being so, where else can the hidden treasure of Zembla be hidden save in the text? Therefore, if the index located the 'hidden treasure' on a particular page, that treasure would no longer be hidden. It is cheering to discover a novel by that curmudgeonly anti-ideas aesthete, Nabokov, providing such a signal confirmation of modern literary-critical theory.

By contrast, *The Sinking of the Odradek Stadium* (1971–2) by Harry Mathews has a richly-detailed and rewarding index in which fictional creations like 'Dexter Hodge', 'Pan-Nam' and 'Spindle, Knights of the' are listed alongside 'Black Sea', 'Clement VII', 'Glinka' and 'Medici'. Mathews's brilliant novel, besides being a mine of information on Renaissance banking practices, is also an epistolary fiction set in modern times, detailing the progress of a treasure hunt in modern Florida. However, Harry Mathews has spent a great deal of his life in France. He was a close friend of Georges Perec and has been crucially involved with the work of OuLiPo (an experimental group of writers and mathematicians based in

France). It may therefore be appropriate to consider *The Sinking of the Odradek Stadium*, as really a French novel, albeit one written in the English language by an American author. It is also easy to detect the influence of Perec on Mathews's index. Perec's own novella, *Quel petit vélo à guidon chromé au fond de la cour?* (1966) reads as a freewheeling satirical sketch of Parisian intellectual life and more specifically as a portrait of La Ligne Générale, a short-lived, Marxist intellectual group. However, Perec, like Updike, uses the index to avert to the metatext. The formal and rhetorical underpinnings of this slight work are registered in the index. Consider the Cs:

Cacemphaton, 41
Cacography, 18
Catachresis, of course
Cataglottism!
Catalectic, 39
Chiasmus, 7, 8
Circumlocution, 12
Citation, 23
Conspectus, 20
Contraction, everywhere
Crasis, 7

Cacemphaton, as every schoolboy knows, means 'an ill-sounding expression'. The trouble is that the whole of Perec's short novel reads so strangely. The book is full of the most contorted stylistic devices and wilful grammatical irregularities. Therefore when one turns to page 41, one finds that the whole page is full of ill-sounding expressions, though there are not obviously more of these on page 41 than on any of the preceding pages. It is hard then to know what precisely is being indexed under the heading 'Cacemphaton'. Disgruntled, we may pass on to the index of Perec's later and grander work, *La vie mode d'emploi* (1993) which is altogether a more agreeable affair. The novel, which serves as a preface to the lengthy index, presents a portrait of a Parisian apartment-block, which is a house of many stories, and we are given a methodical introduction to its contents and the preoccupations of its inhabitants. The climactic index registers both real and imaginary characters, as well as places, works of art and literature, television programmes, newspapers and jigsaws. Perec's professional background in information retrieval and filing-card management has served him well in this work. Taxonomic preoccupations and listings pervade the novel, for *La vie mode d'emploi* is above all concerned with the orderly classification of the disorderly clutter of life. It is not surprising then to find such famous taxonomists as 'CUVIER (Georges Baron), French Zoologist, 1769–1832', 'DEWEY (Melvil), American bibliographer, 1851–1931 inventor of Universal Decimal Classification (UDC)', and 'LINNAEUS (Carl von), Swedish naturalist, 1707–1778' all featured in the index.

Perec was the master of the fictional index. There is no reason to survey the numerous other, more amateurish, attempts by French writers to provide their novels with indexes. Yet it is worth pausing over Jean d'Ormesson's, *La gloire de l'empire* (1971), for this novel (which comes close to being historiographical hoax) is that rare thing, a novel with two indexes. D'Ormesson's book lovingly chronicles the fortunes of two imaginary dynasties, the Porphyre and the Venosta and places them firmly in the context of the real history of the Middle Ages. One of the book's indexes is for proper names and here fantasy rulers like Balamir, Kha-Khan of the Uighurs, rub shoulders with real historical personages, such as the Byzantine Emperor Basil II. The other index registers historical themes, such as Abdication, Administration, Age d'or, Agriculture, Ambassadeurs, Ambition and so on.

It is a common error to think that the indexed novel is a Continental import and, indeed, merely a modern fad. In fact, we British pioneered the practice in the 18th century. It is perhaps the chief claim to fame of Samuel Richardson that he provided indexes to his novels, *Pamela* (1740–1), *Clarissa*

(1748) and *Sir Charles Grandison* (1754). This is why he is commonly agreed to be one of the founders of the modern novel. There are certain characters whose lives in fiction or reality lend themselves to indexing. Consider the 18th-century diarist, James Boswell. Boswell was, as his biographer and editor Frederick Pottle has shown, much influenced by Richardson and, more specifically by his reading of *Clarissa*. It is not surprising then to find Boswell behaving like a rake in a Richardson novel.

A well plotted index can trace the trajectory of a man or a woman's passions more plainly and economically than continuous prose ever can. Take this non-fictional example from Boswell's *London Journal* (ed. F.A. Pottle, 1950):

Lewis, Mrs (Louisa), actress. JB to call Louisa in journal, 84; receives JB, 85; JB's increased feeling for, 89; JB discusses love with, 94–5; JB anticipates delight with, 96; JB lends two guineas to, 97; disregards opinion of the world, 97–8; discusses religion with JB, 101; JB entreats to be kind, 101; uneasiness discourages JB, 104; JB declares passion for, 107; promises to make JB blessed, 107; JB sees every day, 109; JB talks freely of love connections, 122; JB promises to support child, should one be born, 113; makes assignation with JB, 116; consummation with JB interrupted, 117; promises to pass night with JB, 118; JB likes better and better, 121; JB's felicity delayed, 126; to stay with JB Wednesday night, 130; agrees to go to Hayward's with JB, 135; account of her birth, marriage, and separation, 135; spends night with JB at Hayward's, 137–40; JB has tea with, 141–2; JB afraid of a rival, 144; JB feels coolness for, 145; reads French with JB, 145; JB resolves to keep affection for alive, 149; JB incredulous at infection from, 155–6; JB enraged at perfidy of, 158; JB discusses infection with and takes leave of, 158–61; JB asks his two guineas back, 174–5; returns JB's guineas, 187; mentioned, 12, 98, 116.

(I am indebted to John Julius Norwich's *Christmas Crackers* (2nd ed, 1981) for bringing this entry to my attention.)

In the confident, bustling Victorian era, novelists used their indexes to express their personalities. Just take a look at the opening entries of this novel's index:

ARTISTIC effect dependent on indistinctness (!); 241
Barometer, sideways motion of; 13
Bath, portable, for Tourists; 25
Books or minds. Which contains most science? 21
Boots for horizontal weather; 14
Brain, inverted position of; 243
Bread-sauce. What appropriate for? 58

The whimsicality, paradox and preoccupation with gadgets. One knows immediately that this can only be an index by Lewis Carroll. His *Sylvie and Bruno* (1889) is a lengthy fantasy about a fairy boy, Bruno, who is coaxed out of his bad temper to work on his sister Sylvie's garden. It is not Carroll's best book, as it is over-freighted with Victorian moralising; *q.v.* such index entries as 'Church-going, principle of', 'Conceited people always *depreciate* others', 'Happiness, excessive, how to moderate', 'Paley's definition of Virtue' and 'Poverty, the blessings of'. This would have been a better index if it had been attached to *Alice in Wonderland*. But it is better not to dwell on the might-have-beens of literary history and, to return to the actual index of *Sylvie and Bruno*, what was Carroll thinking of? Why are there so few words beginning with A in his index? I will leave that one with you.

We have seen how an index to a biography, such as Pottle's life of Boswell, can present the protagonist's adventures in essence, flayed of their extraneous wordy detail. The index to a novel can achieve a similar effect, as Virginia Woolf so memorably showed in *Orlando* (1928). Woolf's novel is a love poem couched in prose and disguised as an exercise in imaginary biography. The novel is addressed to Woolf's beloved friend, Vita Sackville-West and it is certain that

Orlando's character was modelled on that of Vita. By far the longest heading in the index is devoted to Orlando:

'Orlando, appearance as a boy, 10; writes his first play, 11; visits Queen at Whitehall, 17; made Treasurer and Steward, 17; his loves, 19; and Russian Princess, 24–5; his first trance, 46; retires into solitude, 48; love of reading, 52; his romantic dramas, literary ambitions, 54, 58, 70, 73, 74; and Greene, 59, 63, 65, 66, 67; his great-grandmother Moll, 60; buys elkhounds, 67; and his poem 'The Oak Tree', 68, 79,102, 122, 166; and his house, 74–8; and the Archduchess Harriet, 80–2; Ambassador at Constantinople, 83–99; created a Duke, 88; second trance, 93; marriage to Rosina Pepita, a gipsy, 97; with the gipsies, 99–107; returns to England, 107; lawsuits, 118; and Archduke Harry, 125; in London society, 135; entertains the wits, 146; and Mr Pope, 149; and Nell, 153; confused with her cousin, 155; returns to her country house, 165; breaks her ankle, 175; declared a woman, 179; engagement, 176; marriage, 184; birth of her first son, 209.

This is a rare example of an index heading changing sex half-way through the entry. Given that Orlando lives for 400 years, the length of the index entry is hardly excessive. But the novel does more than trace the trajectory of an Orlando's life. It also presents a cavalcade of English history. (Incidentally, Orlando is not the only historical survivor; see 'Dupper, Mr, 49, 53, 58, 120, 184'.) Sally Potter's film version of *Orlando*, which was released in 1992, is pleasant to look on as a pageant and to think of as a feminist tract in fancy dress. But the film inevitably disappoints at the end, as the book's index was dropped, presumably because it was judged to be not sufficiently 'filmic'. However, I have no inclination just now to tackle the complex issue of films without indexes.

The furnishing of *Orlando* with an index was I believe a symptom of Woolf's desire to make her fiction resemble a work of non-fiction – of history. On the other hand, Lucy

Ellman, in her high-spirited novel *Sweet Desserts* (1988), actually uses the index to advertise the fictive status of her novel (as if that needed advertising). The book offers an episodic presentation of the life of Suzy Schwartz. It chronicles her love life, her aggravations with her sister Fran, and her researches in art history. It is peppered with jokes, advertisements, questionnaires, press-cuttings, nature notes and other miscellaneous materials. Above all, though, the narrative details her weight problem together with the eating binges, the passages of repentance and depression.

Face, mine upside down, 134.
Félibien des Avaux, André, 45; *see also* Poussin.
Flowers, artichoke blossom, 123; arrangement of beer-coasters, 9; azaleas, 123; buttercups, 1; freesias, 123; iris, 113; Jack-in-the-Pulpits, no mention of, Lily, 63; made out of marzipan, 34–5; roses, porcelain, 128, thorns of, 4; surprise, 127.
Footwear, extensive collection of dolls', 2; Pietro Fortuni's retention of light, 52; Franny's black-and-white, 1, 118; Lily's desire for pink, 90, 92; my slippery, 120.
Found objects, *keep*.

This is clearly a feisty index. (No one would think of calling Gissing's index 'feisty'.) Flowers are clearly important to Fran, but the dominant preoccupations of Ellman's heroine are clearly signposted by those entries elsewhere in the index which are marked '*passim*' such as 'Abstinence' and 'Cookies'. At the same time, the idiosyncrasy of the high-spirited author clearly emerges in such entries as '*dada*, take for granted', 'Warholier-than thou, see Campbell's Chicken Noodle Soup' and 'Index, 143–5'. This last may be taken as an inconspicuous, though pleasing, instance of post-modern self-referentiality. The index functions as a register of the skein of *Leitmotifs*, such as 'Cakes', 'Hair, black curls', and 'Toasters', which weave in with one another to create a kind of Wagnerian *Sprachgesang*. As one studies the index, one becomes intensely aware of the part played by humdrum objects and their evocative resonances in keeping the novel moving along. Just as Wagner had his Ring and his Tarnhelm, Ellman has her 'Aerials, TV' and her 'Nightwear, damaged'.

Any literary text has its fractures and omissions and it is these which allow the practised reader to deconstruct it. Ellman offers us some help here, by dutifully logging the significant absences in her index. For examples, compare the index entry 'Jack-in-the-Pulpits, no mention of' with 'Racket-tennis, non-existence of, p.35'. Of course the first entry should more correctly read 'Jack-in-the-Pulpits, no mention of, *passim*'. More problematic is the case of THE SINKIANG FAT-TAILED SHEEP. Although this beast appears in the index, he is not assigned any page number. In fact THE SINKIANG FAT-TAILED SHEEP does appear on page 46, but without any accompanying nature note, or anything else which might have indicated why it has been dumped into the text at this point. It is tempting here to detect a deliberately allusive parallelism between THE SINKIANG FAT-TAILED SHEEP's lack of a textual context with its lack of a page number in the index. Once again we are being alerted to a significant absence. Those of us who are well-up in lit-crit and who know our Jacques Derrida like to read novels in order to discover what is significantly not mentioned in them. Thus one can read Jane Austen's *Mansfield Park*, which is really a novel about sexual passion, in order to learn what it says about sexual passion, which is nothing at all. In much the same way the post-modern reader will take pleasure from his study of the absence from Ellman's challenging novel of both Jack-in-the-Pulpits and THE SINKIANG FAT-TAILED SHEEP.

One gets more of this heady, theoretical stuff in Malcolm Bradbury's *My Strange Quest for Mensonge, Structuralism's Hidden Hero* (1987). In this novel Bradbury addresses the condition of post-modernity and reinvents the indexed novel. Although it is a more or less universally observed convention in literary criticism that the critic never admits to finding anything he has been reading difficult, I found Bradbury's novel hard going. It is austere, self-referential and has lots of French words in it. The text seems to be primarily concerned with 'the death of the author', but I could not see what the fuss was about. We are all going to die some time. As for the index, it is mostly concerned with such abstruse matters as 'Aporia', 'Being, compared with Non-Being', 'Deconstruction' and 'Diachronic axes'. However, 'Vol-au-vent' does get a look-in and I was delighted to see my old friend, John Sturrock, featuring in the index as 'Sturrock, John, 42; excellent index of, 119'. True, I could not find Sturrock or his index in Bradbury's text. (It is a short book of only 104 pages.) This could be regarded as carelessness on Bradbury's part, but, having due regard for the context of the 'error', I am more inclined to regard this as a coded message to the reader, having not a little to do with the author's contention that we are living in 'the age of the floating signifier'. We all have to be intensely aware of the arbitrariness of signs.

The index to Alain de Botton's *Kiss and Tell* (1995) is a rather more down-to-earth affair. In the novel itself (which I am tempted to regard as a mere prelude to and pretext for a satisfying index), the young protagonist sets out to write the biography of his girlfriend, Isabel Rogers. He undertakes this in a doomed attempt to retain her affections by demonstrating that he is not as self-obsessed as she thinks he is. Isabel, who lives in a house off Hammersmith Grove, has not had an exciting life, as can be seen from a sample listing of some of the sub-headings under 'Rogers, Isabel Jane:

    dental work on, 116–17.
    dislike of sports, 38–9.
    disregard for convention, 204–5.
    drinks preferred, 17–18, 20, 23.
    driving ability, 227.

And so it goes on, the itemisation of such mundanities as 'handwriting', 'love of ironing' and 'packing problems'. It is the rostering of the beloved girl's fetching ordinariness – alphabetised banality, if you will. Banality indeed constitutes the potentially explosive molten core of de Botton's novel. After interrogating Isabel about how she applies her make-up, the narrator goes on to observe that the 'banality of such a ritual to anyone of the female species did not obscure its significance. What is most banal for one person strikes another as exotic precisely on the basis of this banality – the thing which that one believes unworthy of interest sparks exceptional curiosity if one happens to be surprised'. More-over, the index performs the secondary function of logging the cultural credentials of Isabel and her obsessed biographer. They go to the cinema a lot and they earnestly sample the classic works of literature. Hence the entries on such subjects as 'Auden, W.H.', 'Barbican, London', and 'Camus, Albert'. Less tangible topics also feature, including 'banal advice', 'empathy' and 'friendship after sex'.

The fictional narrator, whom we are also to identify as the compiler of this index, has self-effacingly excluded himself from it (and there is a strong contrast here with the wretched Charles Kinbote). Only I note the appearance of the subhead-ing 'inviting biographer home, 26', under the main heading 'Rogers, Isabel Jane'. But his self-effacement proves to be not enough to save their affair and the story ends unhappily. (STOP PRESS. I have just found the reference to Sturrock's index in Bradbury's *Mensonge*. It is on page 19, not page 119, as in the index. So it was carelessness after all. Ah well.) Back to Alain de Botton's book. It is the sheer intensity of the narrator's regard and his relentless enquiries into every aspect of Jane's personality which destroys their relationship. 'Isabel woke up one morning and got bored of being understood.' She tells him that they should stop seeing one another. However, one's sadness at the end of the love story is tempered by turning straightaway to a good index. The book's author, Alain de Botton, is still young and it will be interesting to see what indexes he produces in the future.

Novels with indexes are easy to discuss. Novels which do not have them are a different matter. Take William Boyd's *A Good Man in Africa* (1981). This novel won both the Whitbread Literary Award and the Somerset Maugham

Award. *The Times* praised it as 'wickedly funny'. Several of
my friends have recommended it to me. Even so, I occasionally heard regretful utterings about its lack of an index, so it
was a long time before I nerved myself to get down to reading
it. When I did so, I was completely foxed. Since I normally
only read novels with indexes, I wondered how other readers
managed to get through Boyd's book without this vital aid.
Who was the 'Priscilla' mentioned on page 11? Was she
significant? Or could I forget about her, because she was not
going to be mentioned again? Why was the hero, Morgan
Leafy, so worried by a Dr Murray, first cryptically referred to
on page 13 and then quite frequently throughout the book
(though not frequently enough in my opinion to merit a
passim)? By the time I got to page 150, I was wondering
whether Morgan had not had rather a lot of gin for a
character who was only half-way through the book, but
without an index, I was unable to check. In short I was
completely at sea.

For a while I kept turning the pages, collecting snatches of
delayed revelation about Morgan, Priscilla, Murray and
others. I was like a beggar waiting for scraps to be tossed
from a rich man's table. Finally, I decided to go back to the
beginning and compile my own index to Boyd's novel. I am
feeling much better now. Here are some sample entries from
my work, which is based on the Penguin edition of 1982.
This is very much work in progress:

Adekunle, corrupt politician, Morgan first hears of,
100; reader first hears of, 20.
Bilbow, see *Dildo*.
Breasts, fabulous, of black girl, 189; c.f. Fanshawe,
Priscilla, breasts of.
Bunfight, any excuse for, 115.
Cake, icing on the, 116.
Climax, A Good Man in Africa, of, 291–312
Crimean War dressing station, a scene in the novel like,
256.

Dildo, Bilbow, Greg, British Council-sponsored poet misheard as, 246.

Eyebrow, Morgan's, missing, caused by, attempt to rescue baby trapped in burning house, 287, blowback of gas cooker, 265, cigarette-lighter going whoomph, 286, Morgan setting light to derelict car, in order to distract people's attention while he shifts lightning-struck corpse, 258, Santa's sledge shot down in flames, 262, too much brandy on the Christmas pudding, 284.

Fanshawe, Chloe, body forms accentuated, 70; breasts, like empty socks, 188, tumble free of nylon corsetry, 308; buttocks, turquoise globes, 223, corsetry of, 29; prow of her chest, immense, 155; tightly packed and constrained bosom of, 188.

Fanshawe, Priscilla, breasts of, impossibility of, 33, impossibly firm, 106, Morgan allowed to squeeze, 108, pointing by Priscilla, 31, sharp, 105, small, 163, 164, taken in by Morgan for the first time, 54, unbelievably firm and conical, 130, unimaginably pointed of, 98; first mention of (Priscilla, not her breasts), 11; last reference to, 309; Morgan's first meeting with, 98; teeth of, Morgan tries to get tongue past, 104.

Fanshawe, Reggie, see Hatred, Morgan's.

Folklore, Kinjanjan, gnomic trenchancy of, 216

Gin, bought by Lee Wan for Morgan, 88–9, Chloe Fanshawe offers Morgan, 223, Morgan offers Dalmire, 11, rest of into flower-bed, 82, tumbler-full at Fanshawe's, 81, reference to on p. 11 repeated, 206, vomiting caused by, 289.

Gonorrhoea, Morgan unaware he has, 109, still fails to identify correctly, 143–4, Dr Murray diagnoses, 159, nose drops off as a consequence of, Morgan wonders if, 160, treatment for, 170–1, amputation not necessary as a consequence of, 171.

Good Man, 11, phrase repeated, 205, not many around, 311.

Hatred, Morgan's, of accents, Australian 15, Geordie, 15, Welsh, 15; of analogues, visual, used in conversation, 16; of Dalmire 14; of Fanshawe, Reggie, 27; of Murray, 15; of Nkongsamba, 17; of shorts, 13; of work, 23.

Hum, of air-conditioning, monotonous, 22.

Mad, happily tolerated in Africa, 18; houseboy, Kojo, thinks Morgan, 23; Morgan, at Fanshawe, 67.

Lying, doggo, 288; lightning struck body still, in compound, 221; Morgan to Bilbow, 250, to Murray, 262, to everyone else, *passim*.

Murray, Dr, first mention of, 15; last mention of, 312; Morgan's first meeting with, 87, the page where it is at last made completely clear why he is so important to the plot, 231.

PART TWO, begins 87.

Peectures, filthy, 223.

Pencil, Morgan not got lead in his, 166.

Sex, Morgan always thinking of, 24; of lightning-struck corpse, clarified 70; one of two good things in Africa, 41.

Sinatra, Frank, 240.

Socks, empty, see Chloe Fanshawe, breasts of.

Spelling mistakes, see Peectures, filthy.

Status symbol, Peugot as, 34.

Two, it takes to tango, 172. c.f. Sex.

Yard-arm, 11.

Zen master, Morgan empty of thought like, 226.

From the above it can be seen what a useful critical tool a carefully-assembled index can be. Take those breasts (I mean the breasts of Priscilla and Chloe Fanshawe). Do they not seem to have an existence which is more or less independent of their owners? I am reminded of Nikolai Gogol's story, 'The Nose', in which a nose breaks free of its owner and goes off having adventures on its own. As Nabokov observed in his monograph on Gogol, the question whether 'the "fancy begat the nose or the nose begat the fancy" is inessential'. Of

course it is. Inessential and quite irrelevant to any consideration of *A Good Man in Africa*. Besides, come to think of it, I
may have been muddling up Gogol with Woody Allen. (Not
for the first time.) What I was actually thinking of was that
scene in Allen's film, *Everything You Always Wanted to
Know About Sex, But Were Afraid to Ask*, in which a giant
breast goes on the rampage.

Although I am, of course, available to index other people's
novels, the activity is such an agreeably therapeutic exercise
that I recommend that novelists should index their own
works if they can. Most novelists, on reaching the last page of
the story they have to tell, experience the literary equivalent
of post-natal depression. Indexing what one has just written
can serve as a sovereign remedy against post-creative blues. 'It
was among the ruins of the Capitol that I first conceived the
idea of a work which has amused and exercised near twenty
years of my life, and which, however, inadequate to my own
wishes, I finally deliver to the curiosity and candour of the
public'. This is the last sentence of Edward Gibbon's *The
Decline and Fall of the Roman Empire*. He completed the
great work on the night of the 27th June 1787. Looking back
on the occasion in his *Autobiography*, he wrote that 'I will
not dissemble the first emotions of joy on the recovery of my
freedom, and, perhaps, the establishment of my fame. But my
pride was soon humbled, and a sober melancholy was spread
over my mind, by the idea that I had taken an everlasting
leave of an old and agreeable companion . . .' However, I like
to imagine Gibbon shrugging off that sober melancholy and
cheering up when he realises that he still has the index
to do. (It starts with 'Aban, the Saracen, heroism of his
widow'.) An index to a book, whether fiction or non-fiction,
serves as a graceful coda and it confers a richness to the
conclusion of a text which cannot be provided by a mere
FINIS.

Sarah May

BLUEPRINT

HOLDING AN UMBRELLA in one hand, and his briefcase open between his legs, Klaus Konditorei started to feel his way through the rubbish in the bin, layer after layer, moved as always to tears. As soon as he came across anything edible he bent down and slipped it into his briefcase which had been empty at 6.00 that morning.

This was his last stop. There were one hundred and fifty bins in central Nuremburg, all green, with the municipal slogan on them. Some mornings he barely filled his briefcase, on others he had to resort to three, even four overflow bags. One morning his baggage had been so excessive that the security guard on reception at the Department of the Environment short-circuited his monitor, violently. Now when Klaus entered the building the guard raised a handkerchief to his face, like a doctor, using initiative in the face of catastrophe.

This morning's collection was minimal. He snapped the case shut and walked into the building which was black and made of glass. Designed to look impenetrable and useless, it suited heavy snows, high skies, quartz frosts. The heat in the summer made the dust rise as high as the baronial top floor.

Klaus Konditorei had taken the same route to work for the past twenty years, growing during that time from an old to an older man. His work at the Department of the Environment rarely varied, like the work they commissioned from the Institute of Architects, who still supplied him with the second-rate students. The mediocrity never changed.

The Department was always rebuilding, strictly in the spirit of 'municipality' that nowadays had the strange ring of communal love about it. Municipality was being pushed further than it ever had been in the 1890s when it was first perceived that such a thing as the general public existed. Now the general public was a legitimate, literate mass, and he was responsible for carrying out extensive and frantic new building programmes with an overriding architecture of anaesthesia.

The architects he commissioned at the Institute worked on a factory line producing functional spaces that were unlikely to survive a century of history. Whenever Klaus arrived at the Institute which was white and smooth with moderate ceilings, and statues which should have looked ruder than they did, they would take him into corners, behind pillars or up stairwells to tell him in whispers that they were 'all having the same dreams. My library looked the same as Brand's gallery; there's no difference. We aren't dreaming ourselves anymore.'

'It's a form of ecstasy,' Klaus would say, indifferent.

And Frederick, the director of public architecture, who had known Klaus for thirty years, and taught him as a student, would say 'all my young designers have been infiltrated by this culture of substance abuse; they are ecstatic, but clumsy, careless. They are without focus, some of them barely know where they are standing. They aren't even building for their own life-span let alone the life-span of their children.'

'Those are your worst students, Fred. The ones I have specifically chosen.'

'You have made our city so clean we feel uncomfortable walking on the pavements. Everything is so new, the few remaining "histories" have been integrated in a way that produces hybrids, buildings with such deformities they look as if they have been subjected repeatedly to radiation in the womb. Do you really think you should give yourself the right to deconsecrate a church, knock down the nave, then make the tower a feature on a high-rise insurance building? These multi-national corporations you are forever rehousing; do you want people to survive the 20th century only to rediscover feudalism? You are more medieval than you think, Klaus. And the surfaces of these buildings even though reflective are nothing more than two-way mirrors. Every surface is a surveillance camera when our city is already the most sinister in the world. What are you hoping to catch on tape?

'The other day walking home, I saw a man pissing against the wall of the new public library which, as you know, is covered in a particularly imperialistic white marble. The urine trickling down the wall was the most beautiful warm mellow colour on the stone. People need to leave traces of themselves, Klaus. Do you know what people do at the edges of the world to stop their hands freezing off – they piss over them.'

'Urine,' Klaus repeated.

In the beginning a new building was added to his elevated model every month, and he would go home and say to his new wife, 'I'm rebuilding the city, I'm rebuilding the city,'. Then he would take her by the hand, sometimes late at night, and with a set of keys he showed her museums before exhibits, galleries before pictures, libraries before books. And they would stay the night and fill the buildings with their sounds which became the crowds and the furniture.

'I've seen your city, and it's empty,' she would say.

Later in their marriage she would go alone in daylight, and still she would say, 'I've seen your city, and it's empty.'

Klaus stamped 'approved' on another set of plans, then opened his briefcase. He had a plastic lining inside and now, at midday, the morning's collection was sweating and comingling. He ate his lunch which looked better once chewed and swallowed than it did in its solid state. Often he overate and sometimes he fell on all fours in front of the toilet.

Meanwhile, ten floors above Klaus in the General Manager's office from which the whole city could be seen, they discussed a regeneration programme. Their sole audience was a young girl who stood by an urn of coffee, too afraid to replenish cups and too afraid to leave the room, party to information that would later be circulated as Highly Confidential.

'These proposals are for towers of garbage. It's not what I expect from somebody who has twenty years experience of central urban redevelopment.'

'We already have towers of garbage.'

'Areas applicable for potential redevelopment.'

'You saw the cartoon in *Spiegel*? The one where the civil servant has his arm up to his elbow in a litter bin?'

'Something to do with salaries?'

'Whatever. It was Klaus; it was meant to be Klaus.'

'We're getting complaints from the general public now.'

'He's even going into bins on private property, in people's back gardens.'

'People don't want to see civil servants searching through bins.'

'The students are moving in, energetically, saying it's the latest move in a campaign to starve the homeless to death; the tabloids are already using words such as "genocide".'

'Death squads?' There were men in the room old enough to remember, so he used the words bashfully.

'Yes, "death squads" was yesterday.'

'You can't just sack a civil servant. Once people are in these corridors they are here for ever. We have to wait for them to leave of their own accord one way or the other.'

'Make his position redundant.'

'There are people walking these corridors with more metal in them than robots. That girl there by the coffee machine is the first one we've had with two arms and two legs.'

'Well one leg is shorter than the other, I couldn't help noticing,' the General Manager said.

'The last one had a glass eye, a wig, no breasts, and a false leg. Every day I see people gripping files under their chins because they haven't got any arms; I was driven mad by this squeaking noise which turned out to be a stump on a wooden trolley, holding a printer in one hand, while propelling the trolley with the other. Apparently he works in systems support. It's disconcerting to have a . . . colleague who is only as high as your waist. We're a hospital for the living. Klaus Konditorei is of able body and has been with the Department for twenty years, we can't just dismiss him. I don't think anybody's ever been dismissed have they?'

Nobody answered. Nobody was interested for long in Klaus Konditorei.

Ten floors below Klaus raised himself up from the floor clutching his belly and watched as the remains vanished down the toilet; today's waste was bad. It no longer bothered him that colleagues couldn't speak with him, or that his name on paper meant nothing, because he had succeeded in getting them to build his city.

He had seen this city forty years ago, sitting in a pram surrounded by the contents of his mother's kitchen. You could see a lot at three from an upturned saucepan. What he saw was his world as it was then, and his world to come. His mother's bent head was covered in a red scarf; her head was always bent, and sometimes he worried that she was directing her prayers towards him. He learnt that mothers partake very readily in the boy-king ideology, dreaming that before boys become men they will not only save them, but the rest of the world as well.

At the age of three he wore shoes made of cardboard, and they were using glue to thicken their soup, sometimes candle wax if no glue was to be had, until by 1945 they were something other than human, he and his mother. And all she ever said was, 'Now if we were in Russia things would be much worse. And if we were in Leningrad . . .'. He never did find out what happened in Leningrad. For twelve months they moved from ruin to ruin; a corner anywhere was shelter enough for them. He would dig a hole in the ground and she would put the stove in it. Often she would put him in the pram and cover him with the blanket while she went out to look for stray dogs so that she could turn up at the Allied HQ kitchens and beg for the intestines of a cow, or the offal, because she knew that the British were more likely to take pity on a starving dog than a child. And she would get some indescribable part of an animal, wrapped in newspaper which she would add, after taking the meat out, bloodstained, to his shoes or even his bedding. The word *ersatz* for him still smelt of animals' blood, even after the hunger years.

Later, when they had a roof over their head and not much else, his mother still used the dog trick, but by then it was on butchers, and done out of pride rather than imagination. And what everybody failed to see was that this city of Nuremburg was not only a new city, it was his city, a fulfilment of an earlier vision, capable of crumbling before dust had time to settle on stone. And when he watched it, the shamefaced flags of the countries of Europe were replaced by red headscarves. Nobody could remember what the old city looked like, not even the old city in ruins, apart from those who were blind. He had the blueprint of the entire city imprinted on his mind and could find his way anywhere, even in darkness. There were rooms in buildings that weren't shown on the plans and, in every building, there was a small room the size of a cupboard, which he called the site crematorium, to honour the site of a previous building whilst eradicating its memory. Klaus Konditorei was what came to them after the echo of countless numbers of boots, after the stadium screams, after the heartstopping moments when people were permitted instincts; after the bombs.

When his wife still loved him, when they used to argue, she would always shout 'where is the tree you gave me my first kiss under? Where is the building you proposed to me by in the rain? Where is the church we were married in? Where is the old library we would make love in after hours? Where are we?'

'They had no roofs, no windows, no books. You wait, you won't have seen anything as beautiful as this, just wait till I've finished. You won't even have imagined anything as beautiful.'

And he kissed her frown.

'How much money have you got in your pot now, then?' Inge's husband asked her one night, not taking his eyes off the television.

SARAH MAY

'Last time I looked, roughly DM25,000.'
'Last time you looked?'
'Yes.'
'Which was when?'
'Two weeks ago,' she shrugged, but carried on looking at him expectantly.
'Two weeks is a long time.'
'It can be a long time, or a very short time. Depending.'
'Well, this time it seems like a long time. Go upstairs and take your clothes off; ruffle the sheets on the bed and lie on top of it with your legs apart. I'm going to watch the end of this programme.'
She got up immediately and left the room. An hour later he prised her mouth open and ejaculated deeply into it. She poured glass after glass of water from the jug at the bedside to try and quench the burning at the back of her throat, and nearly choked as she tried to speak. Her husband got his wallet out of his jacket pocket.
'You gave me such pleasure tonight. DM200?'
'DM200 isn't very much, I've nearly lost my voice.'
'It's relative,' he said wearily, putting the money in the pot by the bedside for her. 'You must have enough for your fur coat now, surely.'
'The one I want is very expensive. It's exquisite. I can't describe it to you.'
Inge and her husband had been making love like this for fifteen years. Fifteen years ago she asked him for a fur coat and became contemptible to him. He called her words he couldn't bear to hear others speak aloud. She didn't even contradict him, but said that she would work for the money herself, which she did.
And the more he paid, the more they were able to transcend themselves, and a strange architecture of sex, without love, was enacted on the bed. These were moments when, crouched over her with handfuls of still warm coal, he would rub the black dust into her body tasting the bitter freedom of instinct, and remind himself of the fact that he must have wanted to do this even when he loved her. They

86

became familiar with every taste the human body was capable of exuding, she treated him as both man and woman, and often fell down under the weight of the apparatus she was wearing. They disguised their gender from each other, their age, so that sometimes she sat on his knee, sometimes she lay across it, and sometimes he made such genuine infant noises that new parents thought it was their baby waking in the night. Sometimes they were so still, they merely traced the outlines of shadows on each other's bellies, while other times they hurt each other so much, they maimed. He once spent a week at work on crutches. And because there was the exchange of money there was never refusal, or denial or argument. Until one night in late winter with the covers around the feet of the bed, and the mattress laid bare, he saw the shadows of their climax on the wall behind them. He expected to see the head of a monster; a 20th-century monster from a visionary test-tube, but instead he saw a woman sleeping. Despite the last fifteen years they still called it 'lovemaking'.

Klaus Konditorei entered the Institute of Architects for the fifth time that week.

'Much as I love you, Klaus, I could almost get sick of seeing you. You are beginning to smell, you know.'

'I have to come directly to you now; it's no good circulating memos or organising meetings at work, nobody there will speak to me any more. I don't take the pleasure I used to in the matt black plastic covers that bind the proposals. Did you know that they're happy to let the city build itself?'

'Don't tell me that you need a memorial. A plaque?'

'No, but Fred, there is something I forgot, in my original plans, something fundamental.'

'That the Board didn't notice?'

'They would never notice this. They aren't used to wiping their own backsides. We need a municipal waste plant. All this rubbish we are producing has nowhere to go. This waste plant won't be a rotting mountain, it will be a factory where everything is recycled, rejuvenated, regenerated, where nothing will ever die. There won't be any more waste, Fred.' He stopped, and sat still, leaning forward so that his arm covered half the desk.

'Without the Board's permission?'

'Without their knowledge.'

'I don't know, Klaus.'

'Then you're nothing more than a fat baron afraid to watch his own dick piss.'

Frederick opposite remembered a small boy, clean, but with barely any clothing, and torn nails, who was pressed against his mother's stomach as she asked, above the boy's head, if there was any need of a cleaner or caretaker at the Institute. At the time Frederick thought she was asking for herself, but she meant for the boy. 'Domestic staff aren't hired any more, not in that way; if you're looking for that sort of work, then read the advertisements in the papers,' he joked, already deciding that he would take the boy on. It wasn't until Klaus had been working for them for six years that he discovered the graffiti in the toilets. Small bird's-eye sketches, scratched into the toilet doors with a compass or penknife, of fantastic buildings, executed meticulously as if the designer thought there was the possibility they would be built.

'You were the only real student I ever had, Klaus. Why did I let you go to the Department of the Environment?'

'You knew I wouldn't be happy designing summerhouses, hotels, bridges. I wanted the whole city.'

'Your waste plant is impossible. I know the piece of land you're thinking about – it's private property.'

'Then the Department will have to buy it. Who owns it?'

'I can't disclose that information. Anyway, it's irrelevant, it's being built on at the moment. Residential. One of our best students is working on it.'

And that was the last time Klaus spoke to Frederick with any conviction, with any authority. When he got back to the office he was summoned up ten floors and summarily fired. They had found out about the crematoriums and declared

BLUEPRINT

that many of the buildings he was responsible for were
structurally unsound.

The Board was amazed by Klaus.

'Your shoes are held together by staples.'

'The sole came away from the rest of the shoe.'

'Doesn't that qualify for a new pair?'

'The shoes weren't without soles, they were separated from
them.'

'Oh. And your shirt collar isn't lying right.'

'No, it's turned inside out, it frayed. Look, the same thing
happened to my cuffs.'

'My God, your jacket. Sellotape? And red thread? The
buttons, they're National Railway buttons. From a guard's
uniform.'

'One I found, yes.'

'The disgrace.'

And to nearly all his comments he added in a mumble,
'Waste not, want not,' until the end, when he said, 'But that's
not true, is it? Who's going to finish the city?'

'The city will finish itself in the same way that it has built
itself.'

'How much money have you got now in your pot, then?'
Klaus asked his wife, without taking his eyes off the
television.

'Nothing,' Inge replied.

'You've bought your coat?'

He had never, he realised, foreseen this eventual conclusion.

'No. I didn't buy the coat.'

She drove him in the car to a spot fifteen miles west of the
city where a thin line of forest began; the proposed site of his
waste disposal plant. By moonlight, using a torch for the
details, and holding his hand Inge showed Klaus around the
reconstructed ruins of Nuremburg library which the architect
had built around a tree, overlooked by a small belfry which
had been found in Poland.

'There's an altar inside. It's over 600 years old, and the priest from Witzbern can come over one Sunday a month.'

'You're still practising?'

'Every Sunday.'

'Every Sunday for the past fifteen years?'

'This is our garden; our history. I've been working on it for fifteen years.'

'Frederick built it didn't he?'

She barely smiled, walking him round slowly while stroking the palm of his hand.

Behind the ruins of the old library a white house rose up, shaped like a ship so that with the temporary display of moonlight it seemed as though it were moving. There were silver railings around the outside and no windows.

'The roof is sunken and made of glass,' she said watching him move his eyes up and down the walls in panic as if he were already inside.

'The roof?'

'Yes.'

'I've never had a building designed with a glass roof. Glass walls, but never a glass roof.'

'Well, you didn't build this one, I did.'

'And it's more beautiful than anything I could have imagined.'

'Out here we can't see the city. Only the orange of the lights at night.'

They walked towards the house, neither leading the other.

'The city will build itself.'

Neil Rollinson

BIG IN JAPAN

As I pass the gates of Buckingham Palace
I'm exposed in a hundred Japanese cameras,
a fossil, flash-frozen in Kodachrome.

I'm big in Japan, they've seen my face
blossom in a thousand Tokyo photo-labs.

In Wakayama somebody opens an album
to reminisce, and there I am under the apple tree
part of the family portrait.

A girl in Kagoshima
opens her purse by the sea and looks
at a photograph. It's a picture of me.

She can't remember my name, or how
she came to know me, but I'm smiling at her.

Behind my head she can see the traffic
in Parliament Square, the Abbey, the black hands
of Big Ben captured at ten fifteen.

FRUIT

Now that you've got me home, you hand me
the pinking shears with a grin. They are heavy
and cold like the ones my mother used to have.
You lie on the floor and ask me to cut you
free from your dress. So I take the hem
in my fingers, guiding the zigzag blades

with an unsteady hand, opening you up
to the waist, your legs pale in the lamplight.
I've wanted this all summer long, can't imagine
how good you will be. I can smell your heat
like a fruit, hear your breath, deep and slow,
as the mouth of the scissors slides
through your dress. I snip at the neck
and all the green silk falls off you like water,
I cut through your bra with a snap, your heavy breasts
come free from their cups, the nipples like knots.
I run the blunt nose of the scissors over your lips
and throat, your belly and thighs, snick
the white of your knickers, and you part your legs
at last and I bring my mouth down to taste you,
dark and drenched like a flower in dew.
You play with my hair as I work with my lips
and tongue, and fingers, and you flood in my mouth
at last, pulling my head by the root.

Rosie Jackson

A Christmas Letter

DON'T WORRY – THIS won't be another of those gloating newsletters that slide from Christmas cards these days like plums from festive puddings. You know the sort I mean. All those happy families. Wives who've had hits as business execs, romantic novelists. Supermen husbands who leap from building fairy-tale conservatories to summer hiking in the Pyrenees, or winters scuba-diving off the Coral Reef.

It's not that I think they're lying, the writers of these glorious solstice epistles. Just that the spirit of Christmas has carried them away – tinted and inflated their memories till there's no room left for anything but exultation, jubilation. I mean, the children they have – did you ever meet such paragons, such virtuosi? Infant prodigies who play piccolos, pianos, violins; Enid Blyton schoolkids who cheerfully rescue rabbits and visit grannies in distress; diligent adolescents who graduate into lucrative but philanthropic work. Surely the world wouldn't be in such a mess, if it had these model citizens in it?

Anyway, you can rest assured there'll be none of that boasting here. No exclamation marks, no melodramatic prose. Don't they say exaggeration's the enemy of truth? I tell you, our past year's been quite enough without any fancy embroidering.

To start at the beginning. It was uneventful enough. I made the usual New Year resolutions: lose weight, go to yoga classes twice a week, progress to a new word-processing programme, learn how to change a tyre. The only one that lasted beyond February was the promise to make a vegetable patch. By the late autumn I'd actually harvested 19 lbs of runner beans and 99 ornamental gourds – the bi-coloured warty kind, saffron yellow and deep bottle green, like miraculous ice-cream.

But it wasn't because I'm weak-willed that my resolutions proved to be so short-lived. It was the aftermath of what happened in February – Valentine's Day to be exact, the date's etched in our memory.

Samantha, our leggy and – though I say it myself – rather gorgeous eighteen-year-old, was in between boyfriends at the time, but being a great believer in the rituals of St Valentine, she decided her parents should have some romance instead. She persuaded me to book a table for Mike and myself at the trattoria a few miles away and she would look after Thomas – who, believe it or not, has now reached double figures himself.

'Go on, Mum,' Sam cajoled. 'You can't be in your study every night. I'll cook pancakes or something for Thomas. We won't tell Dad, it'll be a surprise.'

I was more upset for Sam than for myself at how badly her plan misfired. Mike was visibly taken aback when he got home from college, expecting a desultory evening in front of the box, chatting with the kids, only to have the prospect of my company – undiluted except for a litre or two of Chianti.

We were only half-way to the restaurant – I was driving so Mike could drink – when he asked me to pull over. I remember parking very deliberately beneath one of those orange street lamps that give a luxurious feeling of being caught in amber. When I looked at Mike to find out why we'd stopped, he was staring through the windscreen as though trying to decipher his script there, like TV weather-men.

'I'm sorry,' he said. 'It just feels hypocritical to let tonight go any further.'

'What do you mean?' I asked.

'This Valentine lark . . .' There was a long pause. I was

used to Mike tossing words at me like bait, expecting me to finish difficult sentences for him, but this time I let the silence run.

'The thing is – ,' he squinted more intently at the orange horizon as if his lines were getting more difficult to read. 'I wasn't planning to tell you yet – not today of all days – but I can't let you . . . There's someone else.'

To my surprise then, I found I was laughing. Yes, laughing. Not the bitter laughter of hysteria or shocked incredulity, but genuine amusement. 'Don't tell me,' I said. 'That graduate student you raved about then haven't mentioned for weeks.'

Mike seemed taken aback, relieved I wasn't causing an angry scene, but stung by my obvious contempt. 'Actually, she's very mature . . .'

'Of course.' I reversed the car out of the amber light into a neat three point turn. 'After all, she must have been in her first term at school when Samantha was born . . .'

I'm afraid that marked the end of the Valentine's date – and the marriage. Next day Mike decamped to his girlfriend's cramped flat in the middle of Brighton where the only reminder of nature was a collection of carved shells and rigid starfish on the bathroom floor. It was I – who, you'll remember, only moved to the sticks to satisfy Mike's fantasy of rural life – who was stranded here in the Sussex countryside with two kids, three dogs, four cats and a menagerie of peacocks, geese and doves.

Don't panic, though. I'm not about to spill depression over you, or bore you with that bleak mid-winter stuff. I've never suffered from an irony deficiency, I could see the funny side of it all. I joked about it with Mike when he collected the kids one weekend.

'So why do you think it is,' I teased him, 'that middle-aged men can get away with it? Turn back the clock, pick up women half their age, have a second youth? While middle-aged women get strapped to the hands of the clock like Catherine on the wheel?'

He gave me a furtive, guilty smile, not sure if I was being

serious or not, then bent down to fondle one of the cats. It was the same tentative smile I've seen on people's faces when they pass beggars or *Big Issue* vendors in the street – a mixture of embarrassment and apology that says sorry, but I'm as helpless as you, this is one of those sad social mysteries for which there is no answer.

I wonder now if it would have been better if I had ranted and raved, been angry or rushed to the doctor for a bottle of valium. If I had, Samantha and Thomas might have reacted differently. Oh, I know it's pointless flogging oneself with perpetual 'if onlies', but when one's children suffer, when one senses them starting to skid out of control, veer towards the cliff edge, it's a worry like no other. It was as though Sam and Thomas took on themselves the disappointment, the rage and darkness they expected me to feel, and the cloud that should have been mine settled on their shoulders.

Not that I knew any of this at first. My excuse is that I was too busy getting by. Mike had always ferried the kids to and from school, shared the night runs when they socialised – we live fifteen miles from Brighton – and without him, chauffering became something of a full-time job. Nor could I call him to pick up shopping I'd forgotten: cat food, loo rolls, tea, so life generally became more hectic, my brain working overtime.

Hardly surprising, then, if I missed the clues. Mike was financially generous to us all and when Thomas's room started filling with new gadgets – a play station, discs, clothes, trainers – I assumed they too had been paid for by Mike's conscience money. In fact I only cottoned on when Mike came round a couple of weeks ago with a pile of presents, and in that half-guilty half-defiant way of his told me he couldn't have Sam and Thomas for Christmas as planned because he'd found a last-minute bucket flight and was taking his girlfriend to Tenerife.

At that, for the first time since February, I flipped. 'Great,' I yelled. 'Can't be a real father, but come round here and play Father Christmas, buying your kids off with expensive gifts.'

I reeled off the dozens of items that had accumulated in Thomas's room over the year, making wild guesses at their value and hurling the sums at Mike as if they were weapons. Only when I saw his surprise was genuine and the shock of the truth hit us both – that we had a child thief on our hands – did I stop shouting and let Mike hold me the way he used to, the way only the father of your child can. Was this why Thomas had done it, I wondered – been so nimble-fingered? Was he trying to reunite Mike and me, to bring us together in our common anxiety and shame? Certainly it seemed to work. Mike left promising he'd come round and sort things out in the new year, though whether by that he means the marriage or Thomas, we shall have to see.

And Samantha? Well, she didn't break the law exactly, though some would condemn her behaviour as immoral. Her response to Mike's departure was to become my angry champion. She wasn't going to have me on the shelf, she bullied me not to 'let myself go', and when I bridled at the discipline of yoga, Sam chaperoned me to dance classes where we would both learn to salsa and jive.

The truth, I realised too late, was that I should have been chaperoning her. Justin, the dance instructor – all concave cheekbones and Bryan Ferry hair – had one of those lithe little bodies I've never found attractive but some women die for. You know – over-tight, narrowly muscular, with the relentless sinewy buttocks of a jockey. Men like that make me feel too solid, as if like Hamlet's my flesh should melt, thaw and resolve itself into a dew. I didn't even think of Justin in sexual terms and it was another great shock to discover Samantha did. Perhaps it was their being birds of a feather that did it, Sam being the same height and skinny with it.

Anyway, by the time this slow-on-the-uptake mother knew what was happening, the dance course and their love affair had come to an end and – despite the enlightened sex education I'd given her – Sam was defiantly pregnant. Justin, to give him his due, offered to marry her, but Sam isn't one to be blackmailed by circumstance. She plans to stay with me, have the baby, then take up her place at university. Ambitious, but as Mike pointed out when we told him, she can do it.

'You've got a good role model in your mother,' he said, 'combining family with working from home.'

'Yes,' Sam ticked him off. 'And a single parent to boot.'

So that's it, this year's family news. One surprise tripping into another, no predicting what the next moment will bring, the somersaults life will deliver. And now it's nearly Christmas once again and the children and I are spending it together. We've trailed white fairy lights along the cottage beams, hung bronze angels and gold cupids in the alcoves, decorated the branches of a spruce tree with baubles and beads. Sam's painted some door panels navy blue with tiny gold stars so they look like the sky at midnight and now she's sitting quietly by the fire, her belly as huge as Mary's once was, pondering the mystery of motherhood in her heart.

Thomas meantime, playing with the dogs at Sam's feet, looks happier than he has for months now the burden of secrecy has fallen away. When I explained his Dad and I both knew what he'd been doing, he was so relieved he asked me to drive him into Brighton so he could leave all the things he'd stolen in charity shops. Like Robin Hood, he said, taking from the capitalists to give to the poor. He's sworn that's the end of it and I shan't punish him. I don't believe in recriminations. Didn't Christ promise Paradise to a repentant thief?

I hope I haven't disturbed you by being so frank and open with you – but I think you'll see now why I had to get away from the usual Christmas newsletters that sound so glib and have so little substance, like pre-packaged marzipan.

Oh, I understand it, of course I do. Christmas puts us under such pressure to want perfection – the faultless day, ideal presents, perfect family. Really, though, it should be the exact opposite. I mean, why would God bother with incarnation if

He didn't love us in all our imperfections, our all-too-human flaws?

I think this year has finally taught me what Christmas is about. Not seeking perfection, but accepting where we are and what we have. Making peace with those parts of ourselves that fall short, loving the bits of our children that fail – Sammy with her reckless belly, Thomas with his quicksilver hands. I even feel compassion for Mike as he turns on the golden sands of Tenerife to bronze the other side and has a pang of homesickness, wondering what we're doing now . . .

But before I lapse into any more seasonal sentimentality, I shall sign off, pausing only to wish you a very Merry Christmas, one and all.

David McVey

DIAMOND ELLA

IT WAS THE sort of morning you wake up and feel like you've died and gone to Paisley. Mid-January, Scotland's cold, dark, damp preview of the grave: gale-driven rain hammering against ill-fitting windows that allowed chilly shrouds of air to come in and enfold you. This particular morning, just after eight on a Thursday, someone was hammering at my door. Brisk, decisive action was necessary.

I slipped out of bed, into a dressing gown, and picked my way to the door. I unlocked and unchained it: a man's voice growled, 'The former Professor Maclaren?' My lift. To a possible job. Money. And I had forgotten.

I let the man in. He was fleshy and pallid from want of exercise, sunshine and abstinence: more than most people I could recognise the signs of a workaholic who drank too much. 'Give me five minutes to get ready,' I said.

I quickly washed and pulled on jeans, a sweatshirt, a scarf and an old Crombie which I felt still gave me a raffish, academic air. It was soaked through by the time we reached a black taxi. When he was in the driver's seat with me in solitary state in the back, we splashed off down the street.

The taxi driver told me his name was Findlay. I never found out whether it was his Christian name or surname. Once, when we jolted to a halt at a set of lights, he turned and looked at me as if he'd ordered Madras and I'd given him Korma. 'All this,' he said, 'must be a bit of a comedown for you, eh?'

That hurt. Because he was right.

After all, there aren't many jobs a disgraced history academic can do. When everything had blown over, I had taken an A4 piece of paper and listed everything I could do. I could use libraries, archives, the Internet, and CD-ROM sources to find obscure information. I could synthesise that information, analyse it, draw conclusions and communicate them effectively: in short, I had the undervalued virtues of the historian's mind. So I set myself up as a freelance researcher, digging out sources for lazy newspaper hacks, writing articles for popular magazines on historical topics, and on good days doing research for TV documentaries – though they insisted that I used a pseudonym on the credits.

I was keen to make the most of whatever offer was about to be made. I had to live – after paying the alimony, anyway. All I knew was that the potential client was rich and female. We had parked outside an ordinary sandstone villa, the kind that was built in thousands when the railways expanded the suburbs. Its cosy design suggested your granny: its obvious prosperity suggested your lawyer.

'The person you're calling for is Ella MacDonald,' he said. 'Just go in and chap the door. Don't worry about the fare. She'll invoice me.'

I promised I wouldn't worry about the fare. I'd forgotten my wallet, anyway. The taxi drove off behind a silver bouquet of spray. I walked up a path flanked by lawns in dull winter green, and chapped the door. Actually, there was a bell to ring. The windowless door opened narrowly and a woman's voice hissed, 'Quick – get in.'

It sounded like an invitation to dive into a supercharged getaway car, not a solid Victorian villa with as much fancy and mystery as a retired chartered accountant. I stepped inside, into a gloomy, linoleum-floored hallway. The woman hurriedly closed the door, chained, bolted and locked it, and turned to face me. I turned to face her.

I had expected a combination of the granny and the lawyer: perhaps the elderly widow of a solicitor, but this woman was enough to cause a few stirrings in those bits of my manhood the booze hadn't anaesthetised. About thirty-five, her face was pretty, a little lined, perhaps owing to the stress that showed through a smile as false as an ad for hair restorer. Her long dark hair was slightly tousled and the general picture she gave was of a rumpled, mildly breathless attractiveness. I told her who I was. Without speaking she led me into a lounge that didn't fit its surroundings, as if the furnishings had been swiftly imported from somewhere smaller in scale, like a council flat or a modern suburban semi. I sat on a soft armchair that had seen better days. Of course, so had I.

'I'm Ella MacDonald,' she said, sitting opposite me on a sofa. 'It's good to see you, Professor Maclaren.'

'Not Professor, any more.' Painful but true.

'But you *were* Professor of Scottish History at South Glasgow Uni.'

'I was. Why, do you want a lecture on 18th-century agrarian change?'

She ignored me and continued. 'You drank. Too much. Your department was being squeezed: you turned to the bottle. There were a number of embarrassing incidents. Finally, after a graduation ceremony where you puked over a balcony into ranks of assembled parents, you were sacked and will never work as an academic again.'

I was rapidly realising that Ella and subtlety didn't drink in the same bar.

'Now you scrape a living doing freelance research.'

'Scrape is right.'

'You're honest, though.'

'I try to be. Look, what is it you want from me? I could be out scraping a living just now.'

'Not at 8.40 in the morning you couldn't.' She stood up and walked around a little. 'I'm sure you read the newspapers, Dr Maclaren – I assume your PhD is still valid?' She had a great voice: I could listen to her all day, especially if I got to look at her as well.

'In the Scottish tabloids you might have read about the Great Scottish Lottery Winner. An old woman won the National Lottery, double roll-over, twenty million. But before the draw she died, and the lottery ticket becomes the property of the only person named in her will. Her only relative – a niece. Me, Dr Maclaren.'

So this was the richest woman in Scotland. I did remember the tabloid unmasking of the woman they dubbed Diamond Ella. Since we weren't yet sufficiently acquainted for me to ask for a loan, I just offered my congratulations. I wasn't prepared for what came next. She yelled at me as if I'd made a sleazy suggestion.

'Congratulations? I don't want your congratulations. On principle, Dr Maclaren, I've never bought a lottery ticket – and now I find myself winning twenty million pounds!' She paused for a minute, as if tired out. When she spoke again, the voice was soft and quiet. 'Can I get you a coffee?'

She told me about herself. She came from an Old Labour, working-class family, gained a degree straight from school and then found work as the recruitment officer for a large trade union. She also attended a local evangelical Church of Scotland. She had opposed the Lottery from just about every conceivable standpoint. And then inherited twenty million pounds from it.

I was still unsure about my part in all this and I told her so.

'When the tabloids found me I bought this house. They haven't traced me here, yet, but they will. I intend to use the money for good, Dr Maclaren, and I want you to help me.'

'How can I do that?'

'The first thing you can do is come to a meeting with me.'

'A meeting? Who with?'

'When you win the Lottery, Dr Maclaren, you also win the services of a committee of financial advisers. We're going there now. Come on, it's 9.20: Findlay will be here soon.'

Ella's room lights were still on. They had to be. Outside the clouds breasted the very rooftops. Rain continued to hammer against the bay window, running on down the pane and out of sight like a loser's wealth. Sure enough, I saw the tail lights of Findlay's taxi out in the street.

I turned again to see Ella emptying handfuls of letters into two plastic carrier bags. I went over to help her: all the letters were addressed to her. 'I'll carry the bags for you,' I said.

'Thanks,' she answered, pulling on a battered, baggy raincoat. 'You'll need them.'

Most of the journey we passed in silence. Findlay dropped us outside an august Victorian building in the City Centre. We drifted in to a marbled foyer where a uniformed security man sat behind a desk. At first he was shocked to see two casually-dressed lowlifes entering his domain, but he did a double-take when he recognised Ella. He was up out of his seat like someone had started playing the national anthem, exuding obsequiousness like some medieval courtier with high hopes.

'So good to see you again, Miss MacDonald. And your young gentleman, too.' It was a while since I'd been called *that*.

He showed us to the lift, indicating the way with a flourish of his arm. The modern lift whirred up eight floors: Ella just grinned towards me. When the doors opened a young receptionist was already waiting for us.

'They're ready for you, Miss MacDonald,' said the girl, indicating a solid hardwood door, some way down a corridor. We followed her there: she knocked, and beckoned us in. As the door closed behind us, I almost fell over. It was like being hauled before the University Court all over again.

It was a lavish boardroom ornamented with sculptures and paintings, which looked like they were there as investments rather than for their beauty or merit. Deeply-polished tables had been arranged in the shape of a capital D, with the straight edge facing us: round the arc were seated five middle-aged men in reassuringly expensive suits. Not comfortable, tweedy, small-town Scottish family accountants or lawyers: these were tigerish, management buy-out merchants, men who thought in columns of figures and whose sentiments had been replaced by spreadsheets. They looked at me in some despair, which didn't disappear when Ella simply introduced me as 'Dr Maclaren, a friend.' One of them made a desperate, well-intentioned grasp at establishing rapport.

'I believe that's a Dollar Academy scarf you're wearing?'

Many of my well-to-do university colleagues had made the same mistake. 'No, actually it's St Mirren.'

'Oh. Not a school I'm familiar with.'

There seemed little point in explaining about the football team I supported through thin and thin. They introduced themselves and then paused, as if expecting Ella to detail my role, but she stayed quiet. They began a long, mournfully earnest discussion on the investments which Ella's lottery winnings were going into, the tax consequences and so on. Their only animation, a sort of communal furrowing of brows, came when Ella specified some large donations to charities, church bodies and to the Scottish TUC.

When the business was over, and the suits were stacking and folding their papers, Ella said, 'There is one more thing I'd like to raise, Mr Abernethy.'

'Yes?' said the chairman, suspiciously.

'The begging letters, Mr Abernethy. Some people have found out my new address. I'm getting dozens every week.' As she spoke, she emptied the two carrier bags of letters onto the table, and stood up behind the resulting heap.

Abernethy took his glasses off (they *all* wore glasses – something to do, perhaps, with too much late-night poring over columns of figures) and said, with cold condescension, 'We did advise you to get rid of them, Miss MacDonald. Burn them, put them out with the rubbish. *We* can dispose of them if you like.'

'Believe me,' one of the others butted in, 'we know from experience that most begging letters are sent by frauds or cranks.'

'And some are not,' said Ella. 'Some are from desperate, struggling people at the end of their tether.'

'Perhaps,' said Abernethy, with a disapproving glance at the suit who had interrupted. 'But it would be difficult, expensive . . . *impractical* to try to sort the sheep from the goats . . .'

'Impractical! Expensive!' Ella was on her feet, now, a whirling, yelling fury. 'I have twenty million pounds to my name! If *anyone* can afford to investigate and identify the genuine ones, it's *me*!'

'What do you suggest, Miss MacDonald? Are you going to set up your own Social Security investigation agency?' As an attempt at tension-defusing humour, it was, I suppose, just what you'd expect from an accountant.

'I suggest,' Ella replied, with a sudden smile, 'that we employ someone to find out which cases are genuine and deserving, and to recommend the appropriate action.'

'Do you have anyone in mind for this combination of Philip Marlowe and Robin Hood?' said Abernethy, still searching for that elusive, side-splitting one-liner.

'Yes I do. Dr Maclaren has the experience and qualities to carry out the necessary research, and the moral sense to advise the appropriate response to cases of need.'

I hoped that they didn't notice how I started up in my seat before their collective gaze fell on me. I had been relaxing, enjoying Ella's triumph, happy to forget my puzzlement at why I was there. Suddenly I was centre stage, the spots full on, and the audience was waiting for the show.

'Errmm, that's right,' was all the show they got.

'Of course,' Abernethy resumed, 'we can only *advise* you, Miss MacDonald. We cannot *compel* you to avoid this course of action, but . . .'

But Ella had already gathered her things and was on her way out of the room. Only a few minutes later, as Findlay drove us back through the continuing rain, I asked her, 'Why me? I'm not a lawyer or a detective or a social worker. Why?'

She smiled. It was good to see that her heart didn't bleed *all* the time. 'I studied History, Dr Maclaren, at South Glasgow. I came out with an honours degree when you were a senior lecturer. I always enjoyed your lectures and tutorials, and I even had a bit of a crush on you . . .'

The following Saturday I followed up the first of the letters. The address was in a small town a few miles outside the city. I stepped off a bus and walked for a few minutes until I identified a particular semi-detached council house. From the cladding, PVC double-glazing, side conservatory and porch, I gathered that Mr Gardener had joined the property-owning democracy. I rang the bell, setting off a lengthy musical chime: a long-haired, chunky man in his mid-thirties, wearing a hooded sweatshirt and jogging trousers, appeared at the door.

'Mr Gardener?'

'Aye. Whit d'ye waant?'

I was unprepared for this level of directness. No chance of a cup of tea here.

'It's about your daughter, Mr Gardener. I . . .'

'Eh? I don't have a daughter.'

'No daughter called Kayleigh? According to this letter, she's six years old, and has a rare bone condition that can only be treated, expensively, in the States. Can I assume . . .'

'Ach, away an don't bloody bother me. It was worth a try, surely.'

Gardener slammed the door, and I was left standing there, teeming, gale-driven rain soaking my ageing Crombie, with twenty minutes to wait for the next bus to Glasgow.

I was a wage slave again.

Brooke Biaz

THE VAMPIRES

A COACH-LOAD of vampires arrived in town this evening. They came with cameras, lights, actresses, opinions. Their coach was silver and its windows were black tinted. It slit our thick salt air like butter. They flashed their pointed teeth at us through the light rain, ordered 'Bourbon. Neat.', over-tipped without mention, then closed their hotel doors on our prying eyes.

At nine a.m., sharp as you like, a call comes from Mr Margolis's room. He is no taller than a table lamp and sways back and forth on his tiny wooden boot-heels as if there is a thunderstorm around him and his long red hair is wet and, weighing his head back, tips his moon face upwards. His face, pocked slightly, is the face of a vampire.

'We will require,' he says, examining our ceiling, 'lunch for fifty at two precisely.'

I agree to this. I am certain already that fighting them is impossible. After all, I was awake last night to hear those footfalls along our airy latticed corridors (splore-footed these vampires turn out to be!). How many screeches of laughter did I count, penetrating these, our moonlit mangrove forests? How many bloodcurdling shrieks along these, our starry unspoilt beaches? I swear that not one of them slept a wink (they don't, of course, their sort). This morning, predictably, they are unaffected.

'We don't eat,' Mr Margolis told me brusquely, over the telephone, 'in the mornings. Get the picture?'

'So much,' says I to Elphinstone, 'for the appetites of the undead.'

Up this way. Load that by hand. Don't pack the PA with the dolly. Forget the limpet and bring forward the steadicam. Matte box in, meat axe out, yoke-a-pock, scrim it up and fourteen scoops, mister, for the fo'c's'le sequence.

Their eyes are red. Their teeth are perfect. They load themselves determinedly into silver pantechnicons from which men (blood slaves, I imagine) in blue overalls with thick arms and bibs and braces jump down. They converse enthusiastically in a strange vampiric language. I've never seen more organised monsters.

At midday, our diamond sea is blowing up rough and brown. The sun can be forgiven for being unusually weak. Clouds slide over it like lattices. Guests from the hotels along the Promenade are asking to take out boats. They imagine our reefs are fairgrounds underwater. They say they have flown to the South Pacific to get close to nature. They wish to let their hair down, to abandon their socks, run our white sand through their soft naked toes, to break into running sweats, eat rainbow-coloured ice from tall pots, sip something on a white balcony, stroke across filtered pools which shimmer and lap, visit our historical attractions (sailing ships, desert explorations, gold mines, railway builders, crocodile farms, wars), perch under palm fronds, stoke the cold hearths of their northern lives. But a storm is brewing and there are vampires in town, and things are not right.

By one, aware of the time, I have stripped the vampires' beds bare. The sheets and slips lay at my feet on the washroom floor, like captured clouds. When Elphinstone surprises me amongst them she makes accusations. Her accusations are distinctive and alarming. Her tone is contemptuous. It comes to light: she has been watching the vampire goings-on along the jetty.

Along the jetty, she claims, both males and females have

been wearing tuxedoes. Some have donned brown bear suits. Some have adopted hair as tall and as white as sails. The men have stripped to the waist. Their bodies are lithe. There is an air of fun about them. Peaked caps are prevalent. They are joking, she says, almost all the time. Their humour is cosmopolitan. They are obviously educated. On the jetty they have been placing their cameras like dancing girls, forwardly spread-legged. They can make fog or rain and carry the sound of wind and thunder in their pockets. They festoon the pylons with silver umbrellas. The jetty, all strangled in kelp and fading fish rope, has never looked better. There is the sharp echo of clapsticks, the slow movement of the circular pan, the glittering of reflector boards, the flash of grey cards, the winding of geared heads. In contrast, she says, I appear to be against beauty. I am moody and unimaginative. I am self-pitying and grudging and downright hard-hearted. I am not fun. 'What has happened to the guy you once was?'

I fear she may have been bitten.

It is untrue to say that vampires are satisfied with only blood. They eat like horses. For lunch, I serve them Chicken Relleno, Oysters Rockefeller, Pork Gulai, Nasi Goreng, Surf n' Turf, Caesar Salad, Lontong. They accept what I offer them with nonchalance. They drink all the while. There is no prohibition, it seems, against talking while eating when dining amongst vampires. They fang and fork their food through conversations as vivid as pacts and as long as tails. There are soon pieces of flesh on the tablecloths and drinks are spilled. I detect amongst the constant talk the elongated barking of their belches. Men slip away to the toilets and return with their hands dripping wet. The women are not poised on the edge but sink back in their seats. They draw their mouths with lipstick the colour of plums and peaches. Their noses grow unpowdered, but they are confident and demonstrative and smoke with their coffee. If I had my way . . .

In dark cafés we'd steal away time. Our feelings would be mutual. As we strolled, locked lip to lip, I would be widely envied. Time, however, would treat us harshly. This would be the price to pay because our lives would be larger than lives. There would be children . . . but they would not wait on tables, sweep carpets, polish the marble steps of a Promenade hotel. They would be more beautiful than gods, their teeth as perfect as pearls, their mouths forming rosebuds. And, with these, they would plunge into the veins of mortals and, not falling a moment to reconsider, suck them dry and then spill, laughing, into the street

By nightfall the vampires have flown again. But where, O where, do they go?

Elphinstone is angry. She twists her wiry black hair around her fingers. She wants to say she is unwell and cannot work but I will not have it. Things have gone far enough. She is serving the other guests with a nonchalance bordering on rudeness. She is cute in her manner. She is sharp in her answers. To the gentleman who enquires about the rendang she replies: 'It is pork in a pickle of fish livers. You want some?' This is untrue. She admits she has, tucked in her apron, three vampiric signatures on three perfectly good napkins.

'To Ms Effie Elphinstone with love,' writes Mr Margolis (in blood, I have no doubt). 'For Effie with affection,' suggests another fang-faced fakir. 'Go get 'em Effie!' quips a third (grammar is not a vampire's forte).

'It is a lie!' I say in a harsh whisper. 'There's nothing wrong with you.'

But she pricks the skin of a lemon chicken with a skewer and the sour steam that shoots out is no more than the acetous fire in her eyes. She refuses to speak another word.

And so, all evening, we are silent, serving eight dozen orders for red snapper and hogget, shoulders of lamb, jackfruit, mangoes, kangaroo, crayfish, mud crabs and barramundi fish while Elphinstone, Elphinstone silent like a pond, cradles the vampires' napkins in the pocket of her uniform.

. . . until midnight and the restaurant is closing.

The guests are returning to their rooms. The night is light

and bright and warm. If she wants to see vampires then I will take her right now, I say. This is a challenge. I am not narrow-minded, I am not uncaring, but each thing in its place, I say, there is a time and place for each thing, guests must be attended to, jobs must be done, a hotel must run or it is no hotel at all. What kind of place are we if we are not for hotels, sunshine, seashore and boating? What are we if not for proper behaviour and tourism? Vampires must wait. But now . . .

We drive out along Palm Parade, past Hibiscus and Orchid streets. The engine of the Land Rover screams out of time. The moon is high and round and white. Three fishing boats are making out from the harbour, coughing across the black water of Pearl Bay, and the fishermen are swaying to and fro across the deck to unwind the nets on the wide arms and the boats are covered in a thousand stars. I cup the gear shift like a knife and cut our way toward the plantations.

At the base of the mountain we turn inland, past the plantation house which is low and brown-timbered and lit and open. Two pied dogs chase us up the track but soon give up and retreat to their sugar sacks, and their pups. Soon, all around, there are only banana trees, slapping across the windshield and over us with their leaves as broad and wet as washing. Night spiders stitching across the track appear in the Rover's headlamps – their webs glittering with an early dew – and then they are swatted out of view and the engine cuts down a peg or two against the grade and I hold the wheel tight in the deep black sand and there are lights now in the distance and Elphinstone sits up.

She has not spoken so far, wrapped in her white towel against the cool wind of the mountain. But now . . .

'Up there!'

She points to the pantechnicons parked in the clearing and then to the caravans which have been anchored on besser bricks and the neat metal trestle tables laid out beneath the strung tarpaulins and the long white car, which reminds me of the seashore and of the bleached concrete of the hotels, and the hum of a generator perched on a new Toyota utility and the washtubs and flyscreens and mirrors taller than persons and tipped back on pedestals to reflect the night sky.

The vampires do not see us approach. We slip through the banana trees like black snakes. They have made their way, some time earlier, into the caves of the peak. Outside it is dark but inside the caves there is an unnatural glow.

Well, I say, here it is. This is what you wanted. This is why we have come.

The moon is cast over by a lattice of clouds. The lights of the seafront are way below us, speckled as on a fine carpet. I can see the lights of the Grand, the Pacific View, the Mermaid, the Island, the Pelican, the Palisades, of all the hotels of the Promenade. I am tired and my feet ache and I must be awake at six. But it is I who lead the way into the caves, because now Elphinstone will not. It is I who must take Elphinstone's hand and refuse to let her return to the Land Rover. It is I who must say:

You have come this far, the least you can do is finish the business.

Electricity slithers inward along its orange cord route, and we follow it. The caves are cast with shadows swirling and turning over along the ceiling and springing now and then from behind rocks. There is a rack of clothing hung in the passageway and a wheeled ladder and tripods and screens and a railway track has been built over the cave floor but nothing is running. The deeper we go the thinner the air becomes, in the usual manner, but the light grows brighter and it is red and there are voices. The air has begun to smell of salt and of sweat and of seawater in a recognisable fashion.

It is no surprise to me to round the corner in the caves and find the sun is rising. It rises over the Promenade, spread out in front of us.

Here also the street is already filling with tourists. Vendors are selling their souvenirs from plastic fish tubs. Each hotel has its banners blowing in the breeze and ours is as welcoming as always (I think for a moment that I see Elphinstone at the window, polishing the glass, but feel her tugging nevertheless on my hand, wanting to go back).

Over there, fishing boats are returning to the harbour and the beach is dotted with swimmers and dogs. Likewise, to add now to the aroma of sea and salt is the wash of hot dogs and pineapples and of coconut oil. I hear a car passing and the sound of wind in the rigging though, looking up, I see only the cave's ceiling. There is a light plane overhead of the sort that has a glass bottom and can show you sharks on the reef. A bell is ringing and the surf laps up against the beach with the steady rhythm of a heart. Lifesavers sprint past in their red/yellow skull-caps, heading for their white wooden club-house. I swear that I recognise their faces. Gulls perch on the lamp posts. There are sail boats in the water and jet skies on the shoreline and a dozen local boys with surfboards are sitting in pick-up trucks.

'You! You there!' I hear.

Mr Margolis is coming out from the cave shadows. His round face is bright and his peaked cap is tipped back and he flashes his perfect teeth broadly and points at Elphinstone. 'What do you think?' he is asking. I want some time to gather my thoughts. I cannot yet make a decision. It strikes me I have lost contact with something. Nevertheless, he is promising already, once this sequence is over, to take me inside and introduce me to myself.

Don Paterson

From APHORISMS

TRADITIONALLY, THE DEFINING moment in a man's life arrives when he looks in the shaving mirror and finds his father staring back; but there is a day so much more terrible that we rarely speak of it – when he catches himself naked in a full-length mirror and sees his *mother* . . .

✻

Innovation consists entirely in the grotesque inversion of the axioms of the previous epoch.

✻

The reader may be witness to the miracle, but can never participate in it; poetry must remain a private transaction between the author and God. The true poem is no more than a spiritual courtesy, the act of returning a borrowed book.

✻

Sometimes I have the fantasy of passing an enormously long unbroken shit, and then looking down to find my brain coiled in the pan. I cannot accept that this shared morphology is coincidental.

✻

Sympathetic proof of hylozoism: imagine a stone lying on a beach, undisturbed for fifty years . . . impossible to think that, walking by, we could pick it up and throw it into the sea, and that it could feel *nothing* . . .

꩜

I cannot regard the time I spend idling in railway stations as lost; it is a waiting liberated from the three temporal vices of regret, anticipation or boredom, the weak echo of that bliss spent between lifetimes.

꩜

It's a singularly bizarre phenomenon that after the first encounter, the face of the beloved-to-be cannot, initially, be retrieved . . . in our mind's eye, we hold the dinner-table of the previous evening, and though we can sweep from guest to guest, fixing in turn the thin-lipped poet, that ridiculous headmaster, the accountant and his horse-faced wife – however desperately we desire to call back her features, there she stubbornly sits, her face as perfectly bright and blank as if she had spent the entire evening with a mirror held up in its place.

꩜

Any idea borne out of *nothing but the leisure in which to think it* will ultimately, whatever its ingenuity and elegance, eventually be revealed as a perfect superfluity.

꩜

If I do not constantly evince an attitude of self-disgust, it is due to nothing more than a lack of stamina.

꩜

Truth only in fragments . . . there is a makeweight of lies in any statement longer than a sentence, longer than a breath, longer than that which can inhabit the present moment.

꩜

If we expect our work to survive our deaths even by a single day, we should stop defending it now, that it might sooner learn its self-sufficiency.

꩜

Our names should be lengthened a little after our demise, by the lovely matronymic of death . . . we should then appear in the conversation of our friends and enemies with our signature cadence gently altered, discreetly informing strangers of our change of status.

∾

Every morning the writer should go to the window, look out and remind himself of this fact: aside from his own species, not one thing he sees – not one bird, tree or stone – has in its possession the name he gives it.

∾

It is perhaps fortunate for us that the majority are convinced that the path of the departing spirit is distinguished by its scatter of holy detritus; they are forever producing bits of shiny rubbish as evidence of His recent passing; but the one thing of which God is incapable is *fragmentation*. The path He has taken is distinguished only by the fact of its godlessness. When we stumble upon anything – a bottle of wine, a poem, a poor suburb, a railway platform – that is incontestably the worst of its kind, we know for certain that we have picked up the trail again.

∾

The sea rehearses all possible landscapes, the sky – invisibly – all possible seas. But the land is a lexicon of frozen hells, and some of us remember.

∾

We can be certain of one thing: that there *is* one thing, at least, which everyone regards as the dullest point of common knowledge, the details of which – by tact, providence, but most likely chance – have been withheld from you. So you will discover, too late in the day, why your house was sold to you so cheaply, or the *real* ingredients of the communion host, or that all left-handed males are culled in their 50th year . . .

Taking a lover often solves the sexual difficulties of a marriage because it then becomes *pointless to imagine oneself elsewhere*.

There are men and women who, upon every occasion one meets them, talk so seamlessly of themselves one wonders how they managed to listen long enough to have acquired the power of speech in the first place.

We grow into our prophesies. Often it is the simple embarrassment of having told everyone we will leave our lover that affords us the courage to do so; but this trivial example calls a deeper system from the shadows. Usually we must open up the path before we can follow it, the air standing – all too often – solid against us. On those occasions we send out the god in ourselves, and follow his empty trail to our salvation. This is why transition often feels like abandonment.

One thing all adulterers will tell you: the anticipated, dreaded return to the marital bed – *how can I possibly betray nothing to this person who knows me so well?* – when it materializes, is such a simple and easy deception that it stands as a far more grave indictment on the spirit than the original misdemeanor ever was . . .

All critics write a review in the sincere belief that the author will read it. What a bliss to deny them this pleasure! Imagine – to write in a style unmoderated by criticism, simply because one had *never bothered to read any* . . . only the badly reviewed, however, could be intoxicated by this idea . . .

No matter how intolerable an event was, it only has to be repeated three times for you to invest it with a feeling of nostalgia.

∾

There can be no such thing, in our human experience, as a smooth progression. The suicide's descent from Beachy Head will have its lighter moments; even the road to hell will have stretches more bearable – which we will succeed in construing as more *pleasant* – than others. We are cursed by these inconsistencies, since they continually give rise to hope.

Robin Robertson

WAKING LATE

I am used to the smell by now,
the stiffness, sudden shifts
in waist measurement,
the bad skin. But my hair
is lustrous, the cheekbones
well-defined, and my nails,
it seems, still growing.

ANXIETY #101

Leaving the building in a hurry, I find myself on the edge of a
wide and empty urban square. Behind me, frightened people
gather in the doorway. Looking into the centre of the square
where the streets intersect, there is something long and white,
slowly revolving. As I walk closer I see it is a 20-foot bone,
one end still carrying shreds of matter, turning on its own
axis – as if something huge had just passed by, and nudged it,
accidentally.

A commotion further on, and I see beasts – hyenas perhaps
– tearing at something enormous and unrecognisable.

John Burnside

KESTREL

so that my mind would be one selving or pitch of a great
universal mind, working in other minds too besides
mine, and even in all other things, according to their
natures and powers

Gerard Manley Hopkins

We found it at the end of Tollcross Lane
between the garage and that borderline of hedge
and stubble, where October snows begin
like stories told to children:
one of those cold, bright mornings; seams of frost
arriving through the grass, the dead bird's feathers
perfect as bronze, the narrow raptor's face
all beak and eyes.
You probed it with a stick; it seemed alive,
or haunted with the aftertaste of life:
the tension in the wings; the vivid claws;
the hooded skull a mutant hieroglyph
for sunlight, or transmigration.
This was the god of silence and the sky
in ancient times, and Hopkins' dapple-dawn-drawn
falcon: Christ
and Horus;
          and though I am no believer, I could find
some blue-bleak ember of an old
significance, some promise that remains
unsayable, laid down between the folds
of flesh and blood;
and though I am no believer, I could think
that what we make of gravity, or fire,
infers a soul:

the light that pools and lingers in the mud,
this sunlit field, the wind that stains the plumage
blue-black, and the warmth that flows between
my fingers and the kestrel's emptied frame.
It's what we make of memory and fear
and how each body wills its transformation:
hoarding a fall against the level air,
each thread of breaking fire it cannot hold
surrendered for new subtleties of gold.

ADAM AND EVE

I always think of them
as innocents:
too much intended for sin
          they walk their garden
stunned with a local wonder
               angels and beasts
inured to everything but them
or lost in unwitting joy
like the dreamed unborn.

          Imagine that first
cold morning: frosted grass
and fruit-falls running to black
amongst the leaves
the meadows they had laced with given names
muffled in snow
          the net of birdsong
gone.

     We get what we least expect
and most require
was all the explanation I received
in scripture class
          the serpent in the weeds
named from the start

the stillness of each blizzard
preordained.
Imagine them surrendering to white
as we do
     when the snow begins again

falling from nowhere on James Street
          then crossing the park
to find the kirk
     like a song
or a prayer learned by heart

or all those games of tag
and catch-kiss
     that we never quite
abandoned
     children
wandering off to the furthest
corners of a snowfall
          calling
softly from street to street
          their half-goodbyes
but never imagining this:

          a sudden halt
between the baker's and the library
lights coming on in houses and crowded shops
the quick wind sealing us in
          or a snowbound silence
fading us out.
     I always think of them
as innocents with something more to learn

much like ourselves when we come to this
surprise
  our bodies
half-inhabited
and finding it harder to live

with others:
    with each new winter
        each new space
the gardens we remember in our sleep
filling with snow all day
        as we come to require
this white-out
    this
sufficiency of names.

THE MIRACLE

con un terrore di ubriaco
Montale

You've seen it too: that gape across the park
where plane trees should have been, the usual film
of blown trees spotting the grass, or a couple of boys
chasing a mud-coloured ball
in the morning air,

and you've stopped, no doubt,
with a nothingness you can feel
at the small of your back,
your shoulder-blades drenched
with an absence of something like wings,

or that sense of the scenery
standing forever in place:
your neighbour's walls;
hedges and far-off hills; unfolding
parishes of lantern-lights and farms.

At once it slips back into place
– but it's still too late –
and for days you will wander like this,
with a gap in your mind
where certainty had been: that good clean taste,

THE MIRACLE

like spring water, lost in your throat
and the moment's grace
you wanted all along, become, for now,
a sickening shift, like a fall
or a drunkard's terror.

Vivienne Vermes

THE SPACES IN HOUSES

YOU KNOW THERE is a rat in the house because you have heard it at night, somewhere between the roof and the bedroom ceiling. Its persistent burrowing makes you think it is trying to bore its way through to your living quarters. He says it is a mouse, or a bird. You know it is something bigger than a mouse, and you know that birds do not burrow, they rustle. But, because he says these things in his drowsy, light-hearted voice, you curl up next to him and go back to sleep in the dawn. You are happy enough because your skins – his and yours – are the same temperature. As if you have the same skin, indistinguishable. Both pink and white and cool.

The day is cold. He jumps out of bed and races across the bedroom to put on a towelling dressing gown. From where you lie, you hear the splash of shower sounds, sharp water cleaning away the small liquids of your late-night love-making. This, by the way, is unsatisfactory to you, but you have not said anything. He is always bounding around, on the phone or clearing up the kitchen. He does most things well, and laughs while he does them which, to your mind, is rare in a man, and very satisfactory. One of these days, you think, you will sit him down and pour him a Scotch and say exactly what would turn you on. You just have to choose the right time.

It is eight o'clock. BBC Radio 4. Six beeps and the news. You like these presenters. They are familiar to you – their grave voices, their intelligence. In Kosovo, houses are burning and the villagers are hiding in the woods, watching the smoke rise. They must be cold now, these women (most of them women, their husbands shot) up in the woods, in late winter, with no houses.

You nestle down between the sheets and draw the duvet up to your neck. You look out of the skylight, a small square of window cut into the slope of the wall where it rises up to the rafters. The glass is spattered with raindrops. It always rains here, in this village, in the middle of England. It seems that you have never woken up to anything but rain. You have thoughts as pitty-pat as the drizzle . . . how good breakfast is, always, in this house, with fresh fruit yoghurt and hot coffee and brown bread taken crispy and hot from the Aga. You will eat breakfast opposite him, and you will think how lucky you are, for once in your life, to have a man whose skin blends with yours, who has shoulders that carry problems without complaint, who laughs at himself and goes to fancy dress parties as a tree. You like all that. You like the village, too, with its trout farm and white wrought-iron tables spread under the plum trees, with its tea-rooms and Tudor mansion and its two ghosts. You like all this, after the city. It had been time to leave the capital. It had been good to you when you arrived, years ago. Of late, it had turned sour, the pavements all dog-shit and vomit, the beggars everywhere (and you never knew who was fake and who was real) and three friends dying in quick succession, and you holding each one's hand in turn, with no words at all, as they left you.

It had been time.

You get out of bed and enjoy the space of the room. A thick clean carpet, the colour of honey. The wood beams, the slanting ceiling. The house is on the edge of the village. On one side there are fields with the first tiny lambs fluffy with the cold. On the other side, just down the road, but sheltered from view, is a house, but you have never seen its inhabitants, only builders coming and going, converting, as they are always doing in this part of the country. There is no one nearby who knows your name, no neighbour. You like this privacy. You walk around the room naked. You stop in front of the full-length mirror, and pull a face. Your body has undoubtedly got fatter since you moved here, but not displeasingly so. It still goes in and out at the right places, it is just that the 'out' is further out than before. Maybe, you think, there are a few more lines on your face – one, especially, you don't like: it goes down the side of your face from your nose to your mouth and beyond. It disappears when you smile, so you smile. You keep smiling even when you hear, in the pauses in the radio interview, the persistent sound coming from that space between the ceiling and the roof. You must speak to him about it, although you don't know what good it would do. That place is inaccessible. You would have to knock out the plaster or drill a hole in the roof to get at it. And this is not his house, or yours. It is rented from a stockbroker and his wife who live in Hong Kong. So what is the point, you think, of talking about the rat, which may, after all, be a mouse or a bird.

He is coming out of the shower and you cross on the landing. He is red and clean-rubbed. You are pale and unwashed and can still feel his stickiness on the inside of your thighs. Although you are probably too old, you may have made a baby the night before. You smile at the unexpected havoc it would cause, and you kiss him quickly, on the cheek.

You go down into the kitchen and find he has already been there. The cups are on the table and the radio is on loud. In a town in Lithuania, the mayor is on trial, fifty years on, for war crimes. The deportation of five thousand Jews. The people of the town are behind their mayor, protesting his innocence, and saying that, anyway, the past is the past. A Jewish woman is interviewed. She runs a museum in the town that is neglected and receives few visitors. She says she will run it as long as she lives, in memory of the seventy-four friends and members of her family who died in the camps. She is the only survivor. She says the houses in the town are like so many empty faces.

You put the brown rolls in the oven, you turn on the kettle, you sit in the big kitchen with its beautiful stone floor with marbled slabs imported, at great expense, from Italy.

He comes downstairs fresh and well-dressed and bustling.

128

You are crying, but you have your back to him. You lean over the Aga as you open the oven so the heat makes your face red and he won't see the tears. They have gone by now, anyway.

You eat your fruit yoghurt and pour clear honey on your roll and he talks. He hates doing business with the Japanese, he says. He is straightforward, a farmer's son, brought up in Canada. He doesn't like Japanese 'tactics'. He is talking of setting up a system of video-conferencing, which means he won't have to travel so much. Your mouth goes down. You can feel the wrinkle slide back into place, and you are cross with yourself. You are always nagging him to stay at home, to be with you. After all, you gave up the city to be with *him*. And now your mouth is going down. If you admit it, you enjoy his absences, you have grown to like the silence of the house, even at night, alone, if it weren't for the sound in the space between the ceiling and the roof.

Now the house is quiet. He has gone to work. You have put the dishes in the dish-washer. You can hear its hum and churn from where you sit in the bedroom, your table facing two floor-length windows, so the cold, early spring light shines on your pen, your page. It is hard to write, thoughts crowd in on top of each other, a jumble – they block you, not the blank cold spring page, but the many little ghosts of thoughts all whispering at once, urgent and together. You walk around the room. Your feet, bare, rasp against the carpet.

You think of your father. You wish he were not so old. You wish he had told you more about his secrets, about the family that disappeared. There is a horror there, and the shunting of trains. You have seen it in his eyes, and, with a child's sense of the hidden, you have kept silent. Once, insistent, you made him take you through old photos. You made him guide you around his village, going from door to door, cousin to cousin. You imagined you were following his stooped back, wondering if this were cruel or kind, this opening of doors on to old corridors, full of laughter, once, and hung with portraits and diplomas, and smelling of goulash and dumplings. He has never been back. For him, the houses now are so many empty faces.

This house is quiet. There is sun, then rain, then sun again, passing across the floor-length windows and the slat of the skylight. You walk and walk. Maybe you walk half a mile around the room, with the weather changing, with your feet rasping against the carpet.

Then you hear it. Faint, at first, then louder. When you walk, when you move, it stops. So you stop. You stand very still, opposite the full-length mirror, and you wait. You are patient. You could stand here, so, all day. The morning light is bright on you. You can see your wrinkle etched deeper, deeper. You can see yourself as a little old lady, so, with lines all over to match. When you stand, so, with the house so quiet, you can hear it quite clearly. It is boring its way through, persistent, coming closer to the plaster. The plaster is flaking, easy, under its claws. It is equipped, it can deal with these builders' fragile surfaces. It has burrowed through earth and walls and tunnels.

You stand quite still. You could go and pick up the phone in the corner of the room and call him. You can always reach him. His mobile is switched on at any time of the day. But you don't call. You stand quite still.

The plaster is crumbling. Small flakes fall on the carpet, like an early snowfall. Then more quickly, the plaster breaks off in chunks, easily, like sawdust, light wood, cut away from behind by the steady little sawmills of claws.

A hole now, as big as your fist. If you move now, make a noise, you could stop it. It would retreat, go back to its quarters, and leave you to yours. You could phone him, even now you could phone him, or call one of the builders down the road, have one of them come quickly and seal up the hole, put another layer of plaster there, get the ratman in, put the poison down, stop up the process.

But you don't. You want more than anything, more than the closeness of his skin, more than the sticky stuff between your legs and the maybe baby, you want to see what has lived

130

and burrowed up in that space between the ceiling and the roof.

It is raining now, hard, against the skylight, insistent drops pattering, beating against the square of glass, little entities demanding entry.

And then, through the hole, it plops on to the floor, on to the carpet. It remains utterly still, as you are still, and you stare at each other across the clean carpet.

It is a rat – large, grey, and its brown eyes stare at you. It does not look afraid, as you are not afraid, yet utterly immobile. If you move towards it, you do not know which way it will go, as it does not know which you will go. So you both stay very still.

You see its ears are twitching at new sounds. The rain on glass, the hum of the dish-washing machine from the kitchen. You do not like it in your space, in your quarters. But it is here.

Your breathing is fast. Maybe your immobility is caving in like the plaster, easy, cracking. The rat knows this. It is quick, this rat. It flashes across the carpet, so quick that you do not have time to get out of the way, it has already streaked past you and out of the bedroom door and into the living quarters of the house beyond. It has rushed past you, and you are relieved it has gone, a grey flash, so quickly. Still you have had time to notice something, in a split second, about the rat's belly, that was big and swollen and slithered under it as it sped across the floor. You close the door and listen to the rain.

You can call now, take the phone and tell him he was wrong. It was not a bird, it was not a mouse. It was a rat. You could tell him with satisfaction. But something makes you hesitate. It is the bigness of the rat's belly.

So you don't call. You sit down at your table and think of what you will say to him tonight.

He will, after all, notice the hole.

Then you might say it was a bird, or a mouse, and decide which builder to call, to repair the damage.

Adrian Mathews

THE GARDEN OF NAILS

LIITTLE THINGS – LIKE what they do with their bits and pieces – can tell you a lot about a person. They can tell you things that the big things never tell.

Madame Vincensini lives with Monsieur Vincensini in a sixth-floor, 19th-century flat overlooking the Jardin Marco Polo on the Rive Gauche. Their flat is two hundred square metres in surface area and, at today's values, would sell for eight million francs, if they ever intended to sell. But Monsieur and Madame Vincensini do not intend to sell. They would never *dream* of selling. It is a beautiful flat. It has gilt-framed pier-glasses and rococo ceilings. From its windows you can look diagonally across to the eight spitting turtles and rearing horses of the fountain at the Port Royal end of the garden. And if you squinny to the right you can see the Palais du Luxembourg and the Luxembourg gardens in all their glory. It is a seat of power.

Of course Monsieur and Madame Vincensini don't sit there all day looking at these things, but they could do if they wanted to – that's the point. And perhaps – it's not impossible – perhaps from time to time they really *do*, if only to remind themselves of the almost single most important thing of all, which is: that they live at a *chic* address. Of that there is not the shadow of a doubt. It looks damned good, that address, on the embossed headed letter-paper, *toile impériale*. It catches the eye on the discreet gold-fringed visiting cards which they carry upon their persons at all times. It is an address which makes things *happen*.

What things?

Tradesmen with a nose for money get their acts together double-quick. Broken-down boilers are repaired in the twinkling of an eye. Deliveries of Petrossian caviar or *petit-fours* from Le Nôtre arrive bang on time. Handsome tips are anticipated, you see, and let it be said that these expectations are not in vain. They are gratified, amply, over and above mortal expectations, to assure deference and the quality of future service.

An alumnus of the Ecole Normale d'Administration, Monsieur Vincensini's card propagates in the wallets of other alumni, as theirs do in his. If and when the occasion calls for it, phone-calls are made; strings are pulled; favours are done. *Le réseau*, he calls it – the 'network' – and he taps his nose with a forefinger and a knowing look. On other occasions it is *un retour d'ascenseur* – sending the lift back down for a friend, as the expression goes.

On one memorable day, after treating a destitute Russian princess to dinner at Fouquet's (before the cockroach scandal there), Madame Vincensini found that she had neither cheque-book nor credit-card upon her. Only the visiting-card – that address! The *sommelier* glanced at it, the delicately engraved fleur de lys in the corner met his eye, the ragged yellow-gold edging gleamed and Bingo! – Madame and her decayed royal were escorted graciously to the door, with maximum bowing and scraping. A cheque, it goes without saying, was in the post the following day.

That's the sort of thing they get away with.

Always have done . . .

I'm not saying they haven't got money: they have. Pots of it. You don't spend a lifetime as PDG of the biggest French cotton importers without making a stash, do you? That's what Monsieur got up to, before he retired. What I'm trying to get at is that the Vincensinis couldn't give a Spaniard's fart for money. True! – that's the honest truth. Money is vulgar, my dear – so *vulgar*! Sure, it may buy a *chic* address, but the address is just the vessel, the vase – hollow, if there is nothing within it. The address is the outward sign of an inner wealth which is *sans pareil*. And what is this inner wealth, I hear you ask? Wit? Imagination? A propensity for charitable deeds? Not a bit of it. Their inner wealth is *class*.

Or so they imagine, the frauds.

That little word *class* sums up everything they hanker for. And I'll allow them one thing: the trappings are all there, materially speaking. The finest silk Persian carpets. The Louis XIV furniture – bloody uncomfortable, which proves it's the real thing. The Lalique light fittings and catholic mix of 18th-century tapestries and modern prints, not to mention the teeny-weeny ever-so-modest little Modigliani sketch in the Green Room (they never call it the 'dining room', for some reason best known to themselves). This sketch is positioned on the wall in such a way that guests do not notice it at first – thus increasing their surprise when they do. Poor old Modigliani! He had lived only round the corner, as they are so fond of telling everyone, but they don't mention the fact that he lived in abject poverty. He probably bought a shot of absinthe with that sketch.

No – there's no *camelote* at the Vincensinis, no tawdry fripperies in sight. Only the best of everything. The best Armani linen jackets for Monsieur. The finest Chanel two-pieces for Madame. But, I repeat, it is not money they are showing off by parading all these wares. It is taste; it is refinement; it is *class*! But what exactly is 'class'? Ah! If only we could help you out with that one, my dear! Class is, well . . . *breeding*, isn't it? It's in the blood. Nobody can put their finger on it, really. It's an instinct, an aristocratic *feel* for all that is best in this miserable world of sinners. But what am I saying! Class is not something one *talks* about at all. It is just *there*. It *is*. It defies description!

And I'll be a monkey's uncle.

Frankly, they make me sick – that pair. Monsieur et Madame Vincensini.

And how they revel in that surname! It is redolent of – what? Italian Renaissance nobility, a modest mimosa-draped palazzo on the outskirts of Lucca, a red Alfa Romeo sparkling under an umbrella pine in the drive. And in the ancestral home, 16th-century Florentine curtains at the windows and school-of Old Masters on the stone-cool, ancient walls.

That's what they'd like to have you believe.

Of course it's *his* name – Monsieur Vincensini. And I remember once coming across some photos in a drawer. Old sepia pictures, with rounded edges, and the stamp of the photographic studio embossed at the bottom. I've no real proof, but the proof was in those faces, wasn't it? You could see at a glance that they were Vincensinis: the resemblance was striking. And who were they? A bunch of *ploucs* – country bumpkins from Calabria, or Apulia, or somewhere like that. The men all fat oafs with fingers like turnips and expressions that would make a herd of cows look intelligent. And the women – well, they were the herd of cows, weren't they? So much for the Vincensinis. No doubt their cherished offspring now run fibre-optics companies in Silicon Valley, or insurance brokerships in Hong Kong. But origins are origins, aren't they? To put it bluntly, a pigfarmer's a pigfarmer, even if he is dressed in designer linen. There's a whiff of sewage in those Vincensini airs and graces.

But the real snob was Madame, all togged up in her hubby's exotic name – on the phone she'd pronounce it *à l'italienne*, with a kind of fiery Latin swing. *Madame Vinchen-SEENi à l'appareil. Que puis-je pour vous*? If he was a *parvenu*, what on earth was she? Well I'm pretty good at finding things out, but getting to the roots of Madame's family tree was no easy matter. She was well prepared, she was – which is typical of her sort. When everything is façade, the façade tends to be perfect. In my line of business, that's one thing you get to learn pretty quick.

No, the façade rarely gives anything away. Creating the façade is one of those things you can pick up along the way. It's to do with shopping – shopping and having the money to shop. There are magazines which tell you how to do it. *Elle Décoration, Vogue*, even *Madame Figaro*. If you've got nothing better to do with your time than stare at pictures of house interiors and read the footnotes that tell you where to buy this and how much that is, then sooner or later you begin to get a knack for it.

So, for example, Madame realises one fine day that the indigo plush curtains do not give the desired effect, the half-shut half-open effect. They need to be held back, rucked up, in the middle. A discreet bit of string would have done the trick. But somewhere – in one of those fat slippery-papered Bibles of style – she saw some twee little silk cords with tassels, the kind that look like upside-down Scottish thistles. And the minute she saw them she knew that they were just the thing. But it had to be *these* ones – the ones in the picture. What really caught her fancy was the fact that the wispy bits of the tassels had three colours, gold, red and blue. Once she'd seen that, nothing else would do. It was the sort of detailing you'd get in a Loire château. But the people at the magazine didn't say where you could buy it.

So what did she do? She phoned the magazine. I heard her. I was there. They gave her the number of the journalist who wrote the article. She left a message on the journalist's answerphone. The journalist gave her the number of the person whose home had been photographed. The person whose home had been photographed gave her the number of an interior decorator in Aix-en-Provence. The interior decorator . . . well finally she got her damn tassels. She had them sent, Chronopost, from a shop in Madrid. But it cost her a whole day on the phone, and God knows what the phone-bill came to. All that, for four gold, red and blue tassels that nobody would notice . . .

Except of course, they *would*. Because it wasn't just the tassels, it was the whole effect, the *ensemble*. The right address; the visiting card; the Modigliani print; the tassels. When you added it all up it all added up to a lifetime with your nose truffling through magazine pics of other people's homes, a lifetime of phone-calls, and a lifetime reciting credit card numbers over the phone. And the desired effect was 'class'. It was an ambiance; something her guests would breathe in, if you get my drift. They would just feel it around them, and be really impressed. Because Madame Vincensini really wanted to impress.

But magazines don't tell you how to talk. They don't tell you how to behave. You can live like a pasha in the midst of luxury, then open your mouth and give the whole game away. I imagine that being Madame Vincensini is like suffering from lifelong flatulence and never having a second to yourself to let rip a good long fart. She had to hold it all in, hold it all back – her commonness. However, what really irked me about Madame Vincensini was that not only did she get the voice right – that knowing sing-song, with the Italian accent plastered over the top to hide the cracks – but she also got away with the content.

The time that sticks in my mind is when the Louvains came to lunch. He had been Deputy Minister of Culture and his wife ran the archives at the Museum of Modern Art. That always struck me as odd. I mean, if it's in an archive it's not modern any more, is it? It shouldn't be there. Anyway, the Louvains were a real coup, as far as they were concerned. Monsieur had met the Minister at a bigwig businessman do, and he thought he'd try his luck with the lunch invitation. And it worked. So even though it was lunch everything had to be *comme il faut* and Madame bust a gut getting it right. The menu changed five times. She had to phone retired chefs from the Ministry to find out what he liked, and it turned out to be asparagus puffs, of all things. So asparagus puffs it would be. But asparaguses were out of season, and no tinned muck would do. She had the damn things flown in from Saint Paul-de-Vence where someone grew them in a greenhouse. Then the pastry had to be just right . . . *feuilletés d'asperges* – but I'm sure you get the picture.

What was really weird was that I was looking forward to the lunch as much as she was.

I was sure she'd put her foot in it.

After all, these were not just everyday impressionable yobs. They were ministerial. They were cultural. She would have to talk about art, about government, about music and theatre and opera. You couldn't get away with that on a few revision notes.

But bugger me if the cow didn't pull it off.

The nobs arrived with a chauffeur-driven black Citroën CX with a high military shine and up they came in the lift. She'd bought an Yves Saint-Laurent number that she'd seen Catherine Deneuve wearing on the telly, and she opened the door, all smiles and how-d'you-dos. She had about two and a half hours – that's how she'd planned it. Twenty minutes in the lounge, with aperitifs and finger-food, up to two hours for the meal, then return to lounge for coffee and, if desired, *digestifs*. It was a three-act play. I knew Act One would go okay. Smalltalk. It was Act Two that would be interesting. Her husband could hold his own just being a businessman but sooner or later that class-seeking searchlight would be turned on her.

I couldn't wait.

Well first of all the ex-Minister was more than a little surprised to see his favourite nosh being wheeled in, those famous asparagus puffs. Was she going to admit to the phone-calls and all the rest? Not a bit of it!

'Really?' she said. 'Why, it's Olivier's favourite too! We always have them for lunch on a Thursday.'

This made me feel like shit. I mean her husband is one thing, but she knew that I knew that she knew . . . see what I mean? But the thought that I knew that she knew that I knew didn't turn a hair on her head. It was as if I wasn't there. Maybe 'class' means having no scruples of that kind or maybe it doesn't. I don't know. But I did know then that I had as much significance in their lives as the yucca in the reception hall. The thought that I was there, listening, looking, hearing the lie and seeing her phoney surprise – well it didn't even occur to her. I might as well have been deaf, dumb and blind.

It was when Madame Louvain said 'We're doing a Rothko retrospective. What do you think of his work?' that my ears pricked up.

She brought up one of the table napkins with the

embroidered crest and wiped her mouth on the corner of it, cool as a cucumber.

'There is a Rothko in Berlin,' she said, 'that I would kill for. It is called simply "Number One". It is a deep, velvet cloud of colour. When I stand in front of that painting I am standing in front of my life.'

Well, everybody was dumbfounded. Even Monsieur who'd had a bellyful of her little ways seemed caught on the hop. It was impressive, really it was. Not only had she got wind of the planned Rothko exhibition and done her homework on the wife, but she'd also upped the ante considerably. She was playing for real *cachet* now, and the stake was that cloud-castle of her reputation. She was risking ridicule.

'How very interesting,' said Madame Louvain after a while. 'It is so rare to meet someone who appreciates that – that ultimate degree of abstractionism, that – how can I put it? – that *scale* of obstinately non-figurative vision.'

'My wife has very eclectic tastes,' chipped in Monsieur. There was a quaver in his voice as if he was still unsure whether her bid for power had paid off.

Then chance tipped the balance. I shall never forget that moment.

'Oh!' exclaimed Madame Louvain in surprise.

She was not reacting to what had just been said. Her eye had simply alighted on the Modigliani in the corner.

A smarmy ripple of satisfaction passed over Madame Vincensini's face. Her guests would not have noticed it, but I did: I and my practised eye. Because, you see, she'd pulled it off. She'd hit the class jackpot in one.

'That isn't a . . . it *isn't*, is it?' asked Madame Louvain.

'Yes it *is*, as a matter of fact,' simpered Her Smugness. 'It's only a little sketch, of course. But there is such . . . such pathos and tragedy in his absolute mastery of line.'

Everything went swimmingly after that and the upshot of it all was that she was asked to help with the hanging of the Rothko show and the hostessing of the private view to which the arty-crafty *beau monde* would all be coming. She was cock-a-hoop – the haggard old débutante.

Later I found the Rothko book under her bed with sound-bites highlighted in Stabilo-Boss. That was no surprise. But somehow it didn't detract from her victory, her bare-faced, brazen cheek. She was a damn good counterfeiter of class, you had to admit. I found myself getting obsessive about her, I suppose. Day in, day out, I observed her, waiting for the mask to crack. Even when I was stretching my legs with her afghan hound I'd go up and down on the pavement opposite, sneaking a look up at the window from time to time in the hope of catching her out. What did I expect to see? I don't know. Secret drinking . . . a discreet spot of nose-picking. Almost anything would have done.

Then one day I found it, that crack in the mask, that fissure, that fatal flaw. She'd been mugging up on Maori handicraft because an antipodean ethnologist was due for dinner and in the kitchen I'd just prepared the kiwi salads and some recipe for nut-roast she'd dug up in a New-Zealand cookbook. She came in and said 'All right, Agnès, we won't be needing you. You can have the evening off. But before you go, would you mind giving the bathroom a tidy-up? I'm afraid I've left it in a bit of a mess.'

'A bit of a mess', for her, normally meant that she'd left the cap off the Helena Rubenstein lipstick, so I knew it wouldn't take me long. And now that I come to think of it, I'd been in that bathroom a thousand times without noticing a thing. Yet there it must have been, all that time, glaring me in the face. It stood serenely on a bamboo table by the frosted window.

It was a Bonsai tree planted in a pretty Japanese ceramic bowl-garden. There was a little mirror-lake, a bridge and porcelain Japs in kimonos that were supposed to be wandering around poetically with parasols in the miniature garden. It was while I was giving the bath-tub a bit of a wipe-out that I noticed it because I had to bend down and my nose came up level with the rim of the bowl. In the bowl she had planted her finger-nail clippings in neat little rows, crisscrossing the fine, sandy earth. I just stared and stared, I couldn't believe it. It suddenly occurred to me that these neat little rows were supposed to be fences, and the fences formed fields on the hill of soil above the lake, to one side of the mirror and behind the Bonsai. There must have been thousands of them – nail-clippings, that is – all arranged in twee little curvy rows. I started to count them and do some arithmetic. With ten fingers and ten toes, let's say she cut them every two weeks. That would make a harvest of forty a month – enough for three-and-a-half centimetres. I was adding things up like that when I had to stop because my head was swimming.

I went up to my *chambre de bonne* on the floor above, but somehow I couldn't stop thinking about it. A finger-nail garden! I knew that I'd catch her out one day, but who would have thought of this? The very idea just left me dazed.

The next day, of course, I packed my bags and went to the agency, the agency that had sent me to the Vincensinis in the first place. I went there and I told them. 'I'm a lady's maid,' I said, 'and she's no lady. I've got my reputation to think of too. It's beneath my dignity to be working in such a place. I mean, when one goes into service one expects something a cut above the common round, don't you agree? One expects some old-fashioned values, nobility and breeding. Not a finger-nail garden!'

'What are you talking about?' she said rudely – the secretary in the agency. That vulgar little hussy had been wiggling her finger around in her ear while I was speaking.

'Class!' I said firmly, and I had to raise my voice to get the idea over. 'Are you deaf, or what? I'm telling you that one expects a little *class* in the proper circles. But *that*, I suppose,' – I gave her one of my withering looks – 'is something you wouldn't know much about.'

Jonathan Wilson

MINI-JOE

IT WAS THIRTY-two years since my father died and I had a pain like hot curry in my left shoulder. Bathylle, Dr da Silva's nurse, directed me into his office. She told me to take my shirt off and then she left me alone. I was there for about twenty minutes so I started to use the doctor's phone. I dialled my wife. She wasn't home. I was about to call a couple of friends when the phone rang. 'Cardiology' I answered, but whoever it was hung up. I *69'd the caller but no one responded. I made one more call, to an old girlfriend, Alison Zawicki, whom I hadn't seen for twenty years. I'd found her number while fooling around on the Internet's 'Search for a Person' and transferred it to a small piece of paper which I'd carried around in my wallet for a month. Alison's voice, when I got through to chilly Edwardsville, Illinois, was, I thought, constricted by the smokey lassoes of time and nostalgia, but it turned out that she was eating a tangerine. Since 1976 when we had parted in anger, joy and pouring rain outside the Hungarian Pastry Shop on New York's Amsterdam Avenue, Alison had married, raised three children, lost her mother to cancer and then her husband on account of an affair that Alison had unwisely embarked upon with a colleague in Marketing. In an impressive coincidence, her sons' middle names were the same as my sons' first names.

'How are you?' she said.

I told her.

'You wait twenty years and then you call me when you've

got a punch in the heart and fire rushing down your arm. That's nice.'

'It's only a pain in my shoulder,' I corrected, 'but you're right. It's bad timing. I'm sorry to have intruded on your life. I won't phone again.'

'Oh yes you will. This has got to be at least a two parter. Of the lousy men that I've slept with over the years you could be the first to die. If you don't pull through maybe someone in your family can give me a buzz.'

'I'll see what I can arrange,' I replied.

We talked for a while about a spring afternoon when we had cycled uptown to The Cloisters. The sky was crystal blue and the wind over the Hudson blew hard toward the Palisades. On hills our young legs hardly required the aid of gears. We kissed at a stop light. At this point in our long distance conversation the unicorn of blissful memory laid its head in our laps. We stroked and caressed until it fell asleep.

'My life has been full of disappointment and regret,' Alison concluded, 'and I'm sorry I stood you up that night at the 92nd Street Y.'

'That must have been someone else,' I replied. 'I've never been there.'

Nurse Bathylle poked her head round the door. When she saw the receiver in my hand she gave me a scathing look.

'The doctor will be with you shortly.'

'It rang,' I said, and put the phone down on Alison.

For the next half hour I read *The PennStater* which had been left lying on the doctor's desk. I have a soft spot for Pennsylvania which I have never visited. I have sometimes entertained the fantasy that I am walking home past the steel mills in Bethlehem after a hard-fought high school football game. There's a light drizzle. I'm covered in mud and on my way, like the young Tom Cruise in *All The Right Moves*, to visit a Catholic girlfriend who has long red hair. When I get to her place I have a shower. She lies on the bed reading because, unlike myself, she has ambitions in the direction of college. When I come out of the shower she puts the book down and we make love.

It turned out that via *The PennStater* you could order a life-size or mini cardboard cut-out of the universities' football coach, Joe Paterno. I didn't want to do this but I wouldn't have minded the souvenir inkstand embossed with the college crest. There were two very boring articles in the magazine, one was about environmental engineering and the other focused on a local muralist. I was reading 'Alumnae Notes Class of '57' when Dr da Silva entered the room.

'It's an odd coincidence,' he said after perusing the results of my MRI and the minutes of my various stress tests. 'You were fifteen when your father died and now you have a fifteen year old son.'

'But I'm not dying,' I insisted.

'That remains to be seen,' da Silva replied. I thought he was probably kidding.

Da Silva ran through a lot of questions of the sort everyone knows. Then he said, 'I have to ask you something. The answer won't go on your medical record. Have you ever used cocaine?'

'Why,' I replied. 'Do you have some?'

It was the wrong answer.

'According to your thallium stress test, your left anterior circumflex may be partially blocked,' he continued after a swift elision of my ten snorts in thirty years. 'You need an angiogram, then possibly angioplasty.' He spilled out a few more sentences all of which featured the words 'heart disease'. I didn't like this at all. By the end of forty-five minutes I had fallen down a dank well. At the bottom there was nothing interesting to eat or drink and two large containers of Beta Blockers and Provachol. As a coda to our discussion da Silva explained what he planned to do to me.

'The process begins,' he said 'when we freeze your groin area.'

'No need to bother,' I replied, 'I've been married for seventeen years.'

'Then we rub in some of that new ointment which restores hair but makes you impotent.'

Da Silva didn't so much say this as imply it. I thought of

the black waves that topped off mini-Joe Paterno and complemented his Roy Orbison glasses.

'What about exercise?' I asked. I had no intention of doing any, but I was trying to ingratiate myself after the cocaine revelations. After all, this man was going to be splashing my heart with dye then running a plumber's line down the bloody streams where my life coursed.

'Do you own a treadmill?'

'No.'

'You could try walking the Mall.'

I groaned.

'Thirty circuits from Bloomingdales round the fountain to Filenes is three miles. It's free and warm. You get the camaraderie of a crowd and the entertainment of various shop windows. I recommend it to all my patients who can't afford a home gymnasium.'

'See Rome and die,' I said.

I didn't go to the Mall or home. Instead I drove to O'Flanagan's bar and ordered a glass of blood-oxidising red wine. The local paper was lying in a pool of beer further up the counter. I fished it out and turned to 'Police Beat.' Item 1. Local flasher seen again at the library. Item 2. Four girls from the high school spend Saturday night in the hospital Emergency Room having their stomachs pumped. I had already heard about 2. The girls had drunk a bottle of vodka as if it were Evian. Two slumped unconscious for three hours, the others were choking on vomit when the cops and ambulance crew arrived. I knew the mother of one of these girls. She was a hard-working person, full of love and care for her children. Her husband wasn't in the picture any more. Every day, she made school lunches and sent her offspring on the clamorous bus to struggle with algebra, read multi-cultural poetry and learn a few words of Spanish. At night she made dinner, laundered her children's clothes, helped with the homework, then drove to rent videos and Nintendo games. Sometimes she shouted, warned, and threatened, sometimes hugged.

Everybody agreed that having your stomach pumped was something to be avoided, but youth would rather swig grain alcohol and try to make death drunk, than stand lost in thought with a finger to its lips.

I ordered another glass of wine.

When I got home there was a message from my cousin Risa on call answering.

'I've had it confirmed,' she began, 'that Meyer Kriss, your grandfather on your father's side's nephew, and husband to my mother's aunt Raisl Oskerovitz, was badly treated by your family on a station platform in London after the war. I'll be in and out all day.'

I called her at work. There was a high tech crackling on the line, like ice on the River Neva pulling apart in spring. My cousin was an epidemiologist. She knew, for example, why women of African American descent were more likely than any other group to undergo hip replacement surgery.

'Bad news for the royal line,' I announced. 'I'm down for an angiogram.'

My cousin shrieked, but then she settled down to business.

It was 1947. The smoke from a recently arrived steam train billowed and flattened under the great roof of Victoria station. My grandfather, the well-known pigeon fancier, religious fanatic, and specialist in unemployment, stood with his three sons in the penumbra cast by the black cylinder of the train. My father held the *News Chronicle* under his arm: Headline. SIX-WAY SPY WAS SO SHY. Down the platform, clutching the refugee's obligatory brown suitcase, came skinny Meyer Kriss. Because sometimes the eye sees less than the heart knows, my family apparently missed history's misery sliding down Meyer's sloped shoulders: the camps, for example, of which they could not speak, and the DP camps which, over a period of eighteen months, had softened Meyer's jowls in a direction away from skeletal.

Well, well, after a week Gramps sent him back. No room at the inn. Too many hungry mouths to feed. No work, no beans. Bye Bye cousin Kriss, the moil of London is not for you, nor its mohels for your children. Return to the displacement camp of your choice and here's five quid for a new suit and a decent meal on the boat.

'I don't believe a word of it,' I replied when my cousin was through. In the first place, my grandfather never went anywhere in a collective. Second, he never had five pounds to his name, which is one of the reasons my grandmother kicked him out. And third, my father once saved a sparrow by splinting a match stick to its broken leg. Is that the kind of man who would spurn a needy relative?'

'Hitler was a vegetarian,' my cousin replied.

I lay on the hospital bed while a nurse shaved my pubic hair to centrefold specifications, then popped me a few pills to make life seem easy and calm. It was six-thirty a.m. The winter sky was the colour of a wild goose's belly. Beneath it, cinder forms in high blocks ordered the patient to look no further. The real prisons, said Albert Camus, are the hospitals, and the real hospitals are the prisons. My wife and her sister sat chatting at the foot of the bed.

'What do you think?' my wife asked. 'Plates or paper plates?'

'It's a party,' her sister Minna replied. 'You don't want to have to do a lot of clearing up afterwards.'

Was it 'party' she said or 'wake'? Could it be check out time for yours truly? Or was it the drugs listening? But why not move on and out? What was there in return to the quiet suburbs except a month of snow shovelling, the endless chauffeuring of children and a slowly defrosting groin? On the other hand, my legacy was incomplete. On this day of potential reckoning I had offered a particularly weak and disappointing choice of last words to be remembered by.

'Can you bring up some toilet paper?'

'Yes I'm a bit scared.'

'I know which parking lot.'

'Can I have a Valium drip?'

'I hate slippers.'

Dr da Silva and his team were waiting for me in the operating theatre. His assistant, Dr Soo-Hoo, looked especially fetching in her grey scrub suit and matching mask. I wanted to ask her to dance but my condom catheter got in fantasy's way. Lights. Camera. Action. We were in hyper-space. My upper torso burned from the inside out.

'*O lac*,' I urged, '*suspends ton vol.*'

These were the first words that I had uttered in French since completing the British equivalent of sixth grade. Time rested its aluminium heel on my chest but didn't stomp. Then it was over.

Dr da Silva leaned in and whispered close to my ear.

'May your children's arteries be as yours, yea unto the tenth generation.'

Was this a blessing or a curse?

Dr Soo-Hoo removed her mask.

'The thallium test was a false positive. It happens only five per cent of the time, and almost exclusively to women.'

My wife and Minna were waiting in recovery.

'I'm clean,' I announced, giving a thumbs-up sign from the supine position.

'We heard,' my wife replied. 'You have the heart of a girl.'

I lay back. The entire futile world that I was so happy to be a part of returned to me in the shape of a white globe and its rip cord flex. My wife squeezed my hand. I thought, on reflection, that my grandfather might have been kinder to his skinny nephew Kriss.

Lawrence Norfolk

BEING TRANSLATED, OR THE VIRGIN MARY'S HAIR

EVERY CHURCH NEEDS an altar, and every altar needs a dead saint. A shortage of the latter in the early 8th century first prompted the practice of cutting up beatified cadavers and distributing their bits and pieces among the unendowed churches. Pity poor Saint Elizabeth whose still-warm corpse was divested of hair, fingernails, and nipples by overenthusiastic relic-hunters in 1231. Or Saint James: one arm in Liège, the other in Alsace, a hand in Reading, part of his breast in Pistoia, a tooth in Bremen, and the rest in Santiago de Compostela. The Holy Family, having been raised bodily to heaven on their deaths, could provide no relics except those discarded during life. Nine different churches claim to hold the foreskin of Christ. Sixty-nine claim vials of milk expressed from the breasts of the Virgin Mary. A lock of her hair has led a separate, highly mobile existence ever since the original hair-cut sometime in the late 1st century BC.

The theological term for such displacements is 'translation'. It derives from that most irregular of Latin verbs '*fero, ferre, tuli, latum*', which means 'to bear' or 'to carry'. The ancient Greek term for the dismemberment which necessarily precedes a multiple 'translation' is 'sparagmos', which is what the Maenads of Thrace did to Orpheus. Namely, tearing him to pieces. His head ended up in the river Hebrus, whence it found its way, still singing by some accounts, to an eventual landfall and burial on Lesbos.

Latterly, 'translation' has become something that happens to books. ('Sparagmos' too, although that now goes by the

149

name 'editing'.) Of course the cutting-up and distribution of saints only loosely approximates the kinds of operations performed upon books. That a single lock of hair from the head of the Virgin Mary might be as efficacious as the whole body, that a saint can be infinitely sub-divided and each part retain the power of the whole (to heal, or save, or guard against misfortune) ultimately depends upon the doctrine of grace, which requires in turn a considerable leap of faith.

These are the same doctrinal foundations which upheld the sale of indulgences; such shaky underpinnings do not inspire much confidence, yet the demands upon the faithful run on. For a lock of hair from the head of the Virgin Mary to have its claimed beneficial effect implies not only that the lock of hair represents the whole body and the body the whole store of Mary's virtuously-earned grace, but also (the doctrine of grace being absolute) that these successive representations must be perfect: the meaning of the hair *is* the Virgin Mary, and everything she means *is present* in the lock of hair. Synecdoche with a vengeance.

Charlemagne believed it and wore the relic around his neck enclosed in a hemisphere of polished crystal. To expect the readers of today to make such a leap of faith reveals an optimism bordering on lunacy, and yet that is the presumption every time a literary translation is published. But, by and large, that optimism is justified. Readers believe in translation. For writers, however, the process is more fraught.

Here, by way of illustration, is a list of books which I did not write: *Lemprière's Wörterbuch, Le Dictionnaire de Lemprière, Słownik Lemprière'a, Lemprière's Ordabók, Lemprières Lexicon, El Diccionario de Lemprière, A Lemprière-lexicon, Het Woordenboek van Lemprière, Kabbalin Kulta* ('Lemprière' being unpronounceable in Finnish), *Dictionarului Lemprière, Lemprière's Ordbog*, and several further variations in languages (Hebrew, Cantonese, Korean, Russian, Japanese) whose alphabets are, to me at least, illegible

The implicit promise of a translation is that it carries within it the original text, that the original writer's expressed intent is present in the new version just as surely as the Virgin Mary's salvific goodness is present in a lock of her hair. In translation, however, there is no doctrine of grace. In fact, as far as I can see, there is no coherent doctrine or theory at all, and the existence of Chairs of Translation Theory within universities the world over no more guarantees the possibility of a perfect translation than the Pope's throne ensures virtue within the Church of Rome.

Foundationless edifices induce nervousness in their inhabitants and all writers are notoriously prone to paranoia. Amongst the worrisome operations performed on one's book (editing, binding, jacketing, publication, reviewing . . .) translation maintains an effortless pre-eminence. It is of course an unignorable signal that the book has ceased being one's own and has become a public property, has stopped being what one *does* and has become something one has *done*. *Opus* has turned into *corpus* and, for the writer even if no one else, a dead *corpus* at that.

Next: the dismemberment. Territorial and language rights are auctioned off. Then – for a long time – nothing happens. Or nothing *seems* to happen. Distantly and inscrutably, translations are underway. One's 'O's are becoming 'Ø's. One's 'C's are sprouting little tails. Umlauts, accents, and all manner of other sigils and squiggles settle over the text, blanketing it in a diacritical fallout. The text mutates and, most obviously, swells. A translated book is usually 20% longer than the original. Sometimes, however, it contracts. The UK edition of my first novel has 530 pages; the Hebrew edition has 431. Translation? Sparagmos? Where is the rest of the Virgin Mary's hair? One simply does not know what happens to one's book in translation, and sometimes it is best not to ask.

But the questions come at one whether one asks or not. They come from one's translators. You anticipate and, to a certain extent, even welcome them. How will they deal with the delicate tissue of half-puns, glancing allusions, and tiny shifts in tone which energise your masterwork? Having ransacked the English language to stuff five synonyms for

'Ship' into a single sentence, you wonder whether your landlocked translators will be able to find a sufficient number in, say, Czech, let alone Slovak. And what about the twenty-five synonyms for 'Book', each one to begin with a different letter of the alphabet excepting whichever letter begins that language's word for 'Dictionary', which must appear with jokey belatedness in the following paragraph? How will this work in Greek, whose alphabet does not possess the requisite twenty-six characters? Or Cantonese, which doesn't really have characters at all?

Actually, all these 'wonderings' can be organised under two successive headings: 'Will my translators recognise how extraordinarily clever and talented I am?' and, if the answer to that is in the affirmative, 'Will they then write and tell me so?'

I suppose this is excusable when one considers, firstly, the mind-warping effects of spending years on end with only a computer screen for company and, secondly, the fact that although most writers need only a medium-sized truck to transport their hypertrophied egos, an oil-tanker would not suffice to carry their attendant insecurities. Anyway, the answers to the above questions usually turn out to be, 'Only out of politeness' and 'No'. A translator's questions, one quickly understands, are not designed to make authors feel good about themselves.

So: 'How many legs, if any, does Captain Roy have? On page 170 he is described as *the amputee* and it says that he has lost one leg; whereas on pages 389 and 478 he appears to have no legs at all.'

Or: '*The coach turned left before the Marché des Innocents as though to cross the river by the Pont Neuf . . .* are you sure you mean left and not right?'

'And by the way (page 284) how can Caltanisetta (Sicily) sulfur come from Cagliare (the "Cagliare", I suppose, on Sardinia)?'

Lastly: '*He had not realized before* – REALIZED WHAT??? Can you just realize like that, without an object?'

To which one is tempted not to reply.

One does though, because one's translators are not only one's closest and most attentive readers but also one's closest and most attentive re-writers. Your text is in their hands. From my Swedish translator, Thomas Preis: 'Thank you very much for an extremely speedy answer. You care about your own work. Not all authors seem to do so. I am right now reading the proof of my translation of James Ellroy's *LA Confidential*; he didn't even deign to write an answer and tell me he wasn't interested in co-operating . . .'. The smart writer remains, at the very least, polite.

A translator's queries centre on inconsistencies and questions of vocabulary. Woe betide the sloppy plotter and the forger of neologisms. But, given that a novel is more than items of vocabulary strung together by a plot, it would be a writer of inhuman confidence who did not, from time to time, wonder what was happening to the other things: style, for instance, or shifts of register, the relative broadness or subtlety of the comic passages, degrees of irony. I have never been asked whether or not I am 'trying to be funny'.

A writer-in-translation is as isolated as a general in his bunker trying simultaneously to direct a war on twenty or more fronts. The dispatches come through (or fail to) but, reduced as they are to their bare essentials, it is hard to know how the conflict as a whole is going. One suspects that those in the field are taking matters into their own hands. Worse, that they are showing initiative, or worse yet, that there has been an outbreak of *creative flair*. The situation is out of control . . .

Not true, or only partially so; control has been devolved. One's book is becoming other books, which should mean that its writer is becoming other writers or, more specifically, a group of translators. But that is where the analogy breaks down. You remain 'you' while your book is reincarnated in Albanian, and Estonian, and Japanese. Who are these impostors busily imitating the 'you' who wrote the book? The spread of a text through the languages capable of reproducing it extends its reach and strengthens its appeal, but the reproductions (by one's translators) of the effort expended in its original writing seems parodic, somehow mocking. Of course it is possible that a translator appreciates only dimly the titanic labours involved in a book's composition; but it is certain that a writer understands the difficulties of its subsequent translation not at all. It is quite common for a writer never to meet his or her translators and to participate in the process of translation only tangentially. The finished book seems to appear *ex nihilo*, effortlessly, or with one's original effort elided.

The process of translation finds an uneasy place amongst those several activities which sunder a book from its author, place the former before its potential readers, and recast the latter as a garrulous puppet in its service. In short, publication. Fraught with misunderstandings and paranoias, translation is the act which makes incontrovertible a book's transition from the privacy of a writer's imagination to the public arenas of the culture and the market. My translated editions are, quite literally, foreign to me.

And they also paid for my house.

The 'translation' as object, by which I mean the translated book rather than the process by which it came into existence, makes writers rich and readers happy. Amongst the activities by which writers compromise themselves in search of an extra buck (always euphemised as 'placing one's work before the widest possible audience'), selling translation rights is at once the most profitable and least venal. It does not involve the writer in tear-jerking accounts of his childhood delivered to suitably sympathetic journalists, or recitations of his work to single-digit audiences, or manufactured feuds with carefully-selected critics. It does, however, close the door on an esoteric but cherished dream.

Imagine this: a book so good that its felicities had the power to turn the debased rhetorical dross of its best reviews into truths. Instead of being 'compelling' (meaning, its author has made some attempt at constructing a story) it would *actually* be compelling. Instead of being 'beautifully written' (meaning, it contains adjectives) it would *actually* be beautifully written. And instead of being 'that rarest of things, a necessary book' (meaning, its author is married to the reviewer) its story would in fact have the force, relevance, and acuity which together add up to necessity. And, instead of instantly running through thirty or more translated editions, its very perfection would render it perfectly untranslatable. What next?

I am sure that those vaguely-sourced anecdotes retailing the travails of dedicated readers who learn Russian in order to read Pushkin, or Spanish for Cervantes, or Finnish (this stretches credulity) for the *Kalevala*, are all apocryphal. Nevertheless, this notional book would be so good (meaning: compelling, beautifully written, and necessary) that readers the world over, instantly and en masse, would take the bookworm's equivalent of the leap of faith. They would begin diligent studies in whatever language it might be written for the sole purpose of reading this wonder-tome.

Instead of the book setting out on the hazardous journey to its readers, wherever they might be and whatever language they might speak, imagine readers propelling themselves furiously through thickets of alien grammar, irregular verbs, slang, arcane vocabulary, and all the other things which once led a friend of mine to describe translation, quite simply, as 'hell'. And finally, having battled with their impatience until their proficiency sufficed for this extraordinary book's delicacies and nuances, they crack open the spine and begin to feast on the hard-won banquet set before them . . .

Pope Boniface IX tried to ban the 'translation' of saints just as later popes tried to control 'translation' of the Bible. All failed, and mummified feet, fingers, foreskins, and the Word of God duly devolved from Rome to the most far-flung churches of Christendom. The paranoias of writers are identical to those of Boniface. They suspect and resent devolution, interpretation, translation; anything which takes their book away from them. But the flow, whether cultural or spiritual, is always outward, away from the centre. The tendency of everything is to spread.

Yet I think that a simple desire lurks within the fog of paranoia that envelopes the translated writer. Everyone would like to write that impossible book: the book which pulls readers into its world and language just as Rome pulls pilgrims into its churches. This is, of course, a mawkish and sentimental fantasy, but its corollary is even worse. As a translated writer, it is just possible to convince oneself that one has already written such a book, except that twenty-odd translators got their hands on it first. Had they not – the argument runs on – then by now one would either be considerably less-read or (the tempting alternative) universally acknowledged as the greatest writer on the planet.

Whether the extreme implausibility of this scenario signals the high degree of writerly paranoia over being translated or vice versa seems undecidable, and perhaps not very important for the odds of either possibility being true are about the same as the Virgin Mary emerging alive, well, and intact (except for a slightly irregular haircut) from a hollow crystal hemisphere which once hung about the neck of the Emperor Charlemagne.

The only real way out of this uncomfortable conundrum is to translate one's books oneself. But, leaving aside the mind-boggling effort required, this involves a peculiarly uncomfortable linguistic straddle. It was touched on by Hilaire Belloc in a lecture delivered in 1931: 'There is a certain degree of familiarity with German which makes an Englishman, especially in the theological field, incomprehensible. There is a certain degree of familiarity with French which makes the English sentence professing to translate a French one unnatural and slightly ridiculous.' If that seems opaque, here is a paraphrase (albeit an unwitting one) given by the duty sergeant from *Hill Street Blues* a mere fifty years later: 'Remember people, let's be *careful* out there . . . .'

Unfortunately, the translated writer can be either 'out there' or 'careful', but not both.

Philip Davison

LENNON'S GUITAR

THE TELEPHONE RANG just twice before the receiver was lifted, but nothing was said at the other end.

'Hello . . . ?'

No reply.

'Hello?'

After the second hello there was a response. 'Say something else.'

'It stinks in here, Jemmie.'

'What kind of a car do I drive?'

'You don't have a car, Jemmie.'

'Wrong, Billyboy. I told you I was buying a car, didn't I? Have you done your homework?'

'I have.'

'Read the whole book, did you?'

'Yes.'

'Right. Read the bit I told you to mark.'

'What – over the phone?'

'READ IT.'

Though Jemmie had raised his voice, he was calm. He had had a vision. Men holding aloft a glowing dog. He took this as a good omen.

The Billyfella pulled a grubby, dog-eared book from his coat pocket and began to read the section he had marked. It concerned the theft of John Lennon's Jumbo guitar. The guitar had disappeared at the Finsbury Empire in London in 1963. Lennon was very upset. The identity of the thief had remained a mystery. Though The Billyfella read with a small voice into the mouthpiece, his words filled the stinking telephone kiosk.

'Good man,' said Jemmie when the short passage had been read. 'Now, I want you to meet up with somebody. He's good with locks.'

The Billyfella patrolled back and forth in front of the telephone kiosk. He whistled a tune through his teeth. He stopped abruptly when he heard a voice in the dark.

'Psst.'

A man eight or ten years younger than him stepped into the light and introduced himself. 'The Bobbyfella. Where do you want me?' Even at eight or ten years younger he had missed his chance at being a rock star, if ever there was a chance. There was that much in common.

'I don't want you anywhere,' said The Billyfella.

The Bobbyfella took up what he thought might be an appropriate position by the telephone kiosk. 'I understand,' he said, sotto voce. 'You can't be too careful.'

'Are you looking for trouble?' The Billyfella asked.

There was an awkward pause while The Billyfella made a token adjustment to his position.

'That's all right,' he said. 'I was told to expect this.'

The Billyfella began to circle him. The Bobbyfella thought he should make another token gesture, but he couldn't think what that might be.

'I brought a torch,' he said.

'Oh – so you brought a torch? Who told you to bring a torch?'

'Nobody. I brought it myself. It's my torch.'

'Why did you bring a torch?'

'It's dark.'

'Don't get smart with me, sunshine.'

'I was told not to get smart,' The Bobbyfella conceded. '"Don't get smart with The Billyfella," Jemmie said.'

The Billyfella moved away to perform some stretching exercises. The Bobbyfella attempted to strike a conspicuously relaxed posture.

'"You do what The Billyfella says," Jemmie told me. "You do what The Billyfella says until I get there."'

'You were told to bring a torch?'

'I wasn't told not to.'

The Billyfella ceased his exercising and again approached The Bobbyfella who had begun to sing.

'Who said you could sing? Nobody said you could sing.'

'I sing if I like.'

'We'll see about that.'

There followed a silence that was punctuated by an occasional disembodied note from The Billyfella which was ignored. Then The Billyfella stepped forwards.

'Hel-lo – what's this?'

'Is that him?'

'No, it's not him. Christ – he's not going to arrive pushing a car, is he? Look at this eejit. The state of the Jaysus car.'

The stranger pushing the Jaysus car was signalling to them.

'Here – what does he want?'

'He's waving at you,' The Billyfella said with a smirk. 'Ignore him.'

'Hoy,' shouted The Bobbyfella, 'get yourself a decent car.'

The smirk vanished from The Billyfella's face. 'Shut it. Do you hear?' Then, he took to shouting. 'Hoy. Turn down Prussia Street. Turn left. Prussia Street. Christ. LEFT. DOWN HILL.'

'LEFT,' The Bobbyfella shouted.

The car was not steered to the left but instead continued on its course and disappeared from view. The two men watched then The Bobbyfella turned to his new acquaintance who felt obliged to say something.

'His sort never listen.'

'His sort? You know his sort, do you?'

'I study people.'

'What?'

'I look at them. And I read about them.'

'Oh – very good,' said The Billyfella making a big gesture of looking at his watch to amplify his mockery.

'There's this bastard comes into the library and he sits

down and he starts to laugh. Hoots of laughter and he
doesn't so much as have a book out in front of him.'

'And . . . ?'

'And the rest of us pretend to ignore him. They ask him to
leave every time he comes in and starts. He gets tired very
quickly. Then, he gets up and leaves. I tell you what, though –
I saw him in the street the other day, so I went over to him. "I
know you, ya bollix," I said. I don't have to tell you what his
reply was . . .'

'He laughed.'

'What is it with these people? Do they have a bad diet, or
what?'

The Bobbyfella concluded with some gruff humming. The
Billyfella countered with some whistling. Then, the telephone
rang. Initially, both men doggedly ignored it. The Billyfella
cracked first.

'Answer that.'

'You get it.'

'He said he'd collect us. Christ on a bike.' The Billyfella
answered it. 'Hello . . . ?'

No reply.

'Hello? Jemmie? Jesus, the stink in here . . .'

No response.

'It's The Billyfella . . .'

'What song did I sing in the Indian restaurant on Thursday
night?' Jemmie asked.

The Billyfella gave the opening lyric of the song and said
that he was unsure whether or not this was the actual title.
Jemmie insisted that he sing the first verse. The Billyfella sang.
The Bobbyfella leered at him through the window of the
kiosk.

'That'll do, Billyboy,' Jemmie interrupted. 'No mistaking
that voice.'

The Billyfella confirmed that The Bobbyfella was there
with him. He asked if the half-wit, as he called him, was
needed.

'I know he's there,' Jemmie said. 'I'm watching you right
now.' And yes, The Bobbyfella was needed.

The Billyfella covertly scanned the vicinity, but could not see Jemmie. There was just The Bobbyfella, who was now crab-walking along the kerb.

'Stay right where you are,' Jemmie ordered.

'What – in here? But it stinks.'

'I'll be there with the car in a minute. And do something about The Bobbyfella. He's not on his marks.'

The Billyfella put down the receiver and opened the door, ordered The Bobbyfella into the kiosk.

'What? Both of us?'

'Get IN.'

The Bobbyfella got in.

'Christ – what a smell. Was that him? Are we in business?'

He was given a nod.

'Now what?'

'We wait.'

'What – in here?'

There was no answer. They separated as best they could. The Bobbyfella took out a harmonica and began to play.

'What the HELL? Stop. Stop THAT.'

The Bobbyfella stopped playing.

'What do you think you're at?'

'I'm practising.'

'Practising? We're on a job and you're practising?'

The Bobbyfella asked if he recognised the tune and The Billyfella said that he did. Did he know the lyrics? Yes, he knew the lyrics.

'Great song,' The Bobbyfella asserted.

'I suppose Jemmie told you to bring a harmonica – just in case, like.'

The Bobbyfella said that he always carried a harmonica.

'Have you any idea what this looks like – you serenading me in a public phone box?'

'I'll play. You sing. Take our minds off the stink.'

'You're the bollix you've been telling me about – the one in the library. It's you, isn't it?'

The Bobbyfella grinned and resumed playing, but stopped

abruptly when there was a light tap on the window. The Billyfella opened the door.

'Well, well,' said Jemmie as a general greeting, then turned to The Bobbyfella. 'What's that in your pocket?'

'A torch.'

'A torch. You brought a torch?'

'I have, Jemmie.'

'I didn't tell you to bring a torch.'

'Bloody harmonica, too,' added The Billyfella.

Jemmie then turned to him. 'We're going to do this right and to do it right everybody has to know his place.'

'Jemmie, there's people looking at us standing here,' The Billyfella warned. 'Do you not think we look – suspicious, like?'

'Suspicious? On the deck, Billyboy. Ten press-ups.'

'Ah here . . .'

'DO IT. You – Bobby. Count.'

The Billyfella got down on the ground and did his ten press-ups. He undertook them in the spirit of camaraderie and adventure. It was a good release for nervous tension.

'Now,' said Jemmie, 'you stand on him.'

'Stand on him?'

'Stand on him. Get up on his back.'

'All right,' said The Bobbyfella, only now entering the spirit of the moment, 'I will.'

And he did. And The Billyfella let out a cry.

'Right,' said Jemmie. 'Anybody looking at us now, is there?'

'No,' gasped The Billyfella.

When The Billyfella had struggled to his feet and brushed himself down, the two fell in behind Jemmie.

'Are we walking to this gig?' The Bobbyfella asked.

'Somebody told me you were a musician in need of a few bob. I wasn't told you didn't come with a pair of feet.'

'No . . . it's just these shoes . . .'

'Pull the women with those shoes, do you?'

Jemmie led them around a corner to the car he had recently purchased.

'A Zodiac,' The Billyfella said aloud. He was impressed.

'You don't see many of them anymore,' The Bobbyfella added. He was less enthusiastic.

Jemmie got them into the car. 'Don't wind down that window. It won't go back up.'

'Fair enough.'

'And no smoking.'

'No smoking. Right.'

'So where are we off to, Jemmie?' The Bobbyfella asked. 'It's all very mysterious.'

Jemmie told him they were taking care of a little piece of history that night. It would be something to tell his grandchildren. 'I've brought an Instamatic. You'll want a picture.'

The car wouldn't start.

'When I tell you to switch on, switch on.'

'Right, Jemmie.'

Jemmie got out and lifted the bonnet.

'Christ,' said The Bobbyfella, 'does anybody in these parts have a car that goes?' The Billyfella told him to relax, but he persisted. 'Might have been a Zodiac once. Pile of shite now, wha'?'

'Expert are you?' said The Billyfella. 'Get your feet down.'

'I'm relaxing. Bit like sitting in the dentist's chair, actually. That kind of relaxing. I was in the chair last week. The dentist's clammy hookers in my mouth . . .'

'Is that where you get your singing lessons?'

'Never had it open that wide before. Thought it might rip. I was trying make my mind go blank. I was looking out of the window, watching the birds fly past . . .'

'I don't want to hear this.'

'Birds don't have a plan. Have you noticed? Is it any wonder they're afraid of everything?'

'There's something wrong with you.'

'Switch on,' shouted Jemmie.

The Billyfella turned the ignition key. Nothing.

'Pile – of – shite,' The Bobbyfella repeated helpfully.

'Right,' said Jemmie. 'Out, the pair of yis.'

It had to be a push start. Jemmie told them they were like a couple of aul'fellas. 'And to think I used to watch you, Billyboy, jumping around the stage for ninety minutes at a go.'

'Are you serious?' The Bobbyfella retorted. 'What band was this?'

'That was a while ago', The Billyfella snapped. Nothing more was said on the subject. 'Bobby,' he growled, 'you give us a tune.'

The Bobbyfella played a blues number on his harmonica as they drove across the city. Jemmie was guided by his glowing dog that shambled ahead of them in the night sky.

'Read that piece for The Bobbyfella,' Jemmie said.

Reluctantly, The Billyfella produced the dog-eared copy of *The Beatles: The Authorised Biography*, by Hunter Davies. The Bobbyfella stopped playing his harmonica. The passage about the missing guitar was read.

'"Where's my Jumbo," says John Lennon,' boomed Jemmie. 'Can you imagine? 1963, and the genius that is John Lennon comes backstage and finds that his guitar has walked. "WHERE'S MY JUMBO GUITAR?"'

'Christ,' said The Bobbyfella. He was very taken by Jemmie's dramatisation of the event.

'I mean, not even Elvis would get a loan of that guitar.'

'And some filthy gouger stole it,' The Billyfella rejoined. He was genuinely outraged.

'They did,' said Jemmie. 'And tonight, we're getting it back.'

'JAYSUS.' The Bobbyfella was astonished. 'John Lennon's guitar . . . IN DUBLIN . . .'

'The grandfather was from Dublin,' Jemmie said, playing down his biographical knowledge to good effect. 'Why wouldn't the guitar end up in Dublin?'

'Absolutely,' agreed The Bobbyfella.

Jemmie stopped the car in front of a terrace of houses built with yellow Dolphin's Barn brick.

'Right,' he said. 'It's around the corner. Number thirteen.

Bobbyboy, you come with me and do your thing on the lock.
Billyboy, when I get out you get in the driver's seat.'

'I get to drive the getaway car.'

'Grow up, willya.'

'Yes, Jemmie. Sorry. It's just the excitement.'

The Bobbyfella was slow to get out of the car. 'Eh,
Jemmie . . .'

'What?'

'What if I can't do the lock?'

'I beg your pardon?'

'If I can't – you know – do the lock.'

'I was told you were a dab hand. Are you telling me you
can't spring a lock?'

'I can – most of the time.'

'Do you think I'd wear leather soles to go climbing through
windows?'

'No, Jemmie.'

'Do the Jaysus lock.'

'Right. I will.'

'Christ. What are you waiting for? Number thirteen.
There's nobody at home. You do your business. There'll be
nobody watching apart from me. I'll be right behind you.'

'Jemmie,' The Billyfella said as the others were getting out
of the car, 'you haven't said what you're going to do with the
Jumbo once we have it.'

Jemmie froze half way out of the car, turned about, leaned
back in to reply. 'What – having it isn't enough? I don't
expect The Bobbyfella to understand. He's too young. But
you – I'm surprised at you, Billyboy. I really am.'

The Billyfella squirmed, then slithered into the driver's seat,
avoiding eye contact.

Initially, The Bobbyfella seemed to know what he was
doing. Jemmie was the nervous one.

'Have you got it?'

'No. I haven't got it.'

'Take your time.'

'I am taking my time.'

'Just do it.'

'I can't do it with you watching me.'

'Who's watching? Do the Jaysus lock and be quick about it.'

'I'm doing it. I'm doing it.'

'I was told I was getting an expert. Christ . . .'

'There . . .'

The lock gave, Jemmie pushed past and advanced up the hall, pushing open first the living room door, then the dining room door for an instant inspection.

'You know this bollix?' The Bobbyfella asked in a harsh whisper.

'Ho – I do, Bobbyboy.'

'Can he be violent?' The Bobbyfella asked, advancing sideways and not quite keeping up. 'I mean, he mightn't be the type that responds to a chorus of Give Peace a Chance.'

Jemmie turned on him sharply in the kitchen doorway. 'You don't see, do you?'

'Don't see what?'

'No sense of history. No respect.'

'No – no, I do see,' replied The Bobbyfella. He didn't want to stop moving, so he shuffled from one foot to the other. 'Hell of a gig, this, getting hold of John Lennon's guitar. Could we do it right now, please?'

'You keep watch.' Jemmie pushed past again and went back down the hall and took the staircase three steps per stride. He wasn't up there long. He came thundering down the staircase.

'Right. It's not up there. Get looking.'

*

Jemmie sat hunched over on the couch. The Bobbyfella stood anxiously by the window.

'Will we go over the whole place again,' he asked.

'We've looked. It's not here.'

'Perhaps he sold it.'

'WHERE'S MY JUMBO?' Jemmie bellowed. The booming words lifted The Bobbyfella off his feet.

'Take it easy, Jemmie. Look . . . don't you think we should be going . . . ?'

'We're going nowhere without that guitar.'

'How do you mean?' There was a sudden shortness of breath in The Bobbyfella's words.

'We're staying right here. Until they come back. Then, we'll find out where the Jumbo is.'

This wasn't what The Bobbyfella wanted to hear. He was beginning to feel ill.

Jemmie ordered a sandwich. 'Cheese and tomato. A bit of ham, if there's any in the fridge. And tea.'

The Bobbyfella turned to make his way to the kitchen. 'Eh, Jemmie . . .'

'WHAT?'

'Brown or white?'

'There won't be any brown.'

There was a tentative tattoo on the Zodiac's horn. Jemmie rose to his feet, glanced out the window, then began to scan the record collection. The Bobbyfella lingered in the doorway.

'You know this bollix very well, do you?'

'I know his wife,' said Jemmie. 'Where's my sandwich?' The Bobbyfella went to the kitchen. Jemmie made a selection of L.P.s. 'Get me a cardboard box,' he shouted. 'I can't carry all of these under my arm. Here,' he said holding out one record sleeve, 'who buys the likes of THIS?'

The Bobbyfella did not come back for a look, but instead shouted to enquire whether or not mustard was wanted.

'Yes, I want mustard. The Billyfella doesn't get a sandwich.'

'Right. No sandwich.'

'Go out and tell him if I hear that horn again he'll be sorry.'

'Right.'

'Christ. Look at that.'

'What?'

Jemmie pointed to an ashtray on the sideboard. 'Somebody's been smoking cigars. Sort The Billyfella. Get the Jaysus sandwich and the Jaysus box.'

'Right away, Jemmie.'

Jemmie ate the sandwich very slowly. He kept The Bobbyfella pinned with his gaze.

'What happens when these people come back?' The Bobbyfella suddenly blurted out.

'Happens? We're going to find out where the guitar is. That's what happens. Then, we're going to get the guitar.'

'Yes but . . . what are we going to say? What are we going to – do? I mean, are we looking for trouble?'

Jemmie stopped chewing with his mouth still full. 'You don't get it, do you?'

'No – I'm with you so far.'

'You just don't see the importance of this venture.'

The Bobbyfella insisted that he did.

Jemmie told him this action wasn't just about the guitar. It was about John Lennon. 'It strikes me that you're just another chancer, Bobby,' he said. The Bobbyfella denied the charge. 'One of these opportunists who expects to make a fortune with the change in the pocket of his leather pants instead of trying to develop his talent . . . such as it is.'

The Bobbyfella didn't like this remark. It hurt. He turned his back on Jemmie.

'Brian Epstein . . .' Jemmie said with a new mouthful. He let the muffled name hang in the air a moment. '. . . he didn't allow The Beatles to run around in the leather pants. He didn't say – "John, you stick to the mouth organ. You four chancers just carry on as before" – NO. He brought them along very nicely. He built on their raw talent and they respected him for that.'

'And?' The Bobbyfella demanded, turning to challenge.

'And look at you. Look at The Billyfella out there. A couple of chancers. A pair of jaded buskers. I brought you in on this to give you a taste of something great. I brought you in to give you an education in how to get on. It's not the guitar I want you to embrace. It's the spirit of the man. I want you to acknowledge the man's willingness to shed the mantle of chancer and to embrace his talent. To acknowledge his willingness to be guided by his mentor.'

There was a brief silence. The Bobbyfella swallowed hard.

'Had you told me this over the telephone I wouldn't have brought the harmonica.'

That was when the telephone rang. Jemmie held up a restraining hand. The answering machine responded to the fourth ring.

'Hello,' a woman's voice said. 'You have reached Brenda and Raymond. This is an answering machine. You know what to do.'

'God's guts,' Jemmie declared incredulously. 'Did you hear that?'

The machine emitted a bleep. No message was left. The line reverted to the open signal. The machine reset itself.

'Some misfortunate person looking for what belongs to him, no doubt,' said Jemmie.

'Not a very nice message, I must say,' said The Bobbyfella.

Jemmie asked him if he was ambitious. The Bobbyfella said that he was.

'I'm ambitious,' Jemmie said, extending himself fully on the couch. 'I was ambitious when I was starting out, but I was misfortunate. I was misrepresented. I was led up the garden path. Unlike your good self, I can sing. I was singing, fronting my own band.'

'Yeah? And what band was this?'

'Never mind what band. Sit down. You're making me nervous.'

The Bobbyfella sat on the arm of an easy chair. He positioned himself so he could see the front gate.

'I'm trying to give you the benefit of my experience,' Jemmie said.

'Go ahead.'

'We were doing all right on the local circuit, right? Not making a penny, of course, but we had talent and we were building the repertoire.'

'As you do.'

Jemmie chose to ignore the sarcasm. 'I was doing a bit of electrical work on the side, to pay the bills. We had this manager – he was trying to get us a deal.'

'A manager – don't talk to me about managers.' The sarcasm had quickly turned to bitterness. This, too, Jemmie ignored.

'The Gerryfella. Full of bravado. Lots of neck. A dedicated, six-cylinder chancer.'

'Chancers – every one of them.'

Jemmie began to pick through his selection of records, stopping from time to time to take a bite from the remains of his sandwich. Evidently, The Bobbyfella had the stomach for neither. He listened to Jemmie tell him about his rewiring job in the rooms above a bicycle shop across the street from where he lived. His wife sent Carmel, Jemmie's daughter, across with sandwiches and tea with a little milk in a flat gin bottle. '"How's your Ma?" I would ask Carmel. See – me and the wife weren't getting on well at this stage. She wasn't too happy with my career moves. Me in the role of father and provider – I wasn't scoring high on either count. See – I was holding out for the big break. "She hates you," says Carmel.'

The Bobbyfella was shaking his head and had a hand raised to indicate that he didn't want to hear any more sorry tales.

'No,' said Jemmie, 'I was convinced it was going to happen. We had made a demo. The Gerryfella was going to get us a deal.'

'And the bastard didn't deliver.'

'Will you WAIT.'

'Sorry.' The hand was dropped. 'Go ahead,' he said wearily.

Jemmie described the morning The Gerryfella called to the flat. '"I've great news," says The Gerryfella. "Swear to God."' Jemmie's wife wasn't prepared to listen. Her understanding was that the band was finished with The Gerryfella – this was how Jemmie described it. His wife wouldn't let him across the threshold. '"I've been around to Kevin and Matt with the good news," says The Gerryfella. "They're out looking for Jemmie as we speak. We have a deal. It's only the most important news your husband is ever going to get," says he. Big mistake, of course. You can't say that to a married woman.'

Jemmie was gazing admiringly into mid-distance now. 'She could hear him calling my name going down the street. Shouting it out. Of course, the minute The Gerryfella was gone she sent Carmel across the street to me above the bicycle shop.'

'She was on the ball, your wife,' observed The Bobbyfella.

'She was on the ball. Now ... picture this – three fat aul'ones dressed like Christmas crackers sitting on the balcony of the public baths sharing a bag of boiled sweets. The wife sits down beside them. Carmel is down below in the swimming pool. They're all watching her showing off.'

'"I hear your husband is fixing the electric for the whores above the bicycle shop," says one aul'one.'

'"They need the electric like everybody else," says the wife. "And we need the money."'

'Fair play,' The Bobbyfella volunteered.

Jemmie said that the whores had to wait. He described the meeting with The Gerryfella and Kevin and Matt. They were off to London.

The Bobbyfella was patrolling the floor. He knew Jemmie's story had to be a tragic story and that was doing nothing for his nerves. 'So what happened?' he demanded impatiently.

'Picture this,' said Jemmie weightily, 'we're sitting in this office in London and there's only the office boy. He doesn't like the name of the band. Sounds Arabic. "Is it Irish?" he wants to know. " ... Jolly good." How come there's only three of us, he wants to know. They were expecting a showband line-up. "There is four of us," says The Gerryfella. "I play the mouth organ." That wasn't a good thing to say. The office boy starts talking business. We're all looking over his shoulder wondering when the big noise will appear. The Gerryfella starts jabbering to me in Irish – not real Irish. None of us can speak real Irish. But right enough, the office boy gets a bit uneasy. He makes an offer. The Gerryfella blathers some shite to me like he's discussing the terms, I grunt, The Gerryfella turns back to the office boy, says no.'

'Ah, don't tell me ...'

'But soon the deal is done. There was no record contract . . .'

'Don't tell me . . .'

'We were to play on some Jaysus cruise ship . . .'

'NO.'

'Glorified buskers.'

'And The Gerryfella knew all along about playing on the
cruiser?' The Bobbyfella was working himself into a rage.

'Correct.'

'I'm sick.'

'When I went home to the wife . . .'

'Stop.'

The car horn sounded again. Jemmie chose to go with the
moment and ignore The Billyfella's impatience. 'When I went
home the wife asked if it was worth all the waiting and the
disappointment and the scrimping. I told her that she was the
only one who could count on me. Her and the kid. But then, I
was counting on The Gerryfella.'

The Bobbyfella said The Billyfella was about to knock on
the door. He went to open the hall door. Jemmie pushed past,
threw open the hall door, wrestled The Billyfella into the hall
and flung him on the floor. He disregarded both men's
protests. He slapped them both around the hall, then he gave
them an impromptu lecture.

'I come from a long line of patient people. Some, of course,
didn't get what they wanted. Went about it the wrong way.
The waiting sapped their strength until they confused being
patient with giving up. With surrendering.'

The Billyfella thought Jemmie was finished so he asked
about Lennon's guitar. The Bobbyfella jumped in to explain
that they were waiting to talk to a couple named Brenda and
Raymond. Jemmie gritted his teeth and continued.

'My Uncle Fergus – he lost his job at the bus depot. He
took a kitchen chair out into the back yard and he sat there
for six months. Young louts from the neighbourhood came
and pegged stones at him. My mother and father tried to get
him back indoors. He'd go in for an hour's kip or to use the
lavatory, then he'd be out again on his chair. Ma used to

bring him picnics. The neighbour used to bring him a hot plate. It's a terrible thing to be on your own. He used to say to me that if a person found the right companion they could live forever . . .'

'Jesus,' said the Billyfella. 'That's very sad.'

'Sad? He just sat there like some bloody primitive contemplating his miserable life. Then, he got a lump on the head from one of the stones. The neighbour took him to the hospital.'

'He's in hospital now?' The Bobbyfella asked. He didn't realise he was rubbing his head.

'No,' replied Jemmie sitting down on the staircase. 'He's indoors now on his chair. Laughs occasionally, when he shouldn't be laughing. That's what can happen to a person if they're the wrong kind of patient.'

'Very, very sad,' The Billyfella mumbled shaking his head. 'Jemmie,' he said, 'it was only when I came round the corner that I realised . . .'

'Realised?' Jemmie said turning to scrutinise The Billyfella through the banisters.

'I realised I recognised this place. This is your house, isn't it?'

There was another silence.

'Yes,' said Jemmie, 'this is my house. Doesn't mean I live here.'

This little exchange stopped The Bobbyfella dancing about and drew a loud protest – 'Ah here . . . AH HERE . . .' He pointed to the telephone answering machine '– does that mean that the Brenda one is your – your wife?'

Jemmie rose slowly to his feet, composed himself at the head of the hall with his back to his companions. 'Brenda,' he said, 'is my estranged wife.'

'And your man, Raymond is –' The Bobbyfella didn't get to finish.

'A bollix,' said Jemmie turning on his heels. 'Correct.'

'But the guitar,' said The Bobbyfella, 'John Lennon's guitar is –' He didn't get to finish here either.

'Mine,' said Jemmie. 'Correct.'

The Billyfella wanted to know where the guitar was. The Bobbyfella rounded on him.

'If we knew where it was we'd have it, wouldn't we? It's missing, isn't it?'

'It's just disappeared,' said Jemmie.

'Yes,' The Billyfella persisted doggedly, 'but who has it?'

'It's a mystery,' replied The Bobbyfella. Now he was gritting his teeth.

The Billyfella wasn't happy. 'Right. I'll be out in the car.'

Jemmie ordered him to stay where he was. The Bobbyfella told him again that they were going to conduct an enquiry.

'Sweat the bastards,' said Jemmie.

The Billyfella didn't want to stay but Jemmie took him by the arm and led him into the living room.

'This place is looking shabby,' he said, in an effort to dispel the tension. He let go of the arm. 'I had it looking lovely. I had it painted top to bottom in Mongolian white.'

The Bobbyfella also wanted to dispel the tension. He began to hum.

'For God's sake,' said Jemmie, 'don't sing. Play your mouth organ.' The Bobbyfella began to play. The Billyfella attempting to embrace the new calm, tentatively inspected the records Jemmie had put in the cardboard box.

'Look at this pile of shite. Who buys records like these?'

'Leave that box alone,' Jemmie said. His forehead seemed to swell in a threatening manner. The telephone rang a second time. Jemmie raised a hand to the others and went to answer it.

'Are we mad, or what?' The Billyfella asked in an urgent whisper. 'Will we leg it?'

'No,' said The Bobbyfella, surprised at his new-found steeliness. 'We won't leg it.'

'Why not?'

'John Lennon. That's why not.'

Jemmie had lifted the receiver in the hall. 'Hello? . . . Is that you, Brenda? – Where's my Jumbo, Brenda? – My guitar. Where is it? – Yes. Raymond is here. I gave him one of his cigars to smoke, then I tied him to the chair . . .'

174

'Jesus,' said The Billyfella, 'that's a bit strong.'

'Brenda . . . Where's my JUMBO?'

The line went dead. Jemmie composed himself. He lowered the handset onto the cradle and came back into the living room. 'She'll be here shortly,' he announced in a mild voice.

'And the guitar?' The Bobbyfella asked.

Jemmie did not reply. Instead, he took up a position at the window and began to suck his teeth.

'You want us to search the place again, Jemmie?' The Bobbyfella asked. That stopped the sucking. The Bobbyfella's steeliness was already slipping away. 'She probably won't be coming back on her own – not after that call.'

Jemmie turned to The Billyfella. 'He doesn't see it, does he, Billyboy? Doesn't see what this is about.'

'No, Jemmie.'

'You see what this is about.'

'Lennon's guitar, Jemmie.'

'I tell you what, Bobby, here's the fifty quid I said I'd give you.' He took the money from his pocket and held it out to The Bobbyfella. 'Billyboy, you have the keys to the car. You take this man back to where we got him. He's not worthy. Go ahead. I can manage this myself.'

*

They didn't drive away immediately. They sat in Jemmie's Zodiac. It seemed the appropriate thing to do.

'I'm glad I'm out of there,' The Bobbyfella confessed.

The Billyfella had his fingers laced on the top of the steering wheel. He was trying to fix on the big picture. 'Tell me,' he said, 'do you think he was there?'

'Where?'

'In London in 1963.'

The Bobbyfella said that Jemmie was too busy rewiring whores. Too busy singing in his band.

The Billyfella took out the dog-eared book, threw it onto The Bobbyfella's lap. 'Read that piece again.'

The Bobbyfella read.

175

The two men looked to each other. It was time to start the engine. If it would start.

It started. The Billyfella drove.

'Where do you want to be dropped?' he asked when they had reached the spot from where they had begun. 'Here?'

The Bobbyfella grunted affirmatively.

'When he gets the guitar I'll give you a call,' The Billyfella said before the front passenger door was closed. 'For a picture.'

'All right . . .'

'If I hear of anybody looking for a harmonica . . .'

'I play the piano as well, and I can sing.'

'Here, did you say Jemmie said he was singing in a band? Jemmie never sang in any band. He managed a band once, but nothing ever came of them. I tell you what, though, he has an eye for talent. I think he did it. He saw The Beatles' greatness. He saw what was coming, so he fecked Lennon's guitar.'

The Bobbyfella stood on the pavement and thought hard on this. Then he shook his head and moved away, playing his harmonica.

Carlo Gebler

BAD JU-JU

Extract from a novel in progress

OUT OF THE corner of his eye, Dessie saw his daughter,
Sharon, look up. She was sitting on the floor with her dolls.
She had three of them under a blanket. Until this second,
Sharon was happy. She paid no attention to himself or his
wife, Sandra. But now, the very instant that Sandra started
blubbing, Sharon was onto them. Had radar, didn't she? As
soon as something was wrong, Sharon knew it.

He saw Sharon get up and start to run towards them. She
wore a check dress with a petticoat underneath. The petticoat
swung as she ran. Sharon's face was anxious. Oh Jesus! this
was all he needed. First the blubbing wife and then the
blubbing daughter. This was meant to be the fucking
Christmas party for Christ's sake and the bloody wife and
bloody daughter, they were ruining it for him.

He looked across the room. There was that fucker Nancy
with his fucking brood. Hundreds of fucking children. And
what was he doing? Nancy and his wife were talking to that
cunt, William, and two older people. Who were they?, he
wondered. Oh, yes, William's ma and pa. Fuckers.

His eye roved on. Everyone in visits that day seemed
happy. Jesus. All having a good time except for him.
Obviously, today, he'd drawn the short bloody straw, hadn't
he?

'What is it, mam?' he heard. It was Sharon. He wanted to
shout at his daughter. He wanted to shout, 'Shut the fuck up.'
But he couldn't. No, he mustn't. He must control himself. Go

177

like that in public, it'd make a bad, bad situation worse. Jesus! How much more restraint would he have to show before the day was out? If only he could let rip. Show what he really felt instead of always holding back. Jesus, what a disaster. The whole day was a bloody shambles.

He stared furiously around the room. He saw couples and families grouped around tables. He saw a child in 'Kiddies Korner', head back, screeching with joy, as he slid down the slide. He heard a burst of laughter. He heard a voice cry, 'Humpty Dumpty sat on a wall.'

He glanced upwards. A blanket of smoke lay under the ceiling. Extraordinary how people puffed away in Visits. Pale sunlight shafted through the high windows and lit up the smoke. The room smelt of women. It smelt of their perfume and make-up and nail varnish, and their perspiration. It smelt of children too. This was a compound of Ribena and cornflakes and those sweet smelling shampoos that didn't sting the eyes or tangle the hair.

This was real life, he thought, but he was not part of it. Nor would he be for years to come. He'd nearly five years done so he'd another seven at least to go, more likely ten, twelve, fourteen. He was, after all, serving two life sentences.

But for one afternoon the outside world was allowed into his world. And what happened? He wasn't able to grab life and gorge himself on it like all the other prisoners in the room. And why not? Because the Santa suit was too hot, the gear was short, and Sandra was squealing. The prisoners' Christmas party came one afternoon a year and he'd blown it. The thought filled Dessie with terrible anguish.

'Mind your back,' he heard the officer McCarthy mumble.

He turned and looked behind. He saw it was Crafty, his red face angled towards the floor. He wore corduroys and a horrible pale blue 'V' necked sweater. Classic root wear. A tiny woman with grey hair walked behind. That was Crafty's mother. Had to be.

'What'd'you say, root?'

Dessie had the question out without thinking, modulated with maximum malevolence.

'Dessie,' said McCarthy sharply. The officer's message was unmistakable. Shut up. Don't start anything. Behave.

Fuck off! thought Dessie, no one talked to him like that.

'What'd'you say, root?' Dessie repeated.

Crafty shot him a sidelong glance. It was apologetic and deeply fearful.

'Sorry,' Crafty said.

Half a second later Crafty's mother came up. There was a whiff of marmalade and old lady. She moved Crafty quickly on.

Dessie watched the pair as they moved away. Crafty was bald and heavily built. He didn't so much walk as roll. Mother moved in a sprightly way. She was a mother bird harrying an overgrown chick.

Mother and son reached the cubicles. Crafty opened a door and they slipped in. The door clicked shut. Dessie felt the clean and delicious feeling of pure unbridled hatred.

When he returned to the wing, Dessie picked up John and Jim. He sent Jim off to get a loaf of Mother's Pride. Dessie fetched a razor blade from its hiding place in his mattress. He slipped the blade under the cuff that ran around the top of one of his Santa boots.

The three men went and stood at the end of Crafty's corridor. They waited and talked quietly. After a few minutes, Jim touched Dessie's wrist.

'He's there,' said Jim.

Crafty was gliding unobtrusively along the corridor.

'Let him go in home,' said Dessie.

'Unlock,' Crafty called.

An officer came up the corridor and unlocked Crafty's cell. Crafty went in. The officer went away. The door was left open.

'Count a hundred,' said Dessie.

The three prisoners began to count, quietly. They finished counting. The corridor was quiet. No one around.

'Rock and roll,' said John, when he reached a hundred.

The three men slipped up to Crafty's cell.

'Hello, Crafty,' Dessie called from outside.

He propelled himself through the doorway.

'It's Christmas,' he said, 'and I've got a present for you.'

Crafty was sitting in his chair. He looked up and opened and closed his mouth. Crafty's lower jaw was set back from his upper jaw. His front upper teeth jutted out. There was something about Crafty that reminded Dessie of a fish. He saw at once that Crafty was frightened. It annoyed Dessie and, at the same time, it excited him.

'I've brought John and Jim. They want to see you get your pressie.'

'What is it?' blurted Crafty. He glanced at the red panic button in its dirty metal collar above the toilet.

'Don't even think about it,' said Dessie.

He sat down on the bed. John sat beside him. Jim stood in the doorway, blocking the entrance.

'Give us the bread,' said Dessie.

Jim threw him the loaf. Dessie undid the sealer stamped with the sell-by date.

'Oh, we're in luck,' he said, reading the sell-by date. 'It's still safe to eat.'

Dessie pulled out two pieces of bread. He ripped off the crusts and threw them in the bin. Then he squeezed the bread that remained into a moist slightly grey pellet. He put his hand under the cuff around the top of his boot and felt around. He found the blade and brought it up into the light of the cell.

Crafty went, 'Oh God, Jesus no.'

Dessie said, 'Look, I'll make it easy for you.' He broke the blade in two, lengthwise.

Next Dessie broke the bread pellet in two. He pressed a half blade into the middle of each pellet and then moulded the bread with his fingers so nothing of the blade showed through the dough.

'Fucking eat,' said Dessie.

All the anguish that plagued him that afternoon was now gone. Dessie felt clear and cool and utterly determined.

*

Nancy sat on the edge of his bed. He smoked one of the Benson & Hedges Marie-Louise had slipped him at the end of the visit. He shouldn't really. He shouldn't use his treats up so soon after a visit. But what the hell, it was Christmas.

He felt happy because he had seen his wife and children for a whole afternoon. At the same time he felt sad because he wouldn't see them all together like that until sport's day in the summer. This was the next big family event in the prison calendar. The combination of the two feelings was bitter sweet. It was both almost enjoyable and it hurt.

He wondered were the two feelings at war? And if so, which one would win out over the over? Immediately after this, an unwelcome thought crossed his mind. If it was war, it was obvious which feeling would win and which would lose. He saw an evening of misery stretch ahead. He must distract himself.

He looked around. He noticed the roll of Sellotape he had borrowed earlier. There was writing inside the cardboard roll in the centre. He squinted at the message scribbled in blue Biro – 'Please return to Crafty,' it read.

He nipped the end of the cigarette expertly. The hot ember plopped into his metal bin, smouldered and died. He'd scoot around. Return the Sellotape. Come back. See if William wanted to come to the gym for ten minutes. Or have a chat with Lyle. Or Copper. He must not sit and fester. He must be busy.

Nancy stood and grabbed the Sellotape. At that moment, William appeared in his doorway.

'Where you going?' said the boy.

'I've got to give Crafty this.'

Nancy waved the Sellotape.

'I've got us a little treat,' said William. 'It's about four inches long, it's in a King Size Rizla and it's got our names written on the side.'

William measured the length of a joint in the air.

'Before tea which will be rotten,' continued William, 'we have to have something to cheer us up.'

Nancy thought he'd forget the Sellotape. Then he thought

181

better of that idea. Crafty was always quick to retrieve his things when he lent them. He imagined Crafty at his cell door when he and William were half way through the joint. It would annoy him. He must do his errand before the smoke.

'Fab-tastic,' he said.

'Fab-tastic – what's that? What are you on?' William asked, mock-seriously.

'Got to whizz this round to Crafty,' said Nancy, 'before we ah . . .' He shook his head.

'I'll come with you,' said William, cheerfully. 'Then we can come back and ah . . .'

They walked around to Crafty's corridor and went straight into Crafty's cell without knocking or calling. That's how it was. Prisoners just went in and out of each other's cells. As soon as he was through the doorway. Nancy collided with someone and a second after he felt William colliding into him from behind.

'Oh, I'm sorry,' Nancy blurted. He saw the back of the prisoner he'd run into. It was a muscular back. He saw muscles standing up and little shadowy dips where the muscles went in.

'Crafty, I've got your Sellotape,' he said.

Nancy realised he'd run into Jim. Crafty was on the chair. Heart sinking, he looked at Crafty's bed and saw Dessie sitting there beside John. Dessie still wore his Santa suit from the Christmas party. His hat was crooked. He had pulled the beard down and it hung around his neck.

'Put the Sellotape on the table,' said Dessie. He sounded unusually polite and reasonable. Nancy was puzzled. Hadn't he heard Dessie cursing Crafty earlier? And now Dessie was in Crafty's cell, with his cronies. Nancy tried to gauge the atmosphere. There was no overt hostility yet this wasn't right. Dessie didn't belong in here. Dessie hated Crafty.

'How are you, Crafty?' asked Nancy. 'Good visit?'

Nancy looked at the older prisoner. Crafty didn't look up. He, Crafty, was looking at his hands. There was something long and white on each palm. It was bread, wasn't it? It reminded Nancy of a bait pellet for a fish hook, only much bigger. What was going on? he wondered.

'Did your mam like the doll's house?' Nancy asked.

Crafty said nothing.

'Nancy, put the Sellotape on the table,' said Dessie, 'and go.'

Nancy put the Sellotape on the table. He heard Crafty sniffle. A tear rolled off the end of Crafty's nose and landed on the bread pellet sitting on his right palm.

'Go,' said Dessie. 'Go now.'

'Are you all right, Crafty?' Nancy asked.

'He's all right,' said Dessie. Then he added, 'Aren't you?'

'I'm all right,' Crafty mumbled.

'He said he's all right,' Dessie repeated.

Jim turned on the spot. This brought his face to within inches of Nancy's. Nancy felt Jim's breath. It smelt of Spearmint and toothpaste.

'We're sorting a problem out for Crafty. Nothing to do with you.'

Nancy felt Jim shunting him backwards into William and a second later he was in the corridor and Jim filled the doorway, completely blocking it.

'I'll be all right,' he heard Crafty call from inside. It was fake bravado.

Nancy saw Jim nod at him. He and William were to go. Nancy began to walk away. He sensed William at his side. This had nothing to do with him, he thought, whatever it was. If he hadn't taken the Sellotape round, he'd be smoking, and if he was smoking he'd be none the wiser. He shouldn't stick his nose where it didn't belong. Hadn't he given William this advice the day he arrived? He should follow it himself.

'Do you want to smoke?' said William.

'Yeah.'

They went into William's cell. William lifted the mirror and took the joint from the small space in the wall behind. William lit the end of the joint. The two men sat down on the bed. Suddenly, the alarm bell began to ring and many of the prisoners on the wing began to jeer back at it. They always did. The deed was done, Nancy guessed, and Dessie or John or Jim had hit the bell as they left Crafty's cell.

Nancy heard clamour and hubbub outside. He heard the bulkhead grilles slamming shut. He heard the C & R team rush down the corridor.

'Lock-down,' McCarthy bellowed outside. He sounded anxious.

William put the joint out. Nancy went to his cell and was locked in. Half an hour later the door was unlocked.

'Excitement over,' said McCarthy.

'So what was all the excitement about?' Nancy even thought he sounded innocent.

'Crafty ate a blade,' said the officer.

'How is he?' asked Nancy

'What do you think? They've taken him away. City hospital I think.'

Nancy took his plate and bowl and cutlery from their place in the sink. This was where he kept his eating things. There was nowhere else in the cell to put them.

'What's for dinner?' he asked.

'Chicken, judging by the smell,' said the officer.

'Lovely jubbly,' said Nancy without enthusiasm.

He went across to William's cell. He found the younger man drying his plate.

'Crafty ate a blade,' said William.

'I heard,' said Nancy.

They went down to the dining-room. They joined the back of the queue. Everyone in the room was talking about Crafty. As Nancy shuffled forward he tuned in to one conversation after another. In every case the explanation was the same. Unable to face the misery of Christmas in jail, Crafty swallowed a blade in order to get a fortnight in hospital. There was no mention of Dessie.

Nancy and William each got his portion of chicken; it was served in a lumpy white sauce with sweetcorn. There was no point eating in the dining-hall. There would only be one subject of conversation and no one had anything to say on the subject that hadn't already been said. Nancy and William took their meal back to Nancy's cell. They sat.

'Are you all right?' asked William quietly.

Nancy shook his head. No, he wasn't.

The two friends ate in silence. Nancy was grateful to William for this.

After they had eaten, William went off to play pool in the recreation room. Nancy sat in his chair and looked at his dirty plate. A skin had formed on the left-over white sauce. It was dull yet it had a sheen to it. It was like candle wax. He should get up and wash his plate in his sink, he thought.

He heard a noise at his cell door. He looked up. Dessie stood in the doorway, John and Jim behind.

Dessie was there to scald him. Nancy was certain of it. Nancy reached for his pillow without thinking. If he could get the pillow in front of his face, he could save himself.

He grasped the pillow. At the same time he looked wildly at the door. He expected to see Dessie clutching a coffee jar wrapped in a towel. That was how boiling water was carried around the wing. To his surprise, Nancy saw Dessie was empty handed. He wasn't there to scald him. Nancy let go the pillow.

'Your fucking little friend had better not tout,' Dessie said.

'Who are you talking about?' It was imperative, Nancy knew, to suggest he wasn't trying to argue, that he wasn't trying to be awkward, and that he was just trying to establish the truth.

'You know who,' said Dessie, grimly. 'Your little friend, William.'

Dessie modulated 'little' in a vile way.

'What would he tout about?' asked Nancy. He tried to sound as if he really didn't have a clue what Dessie was on about. At the back of his mind he had the idea that perhaps he just might convince his visitor that he did not connect Dessie's visit to Crafty's cell with Crafty's eating the razor blade a few minutes later. It was not a strong plan but it was the only one he had and it might work. It might.

'Don't be a fucking idiot. You know what I'm talking about.'

'No, I don't.' Nancy spoke calmly, slowly. With lunatics you had to talk like this.

Of course Nancy knew exactly why Dessie was there and what he meant. It was obvious. He and William saw Dessie and his two friends in Crafty's cell. A few minutes later Crafty ate the razor blade. In a few hours' time the wing would be full of policemen. They would interview all the prisoners about Crafty. Who made Crafty eat the blade? That's what the police would want to know.

Of course, Nancy had no intention of telling the police what he knew. Nor had William. What happened between the prisoners was the business of the prisoners. It was not the business of the authorities.

And if a prisoner broke this rule (and it had happened) the punishment was dreadful. Everyone in the jail turned against him. Those few prisoners who had co-operated with the police in circumstances like these, along with those prisoners who had given evidence for the prosecution in criminal trials (they were also hated), could not live on the wings. They could not even live on the Punishment and Segregation Unit either, where recalcitrant prisoners were held. Those prisoners who had co-operated or turned Queen's evidence, had to live in the Special Unit as it was known officially, or Touts Hole as it was known to the prisoners. The Special Unit was inside the compound where the C & R teams trained. It was supposedly impregnable yet a detail of prisoners on gardening duty had got inside the C & R compound the previous year and set the Special Unit on fire. Since the fire, the Special Unit had a permanent guard day and night, and the authorities were in no doubt another attempt would be made to kill the occupants of the unit. If Nancy told the authorities what he knew (which wouldn't necessarily convict Dessie anyway) it would be to sign his own death warrant. So he wouldn't blab and nor would William either.

'I don't know what's worrying you,' said Nancy, 'but

whatever it is, you don't have to worry about me or the boy. You know you don't. We don't believe in loose talk.'

Dessie stepped into Nancy's cell and the other two filled the doorway behind.

'Nancy, you know what I'm talking about.'

'No, I don't.'

'Yes, you do.'

'No, I'm don't. I haven't a baldy.'

Nancy said this in his sincerest voice.

Dessie glowered from the doorway. 'Don't be an arsehole. You know exactly. Now don't fuck about.'

Nancy saw his plan would not work. He could not convince Dessie he knew nothing. In which case, there was only one alternative. He had to state Dessie had his friend all wrong. He had to do this in a strong and categorical way.

'William's not a tout,' said Nancy. 'I know him. He's a good boy.'

Dessie stopped glowering, which was progress. Both men now knew what they were talking about. It was in the open.

'Just tell him, keep his nose clean,' said Dessie.

Dessie touched his nose again. Then he raised his hands like Jesus Christ showing his stigmata, and vanished.

Nancy began to tremble. If William hadn't been with him when he returned the Sellotape, none of this would have happened. But he had had William with him. William stumbled into Crafty's cell after him. And from this simple accident, trouble was going to flow. Nancy knew it. Dessie didn't like William. He never had. But he didn't have anything on William. Before now Dessie had no reason to turn against the boy in public. But now he had. Henceforth, if Dessie had any trouble with the officers, he could blame William. Or even if he had no trouble with the officers, he could still go around and say that William had told on him. There was no doubt about it, out there was going to be trouble. He knew it. As surely as night followed day. Dessie was going to start a rumour that William was an informer.

Oh God, Nancy thought, what could he do? Did he tell William? Did he suggest to his friend that he ask for a transfer to another prison? Or did he say nothing? Maybe it would all blow over.

'Lock-down,' an officer shouted, and out in the corridor, Nancy heard one door slamming shut after another.

After his door was locked, Nancy smoked three of his precious Benson & Hedges one after the other.

Neil Ferguson

SPINACH

LIKE A LOT of non-native speakers of a language, even good ones, she had a tendency to use some words and phrases more than others, much more than was – from a purely linguistic point of view – appropriate. For a time, *absurd* was one of these words.

'It's *absurd*!' she exclaimed. 'Here I am, a beautiful woman. I like sex. I have always liked it. Why not? It is one of life's great pleasures. And look at me! I have fallen in love with a man who is not only ugly but he is also *short*! He wears spectacles! And he could lose some weight if he wanted to. A man, furthermore, who does not give a button for me! God, I must be desperate! It's *absurd*! There is no other word for it!'

The occasion she chose to deliver this outburst was the end-of-term College party. We were leaning against the corridor wall outside the canteen, holding plastic catering cups from which we were drinking passable Bulgarian red wine, smoking her cigarettes. I am not normally insensitive to the price of a packet of Marlboro Lites for a person on the receiving end of Social Security, but equally I can recognise a generous gesture when one is made to me. It obviously gave her pleasure for me to accept this small gift from her.

'I have beautiful breasts!'

Nush clasped my right hand – the one holding my cigarette, which she first took from me – and cupped the palm around her left breast.

'You see! Isn't that nice?'

I wondered how long I ought to leave my hand where it was before I could decently remove it, before one of my colleagues glanced my way.

'Well?'

'You know, we have a policy in this College,' I said. 'To deal with acts of sexual harassment.'

'Oh, don't be so pompous! Haven't you ever touched a woman at a party before?'

The only way to deal with Nush when she was in this sort of mood was to give it straight back to her. You had to fight fire with fire. She expected you to. She despised weakness, especially in a man.

'If you're as fanciable as you claim,' I sneered, 'how come you can't get a more prepossessing bloke to smoke your Marlboro Lites . . . ?'

'Pah! You think I couldn't! I could! Easily! I just lack the opportunity to meet real men! God, I haven't seen a good one since I arrived in England! Some of these Afghans and Eritreans and Somalis are very good-looking boys. Khalid, for example, is gorgeous!'

She tossed her splendid black hair with contemptuous respect in the direction of the Afghans, Eritreans and Somalis who were disco-dancing behind us.

'I don't want a *boy* – one who is almost certainly a virgin! I could eat Khalid for breakfast! What I'm talking about is a *man!* Someone I could think to share a couple of bottles of wine with and then take to bed with me. A man with blood in his veins and iron in his blood! Where am I going to meet such a man? Tell me!'

I couldn't tell her and she didn't really expect me to. I was privy to enough of her recent history and current circumstances to know that she was right. She was in a rotten position. Thirty-two years old, with fine middle-European cheekbones, lovely dark eyes and, I could now attest with the authority of direct experience, beautiful breasts, Nush was the mother of a three-year-old girl whose father had disappeared during the recent conflict in her country. Altogether, in the form of family credit and child benefit, she and her daughter received

£98.67p each week, which she supplemented with a few hours cleaning. But Nush was a university-trained civil lawyer in her own country, where she had worked in a Government department in some or other judicial capacity.

That country, unfortunately, no longer existed. Every vestige of it had gone, vanished into thin air. Men shot their neighbours and their neighbours' wives and babies and left their bodies in the street to be eaten by dogs. The last thing the place needed at this moment in its history was civil lawyers, since every agreed form of civilised behaviour had been abandoned. Each side had adopted a scorched earth policy towards the other, routinely massacring and raping non-combatants as a matter of military strategy.

One day Nush had been swanking up the steps of some prestigious Ministry of Justice in the regional capital wearing an elegant black two-piece ensemble, 15-denier French tights, Italian shoes and underwear of heart-stopping expense; the next she was sharing a single bed-and-breakfast room off the Edgware Road with an infant daughter who cried all night. She had no money, no family, no status. ('If it were not for my box of photographs, I wouldn't exist!' she claimed – or, rather, exclaimed, because she tended to speak with invisible exclamation marks at the end of her sentences. 'I would have no past!') Even the few items of jewellery she had escaped with had been stolen during her first fortnight in London. She had lost everything, not least her husband. It was a humiliation to her that she could not afford to buy the cheapest bottle of wine in Tesco but, instead, went there to exchange for milk the tokens to which she was entitled. She was right. It was *absurd*.

And yet – because of the droll way in which she talked about her misfortunes – it was also very funny. Absurdity no doubt requires this element of pointless hilarity.

I was fond of Annushi Broblinic but I was careful to regard her with a professional eye. With her engaging arrogance and erect posture, dressed up for the party with as much flair as she could muster, a scarlet gloss on her lips, a drink in one hand and a cigarette in the other, she looked superb – with more than a passing resemblance to Morticia of the Adams Family, as played by Angelica Houston. She had come a long way from the day in September the previous year on which I had interviewed her for a place on my course. Shaking with anger, shame, resentment and frustration, a fractious toddler snapping at her heels, possessing only the clothes she stood up in, she had reached the end of her tether. She had burst into tears. Seven months later, her child had a full-time place in a community nursery; the housing department had granted her a brand new flat; she was following an advanced English course at her local college alongside students from Russia, Eritrea, Somalia, Iraq and Former Yugoslavia. She was also – the truest barometer of her well-being – in love.

Nush was a joy to teach. Refugees nearly always are. The way I do it is to provoke authentic speech acts on subjects that arouse strong emotions. By means of controversial topics – state torture, capital punishment, sexual equality, religious persecution, freedom of speech, the Slave Trade – I try to put the cat among the pigeons. Is there any justice in the *fatwa* against Salman Rushdie? Should the law punish women and not men for adultery? What is liberty? I introduce items of grammar which they need to negotiate in order to address these important issues. Throughout our discussions, which often become quite heated, Nush sits like a bored sleepy cat, half-watching us, waiting for the moment to strike the pigeons in question. In her own time, with great passion but also with a civil lawyer's regard for clarity, she demolishes every argument that is reactionary, bigoted or intolerant. In the event of a fellow-student coming out with something truly daft she would openly scoff at his simple-mindedness. She had no deference towards Muslim attitudes to women, for example – having lived cheek by jowl with Muslims all her life. On the occasion young Omar attempted to justify his view that women could not be fire-fighters on the grounds that they are not as strong as men, she rose from her seat and advanced upon him. Towering over the poor boy she offered to arm-wrestle him on the spot in her hilarious deadpan way. The rest of us were weeping with delight, hooting for Omar

192

to accept her challenge – which he had the good sense not to do.

Omar can take it. Nush can take it. Having been deracinated and humiliated, impoverished and deskilled, they are not inclined to get on their high horse in a hurry. Over the year they draw closer to each other. And also to me, the circus master extraordinary.

Abrehet Soloman, who is nineteen, had been a little girl playing in the yard of her parents' house in Asmara when the rocket struck her house and killed her father. Salima is a Kurdish ex-freedom fighter, mother of five, who carries a fragment of a Kalashnikov shell in her hip, which accounts for her limp. Nina Matrashkova had been a dancer at the Georgian State Ballet in Tblisi. Helen Orlovic is a paediatric nurse specialising in complaints of the ear, nose and throat. In such company Nush is nothing special.

'Well?'

'Well what?'

'Will we go to bed?'

I wish she would learn not to use verbs in an indicative mood to convey matters that have a doubtful, not to say unlikely, outcome.

'No!'

I had made the decision a long time before never to sleep with any of my students. To do so would be to betray a trust. I would not be making an unequal relationship more equal but less so. Although a certain amount of transference inevitably takes place when a professional works with a vulnerable client of the opposite sex, only a prostitute sleeps with a client. As well as my professional qualms I also had a sneaking suspicion that the moment I stepped off my circus-master's pedestal and removed my trousers I might have difficulty getting them back on again. I would be setting in motion a chain of events I could not control. I would not be fighting fire with fire but playing with it. At heart I am a coward. Like most cowards I can always find a good reason to avoid taking a risk. If I don't take any risks, I won't make any mistakes.

'You are worried that your wife will find out?'

Her question had the force, if not the grammatical form, of a statement of fact.

I shrugged. What I worried about was none of her business. In any professional relationship there is always an area that the client does not have access to.

'Oh, you bourgeois little English shit!'

The following September Nush enrolled onto another course at the College and I made sure it was one that I did not teach myself. We still bumped into each other in the corridor now and then, or met in the canteen where we talked over the state of her application for refugee status, which had been turned down by the Home Office. She had been granted what is called Exceptional Leave To Remain, for what that was worth. I put her in touch with a solicitor friend of mine who specialised in immigration procedure, to handle her appeal. I persuaded a local charity to award her a grant. She was grateful to me for this help, although I insisted that she should not be. I was simply doing my job. I had not done anything for her that I would not have done for any other student in a similar position. All I had done over and above the call of duty for Nush Broblinic was to ask my wife to hold back for her little girl some of the clothes that our own daughter had outgrown.

'I'm having a little party for Eid,' she announced towards the end of Ramadan, which puts it towards the middle of March. 'Just a few friends.'

'Why? You're not a Muslim.'

'Oh Christ! Don't *you* start! I left my country to escape that nonsense! Who cares what I am? Or what you or my friends are? At home we all make little pies and cakes for each other at Eid, Muslim or not. It's a traditional festival. Well, before the war it was. Anyway, if you want to meet some more lugubrious Slavs, you are welcome. You still haven't seen my flat.'

'Thank you. Of course I'll come,' I said. 'I'll bring the clothes for your daughter.'

'Good! You keep talking about doing that.'

'Would you like me to bring a bottle of wine? Or would that be inappropriate for a celebration of Eid?'

'Don't be *absurd*! Of course you must bring a bottle of wine! Bring *two*! At home even Muslims drink wine at Eid. We are a great wine-drinking nation. Well, we *were* – when we *were* a nation.'

It was a warm spring morning. The leaves on the lime trees in the streets in West London were luminous. I was the first to arrive, two bottles of Aussie red under my arm and a bunch of daffodils. Nush, her hair up to reveal her fine neck, looking radiant in a white blouse and a shortish black skirt, offered me her cheek to kiss. While we waited for the other guests to arrive she proudly showed me around her new flat, which had been recently redecorated and carpeted. Sunlight filled the almost-empty rooms. I was delighted and impressed. While I inspected the view from the windows onto the communal gardens below Nush looked through the clothes I had brought for her daughter Anna, dresses and t-shirts that my own daughter had worn two summers before.

'But they're *adorable!*' she cried, melting at the sight of the expensive labels.

For a moment I thought she was going to hug me so I opened one of the bottles of wine and poured us each a drink. We walked around the flat, drinking and talking about it. Despite – or perhaps because of – her happy mood I began to feel uneasy. Something wasn't right. I hadn't half-finished my glass before the penny dropped.

'Where's Anna?'

'She's staying with some friends.'

I glanced in the direction of the door to the flat, without holding out much hope that it would open.

'You bitch!'

Nush looked at me aghast, pretending to be shocked.

'There isn't going to be a bloody Eid party, is there? Nor any other lugubrious Slavs to meet! You brought me here under false pretences!'

Unable to maintain the fiction a moment longer, she exploded into laughter.

'Peter! If you could just *see* your face!'

'Bugger my face!'

'I *will*, darling – if you just give me the opportunity!'

Now it was my turn to be shocked. I had no idea that she possessed such a firm grasp of the vernacular. There was a worrying intimacy in our exchange of taboo language.

'Please don't be angry with me. How else could I have persuaded you to come here? Now we can have a nice quiet lunch – just the two of us. And it's such a lovely day. I've made spinach pie – and paklava. These are traditional on Eid in my country. I hope you like spinach.'

'I hate it!'

'Well, it's what you're going to have to eat.'

She refilled my glass, relishing the absurdity of the situation: the adorable circus-master had stepped into the tiger's cage. I prowled the room, alarmed and ill at ease. I had stupidly strayed from my safe professional territory into the emotional battlefield that for this woman was a normal, if not desirable, state of affairs.

On the mantelpiece in a cheap perspex frame was a photograph of a man in a linen suit seated next to Nush, who was wearing a sleeveless summer frock and looking very beautiful, happy in the dappled sunlight. The photo had been taken under leaves, at the conclusion of an *al fresco* meal. The man looked Italian, I thought, or perhaps it was just his suit that did. He had a moustache and an irresistible charmer's smile. A real man. They were leaning against each other, his right hand embracing her sunburnt shoulder. Grinning at the person holding the camera, they both looked a bit drunk.

'Is that your husband?'

'He's my daughter's father, if that's what you mean.'

'Where is he? Do you know?'

Nush shrugged.

'I have no idea.'

'Do you think he's dead?'

'I would have heard through the Red Cross if he was alive.

As you know, I'm no optimist. My fear is that his body is lying in a hole in the ground somewhere in the hills around our city, being eaten by ants and worms and – those disgusting wet things . . .'

'Slugs.'

She turned the photograph to face the wall.

'He could have left when I did but he chose to stay – although he could not have stayed and not fought. That would not have been possible. They would have shot him anyway. By then a man had to take sides. There was no middle course, no room for a stupid English compromise. I didn't want him to stay but he said that if everyone ran away from the country it would mean the country wasn't worth fighting for and who wanted to belong to such a country? He refused to run away. He preferred to die.

'If he is dead, I know he died with his face to the enemy, as we say in our language. He was a man, you see.'

She let her lovely dark eyes rest on mine for a moment, but not as if she were measuring me for her daughter's father's linen suit that she had no use for any more. She wanted me to take her in my arms and hold her, to embrace and take responsibility for her bruised and desperate passion. I did nothing of the sort and the moment passed – as such moments do if you wait long enough, I've found.

'I'm sorry for all those horrible things I said to you at the party. I didn't mean them, you know.'

'Why are you sorry? My wife thought you hit the nail on the head.'

'My God! You mean you *told* her! She must think I'm a terrible person!'

'You *are*!'

'I was cross at you because you were being so *absurd*. You're not as ugly as all that – nor so short. And I think your spectacles are *adorable*! I could never consider going to bed with a man I really thought was ugly.'

Adorable was her latest favourite word.

She moved towards me. Pulling me closer to her by the

lapel of my jacket, she placed her left cheek against mine and spoke softly into my ear.

'Do you forgive me?'

Just as softly, but with an emphatic downwards intonation, I told her.

'*No!*'

We sat down and ate a nice quiet lunch together, just the two of us, drinking some more-than-passable Australian red wine while daffodils adumbrated the English light. The truth is I am not all that fond of spinach, never have been, but in Nush's pie the leaves had been chopped very fine and mixed together with some other creamy and spicy ingredients, folded into what I believe is called filo pastry. I had to admit that it was delicious. I told her it was adorable and so, pleased, she pressed a second slice on me, assuring me that fresh spinach possessed remarkable restorative properties and put iron in the blood. It has what is especially necessary for a man.

We finished the first bottle of wine and then – thirsty after a hilarious and fond remembrance of Omar, Khalid and other members of her old class – started on the second.

'You see! I bet you're glad no one else is here *now*!' she said.

Then we ate her delicate paklava, accompanied by an unusual alkaline fromage frais. For a civil lawyer she wasn't half a bad pastry cook. At the end of the meal she gathered up the plates and pushed her packet of Marlboro Lites across the table towards me.

'Will we have some coffee?' she said.

'How should I know? I'm not a clairvoyant,' I teased her.

'Yes, of course. *Shall we*? would be better. *In a suggestion the future is coloured by doubt. It isn't a statement of fact.*'

I lit and smoked one of Nush's cigarettes while she prepared coffee in the kitchen. After a few moments she returned holding a tray with an Italian espresso machine on it, a bowl of sugar, some little white cups and a bottle of clear spirit of some sort. Her long black hair was down, falling onto her bare shoulders concealing her fine neck. She was wearing only a black bra and matching panties.

Unselfconscious, proud of her superb body, clothed or unclothed, she placed the tray on the table, sat down opposite me and began to pour out the coffee as if in her country the removal by your hostess of her skirt and blouse and tights in the middle of an Eid party was a perfectly normal event. To be expected even.

'Sugar, darling?'

I could – and should, I suppose – have left then and there, but I didn't. I had consumed too much wine and, I hoped, enough spinach. In Nush's world there is no middle course, no room for a stupid English compromise where the nice qualms of a coward can flourish. A man, if he is a man, has to stay. He has to stand and fight fire with fire. I couldn't have stayed and not faced the enemy. That wouldn't have been possible.

Jamie McKendrick

The Belen

It all seemed natural till some strange things came
and left. Butterflies eyed with pink and ochre,
a dazzling blue beneath, sauntered through the mild air

then disappeared. The river flowed both ways at once
the way a road does, but without a barrier.
It was then the bird arrived and I stopped dead

to understand it – its feathers
were the oiled russet of crushed saffron
and sown with spots that glinted like tinfoil.

Like the ruse birds have to lure a predator
away from their nest, its brief awkward flights
seemed meant to have me follow it on

through high grass right to the ends of the earth.
I wondered was this maybe some new type
of jay or hoopoe, only bigger, or

was this the bird that crossed your path and died
beside you. A woman standing on the wooden bridge
said it's just the Belen. As a doctor

she'd seen it many times before, to her
it all seemed natural but to me that bird,
which then dipped its beak and wings and tail

behind a concealed horizon in mid-air,
diving through the line of its erasure,
was as suddenly other as being born.

200

HARVESTING

The novice keepers, togged in gloves and goggles
smoked out the spirit of the hive and laid
three trays, each caked with hexagons,
on the oak table where they sat and ogled
the gold light trapped in the grid of cells
till their lids grew heavy and they trudged to bed.

Lying beside her husband, she wasn't sure
if she was the burglar or the burgled
caught napping as the whole place was stripped bare
but she dreamed herself on the crest of an elm
where a swarm was scouring half an eggshell
whilst the piping of the queen bestrode the air

dainty as a sea-chest in a maelstrom.
She woke to find a double stream
of bees, one coming down, the other climbing
the chimney, heaving bags of it back to the hive,
and when the last ingot had taken wing
the hearthstone was backlit like the gate of heaven.

Derek Sellen

DUNGENESS

The cross-tide discloses
a triangular acre of possibly radio-active mud,
not the right attributes for a beach.
The gulls are giant and ferocious,
having found something flayed
and succulent in the sea-garbage
which they dissect membrane by membrane.

The Jarman garden
sprouts rocky phallic circles;
the shingle-people rise like planted dragon's teeth,
slump-shouldered, lump-hipped Adams,
and cactus-Eves with spiny pads of breasts.
This isn't God's idea of a garden;
viper's bugloss wouldn't grow here if it were.

Donne's 'Busie old foole . . .'
is written on the tarred cottage wall, re-slanted
for a house of gay love. Contours change,
hard to decipher. They even had to build
three lighthouses as if they were uncertain of the shape,
though they got the power stations right first time –
Dungeness A and Dungeness B: squat and square and huge.

Away from all this,
two small boys, ten-year-old philosophers,
are lying daubed in mud on their stomachs,
discussing things with the sea breathing over them.
They are perfectly formed and perfectly innocent,
Archimedes and Aristotle in their youth.
We hope there's nothing nasty in the ooze.

AT·CHESIL

Ten-metre breakers are charging Chesil Bank,
chaos theory in action, this land, this lagoon,
created by criss-cross forces of no intent
except to jostle, a territory of disturbances,
a formlessness capable of such fine distinctions
that each pebble is graded by its position on the shore.

Between the 1300s and now, a monster's four times
surfaced off the beach, half fish, half sea-horse,
not hard to explain – cheap lure for tourists,
a drunken man's hallucination, a hoax, an error.
Or did a conjunction of the tides and winds,
a random pattern of the waves, a special frequency,

produce an excitement in the brain to match?
We saw the monster, which, being seen, existed,
as tall as a tall ship, as vast as a stone hill,
had attributes – a crest, fangs, scales, claws, fins.
It was there, as undeniable as love on the four occasions
it was seen and then not seen again.
          Just vacancy. Just sea.

Jonathan Treitel

A Romance Meat

'SWEETER THAN CANDY, softer than butter,' to her. And to him, 'It's like the tenderest, juiciest beef you ever had in all your born days.' Answering the question ('What does it taste like?') which neither of the hunters had actually asked, but which he, Trapley, felt should have been interjected into his monologue at that moment as a prompt, and would have been if the hunters had spoken fluent enough English.

He was guiding the hunters himself, standing alongside them at the back of the pickup, bumping against them as the Toyota bounced over the frozen ground, and breathing the good air. The joy of being in the open, out on this prairie which was all his, thirty-five thousand acres of it, as far as the horizon. He gestured with his Colt Sauer 458 at the sunrise. 'Like a buffalo's afterbirth,' he said. Both the man and the woman nodded, though he didn't suppose they'd understood. Over the rough patch near the creek the vehicle slowed and swayed then gathered speed again. Puddles of snow, here and there: a tawny glitter.

'It was almost extinct,' Trapley announced, in an ultra-clear explaining voice. 'Once we wiped it out, nearly. But now it's coming back strong.'

The man, Ryuji, was wearing basic Levis and a fur hat. His young bride, Noriko, pretty as a picture, was in a total Annie Oakley outfit, down to the fringed buckskin vest; well, it suited her. In honor of his guests Trapley was featuring his antique Stetson with the lucky jack of spades tucked in the brim, and he'd combed a dab of Grecian formula into his moustache. Trapley had nothing against Japanese hunters; and he'd had Germans also; let bygones be bygones. Not like his Pop, who'd been conscripted into the Air Force, basic trained and sent out to Guam just one week before Hiroshima. Glad, sure, when the Bomb dropped, but sore too at missing out on the whole shebang. So Pop, with zero combat points, had been bottom of the demob list – eight months on Guam with nothing to do, island fever was the name for it; Corporal Horowitz had tried to build a raft; there were still Japanese in the jungle who didn't know the war was over and just to pass the time Pop and his buddies had gone out in search of them – a kind of R&R, a mock engagement, an historical reenactment . . . But Trapley didn't buy that. 'In fact I prefer you people. You know the rules. You appreciate it's a fantasy with limits: go out there, shoot the trophy, haul it home, eat it, mount the head, whatever – mission accomplished. And Europeans too, they don't get carried away. But those yuppie thrusting citified male-bonders . . . I once had a group from Fort Worth . . . they want danger, Christ knows what they want – they're praying the lead bull'll charge them headlong – they won't be satisfied till they're scalped by a raiding party of Comanche!'

While the old rancher was babbling away, a flight of pheasant, bred for shooting, shuddered diagonally off the prairie – Ryuji thought of the good-luck redheaded cranes embroidered on his wife's wedding kimono . . . He got the gist of the American's message, and it was true: all of them were only playing at being Big White Hunters and that was how it should be. Once, not long after they had first met, he and Noriko had spent an hour together in the Wild West bedroom at a Love Hotel conveniently located near Shinjuku station . . . and this whole Wyoming experience, this honeymoon, was just a grander version of that. Meanwhile Noriko was gazing down at the passing ground – each clod of earth, of frozen dung, each nail of stubble – wonderstruck by the sheer fact of herself and this world coinciding. She wanted to leap from the pickup, to grab and hug the soil, to eat it.

'Now a fourwheel isn't as picturesque as a quarter horse, but you don't get saddle sores.'

Ryuji considered he had invented Noriko, the Noriko capable of enjoying an expensive exotic jaunt like this; for a girl of her background, if he hadn't come into her life, such an adventure would have been scarcely dreamable. He had picked her up in, of all places, Wayne's, a trendy US-style diner on Ometasando Dori. She was the waitress. It was early, before work. She had brought him breakfast Number Five (sunnyside-up, hash browns, miso soup, muffin with grape jelly, regular coffee) and he had overtipped her . . . She had no family, to speak of. A generation ago it would have been unthinkable to marry without a thorough investigation of the family tree, but now . . . At the wedding breakfast speeches had been made by her 'wealthy uncle' and her 'former boss' – both of them actors, of course, hired from an agency that specialises in such services; and he knew this, and she knew that he knew, and he knew that she knew that he knew and there was nothing amiss because it was only a shared makebelieve, not to be punctured.

'You're a *real* cowboy.'

Trapley reckoned these were the first words Noriko had spoken to him. So she did know some English. He smiled back at her. A broad grin under a grizzled moustache – a shadowy dip in the frosted earth. 'I guess I am too.'

Maybe he was a little embarrassed because next he made much show of inspecting the terrain through his telescopic sights, and passing the instrument to Ryuji and Noriko so they too could magnify the herd – speckles of pepper into solid forms – then yelling to the driver, 'Whoa! Doug Troll. Whoa!'

The pickup stammered to a halt. Doug Troll pushed his head and a large part of his torso through the side window; glanced up at his employer. Trapley gave orders. The vehicle drove off toward the prey.

'*How does it taste?*' Trapley said to Noriko. 'Repeat after me: *How does it taste?*'

'How does it taste?' On her lips the common words were chosen, enunciated, special, tasty.

'*Sweeter than candy, softer than butter*. Now you say it.'

'Sweeter than candy, softer than butter.'

Noriko remembered how she had seduced Ryuji. She had passed by the customer's table with the pot, and refilled his cup without asking. 'It is the *bottomless cup*, sir' – using the American idiom, which he had not understood, the way they never do at first – of course they know *topless* as in *topless bar* so they think she is making some crude suggestion and they stir on their seats and flush until she has explained, 'You may have as many cups as you want for the same price.' 'I can have a hundred?!' 'Ten thousand!' She clinked her pot against his cup. He toasted her in coffee. 'Ten thousand!' they said in unison. '*Cheers!*' Then she presented him with his individually-wrapped mint flavor toothpick, the paper package stamped *Wayne's*.

'This is yours?' she asked the rancher.

'Oh, it's all mine.' Waving an arm at the herd of buffalo, becoming larger every second (reality matching what had been viewed through the sights) and the frost-bright prairie and the blue sky. 'And this is yours . . .'

Trapley held out the Smith & Wesson .44 magnum ('You specified a handgun') butt first for safety sake, passing it – not into the open hand of Noriko, but to Ryuji, naturally. He added a bonus of six green-tipped cartridges ('SSK-KTW high penetration ammo – the only kind that can do the trick') and the Japanese prepared his weapon. Meanwhile Trapley inspected the safety on his own Colt, and mimed clicking it; his trigger finger squeezed air. He stowed the gun in his DeSantis shoulder rig.

'They say a buff will attack only if you get too near the goldies – that's what we call the young calves, before their coat has turned. A cow afraid for her calf will whup you harder than the mightiest bull.'

The vehicle swerved around a thicket, causing the riders to cling to each other and the railing of the tailgate. The American was sandwiched between the honeymooners. They spoke to each other across him, in a language he couldn't possibly understand. ('*Are you scared?*' '*No. Are you?*' '*I love you.*' '*Of course you love me.*') Ryuji loved his bride in all her manifestations – as uniformed waitress; naked; in a richly brocaded wedding kimono, a million yen's worth, so vast and heavy she could scarcely lift it, posing for photographs in front of the Yasukuni shrine where the war dead are honored (his grandfather and four great-uncles had all gone missing, somewhere in the Pacific); as well as in western style wedding dress, unblushing while her 'former boss' delivered a commendation of her 'devotion to duty'; cowgirl guise now too. As the Toyota surged on, Noriko imagined the mass of beasts was stampeding toward her – or there again that she was a buffalo herself, racing to join her herd. ('*I love you.*')

'*I wake in a cold bed./ Try to sleep again. A buck antelope passes/ from Montana to Wyoming.* It's my own. I recited it at the 1996 Cowboy Poetry Convention at Elko, Nevada, where it was broadly welcomed. It's a haiku, one of your sort of poems, so I guess you know all about that.'

'Yes. I also speak haiku,' she said. (To her husband's suprise. It was the first he had heard of it.) She recited phrases in Japanese, prettily, self-consciously. Literally: '*No smoking, please/ Fasten your safety belts/ In five minutes we will land in America.*'

'Mighty euphonious.'

'My wife is a talented woman.'

'They have springs in their feet. At night they play tag.'

'How do you aim it?'

'She is not – how do you say it? – just a pretty face.'

'You align the crosshairs . . .'

'*Say you love me too.*'

'A buff will chase a dog like a dog will chase a cat.'

'*I love you because you want me to say I love you.*'

'You know what they say: buffalo are easy, ten trained experienced cowboys working as a team can persuade a herd of buff to go the way the buff want to go!'

'That one's so big!'

The Toyota was glide-jolting parallel to the herd, keeping a distance of a couple hundred feet. The dominant male was veering over to investigate.

Trapley's scream . . .

. . . becoming comprehensible as words:

'Brake, Doug Troll!'

The engine off. Quietness.

Think of Doug Troll cozy in his driver's seat, with the side windows rolled up and opaqued with his own exahalations, listening to country music on a Sony Walkman. A man present but elsewhere, not part of the action . . . Our representative perhaps.

Think of three humans up on the back of the pickup, stock still and watching. Breath from their mouths steaming in the cold air – and, not so far away, from the trophy bull's likewise . . . Let him too be our representative.

All but silently Ryuji slid down from the vehicle. One long step away from it. This was his moment. He stood on the earth, orienting himself with care and awe. Free. Alone. A Japanese businessman in Wyoming – Neil Armstrong on the moon. He readied his magnum, gripped it in both hands, extended it before him in firing position. He held himself static, as if it was his own head which was set to be mounted, his own hide to be tanned and put on display. Meanwhile the rancher, up on the tailgate, behind and above, was aiming his own weapon, covering him. The two men were concentrating, busy, doing their jobs; the woman, hovering somewhere near Trapley, seemed irrelevant now – the ultimate instigator and inspirer of all this male activity, yes, but here and now apparently beside the point.

The sound of it. Ryuji staggering back from the recoil. The bull looking around, uninjured; we would say 'puzzled' insofar as we can attribute thoughts to what goes on inside its head. Its huge head; that beats any President's on Mount Rushmore. And the other creatures, more timid, shuffling away. Trapley shrieking, 'You gave the critter a goddarn earache! Fire again!'

Again. Now the massed herd is drumming the prairie as it turns and heaves itself into the distance. All except for the trophy bull which is slipping to the ground. 'Slipping?' No that's not right, more dramatic than that; but you couldn't say he's falling, not sudden enough, and it's not as if he's become an inanimate object yet. More as if the earth itself is doing the collapsing – shifting down and inward, becoming unstable, no longer good for any living creature to rely upon . . . Ryuji is walking steadily toward his prize.

'Give the buff an insurance shot!'

But the Japanese is not firing. Maybe he doesn't understand the idiom? Maybe he doesn't want to understand – who can know another man's definition of courage? Maybe he empathises with the bull, envisages himself in place of the bull, more than a hunter ought?

And up on the Toyota, Noriko – tense, desirous, in love with something, let's guess with this land, in control.

And Ryuji pacing closer.

And Trapley part of the situation but not somebody whose will and wishes need to be considered at this juncture any more than the buffalo's; say that he (like Ryuji, like all men) is a means to an end.

And the triumphant honeymooner combing the thick tangled mane with his Smith & Wesson.

And the crosshairs aligned still. Even now the Colt Sauer 458 is aimed (just in case, because you never know) at the surely already dead beast's head.

'You don't have to,' around sunset, as Trapley winched the carcass off the roll-in table into the windowless cement outbuilding. 'If I need help, I guess I can always beeper in Doug Troll.' But Noriko had put on rubber knee boots and apron, and seemed eager to assist or at least watch. She had signed up for the whole experience and had no intention of missing out on anything. What happened next can and will be put into words – clean, odorless words – but don't suppose they more than approximate the dirt, disorderliness and stench of reality. Trapley split the hide down the belly, using an air-knife. He skinned out the legs. Then he proceeded to cape-skin the head and shoulders, beginning by cutting and loosening the pelt. He fastened a hoist and literally pulled the skull loose, while Noriko helped peel the neck-skin off, easing it free with a razor-sharp knife. Another hoist around the legs and the whole hide was removed, unnicked, perfect. Trapley gutted what remained and together they hung it up on the carcass rail. All the while Trapley was making comments such as, 'You can make a good-looking rug out of the skin, you just have to spread it and salt it and scrape it and let it dry,' and 'The head you can mount on your wall, talk about a memento' . . . but Noriko was silent throughout. It seemed she had forgotten English: but he reckoned she understood enough; maybe it was that she had said all she needed to say, and knew the value and power of silence. Or suppose that, not belonging in this land and so not properly here, by virtue of her silence she was absent, not responsible for whatever might be going on. 'And as for the meat,' the rancher continued, 'it's . . . go on, *you* say it.' But since she was saying nothing he pressed his bloody gloved hand against the small of her leather-vested back, a ventriloquist coming to terms with his dummy, and went in a high funny-sounding tone, '*Sweeter than candy, softer than butter* . . .' then in his normal voice: 'That's right, Noriko. You're right. And, you know, irrespective of market conditions, it'll always command a premium price, it's what we in the business call a "romance meat".'

Harry Clifton

THE LAND BRIDGE

All the way south, there was only this road
Twisting through the mountains
To Siena and beyond. A sanded track
Beaten flat by pilgrimage,
Littered with axles, broken felloes,
Endings. Flooded
Out of season, losing itself,
Re-appearing, in the moon-landscape
Of the Alpine foothills,
Ghastly with mile-high silence, unbroken
But for bird-caw and rockfall,
And suddenly the olives, silver-grey,
And the true south starting.

                    In the distance
Siena, allegorical,
Dreamed of before ever met with,
Shimmered before us. Then, the long approach
Between sanded tumuli, the feminine swells
Of the Tuscan hills, with the factions
Perched in their hawks' nests
Jealously watching, and the skies
Ever bluer, the heat increasing,
And Paris, from where we had started,
So far behind us,
In a space measured only by footfalls.

Through the North Gate we entered,
To a pride of spires,
Fine counting-houses, streets full of rats
Big enough to feed on

In siege-time. Vain women, vain men,
With a preference for red
Like their painters. Coinage, stamped
With the she-wolf, stolen from Rome.
A delicate skein of allegiances
Quivering, unspoken,
On every breeze. The Romans, the French;
To the east, the Florentines;
North, on the pilgrim route from Augsburg
Through the mountains, the Emperor on the move
With his flaxen-haired soldiers . . . .
                                        Autumn –
From tree to tree, the mist-nets spread
For migrant birds, and the nets on the ground
For olives. Venison, game, good wine –
Winter and Spring, we lived in that ideal,
Under the sign of gluttony, science, art,
Then started north, with the road still open,
And the skirmishes, out to sea,
Already visible. Over our shoulders
Siena, dwindling, still could be seen
When the first buboes purpled us.
By the mountains, in the ghastly foothills,
Our dead, unburied, swelled and burst
At every turn. How many rats
Were travelling with us, anyone might guess,
But that we were carriers
No one doubted – plague spots on our faces,
In our pockets, new cosmogonies.

James Lasdun

AMERICAN MOUNTAIN

I

Our Queen's English accents
kept the class-conscious English masses
at bay, while our looks and name
did the same for the upper classes.

Being there,
as opposed to just stopping by,
was a matter of what you arrived too late
to arrange: your ancestry.

'We're not English' went the family saying.
What were we then? We'd lopped
our branch off from the family tree:
anglophone Russian-German apostate Jews

mouthing Anglican hymns at church
till we renounced that too . . . Self-knowledge
was knowledge of not being this or this or this.
We were like stencils: our inverse had the edge

over whatever it was we were,
not that that would have mattered had I not
happened not to enjoy that throttling
knot of annulled speech gathering in my throat,

or the sense of not being in a room
I hadn't left, or being too light
to plant my feet. I was my opposite;
I chased myself across the planet

214

till I vanished through the looking glass
of the Atlantic ocean –
and woke up clinging to the tilted
patchwork of an American mountain.

II

A FAMILY TREE

The locals,
Esopus Algonquins,
having already been massacred,
there's no-one with greater claims to an acre

than you have. As for your ancestry, it's yours
to choose from whoever cleared a spot
anywhere on these tough-fibred slopes and hollows.
Patent your own coat-of-arms; why not?

Elect your forebears from the pitch-brewers,
colliers, tanbark-peelers, the German
smelters at DeZeng's forge hammering molten
pigs of primordial bog-iron; shingle-splitters,

Dutch buckwheat farmers
who felled a white pine to pitch their claim,
cleared the land, then when the tree
rotted, had them a home;

apostate royalists who took 'The Test';
I have it by heart: *I the Subscriber*
Do most solemnly swear
that I Renounce all allegiance to the King of Great Britain . . .

Take your pick, you'll know them
by what they left behind –

great bluestone dolmens the Irish quarrymen
cut and hauled down ice-roads, then abandoned;

abandoned orchards from Prohibition
when a backwoodsman could stay afloat
on twenty barrels of hard cider,
his knobbled trees still cranking out squint fruit;

abandoned houses – middle-income,
cathedral-ceilinged, faux post-and-beam
'Woodstock Contemporaries'
dotted along the creeks for IBM

before they downsized; abandoned grist-mills, graveyards . . .
(and what landscape isn't finally the sum
of others' abandoned efforts to turn it
into themselves? Only the too-tame

or the impossibly wild . . .)
As for my own family tree, I'd gladly
grandfather in our predecessors
here on this slope of the mountain: glassblowers,

Bohemians mostly, shipped over
between the Embargo boom and the peacetime crash
– a brief, bright window –
to couple the virgin forests of Keefe Hollow

with the sands of Cooper Lake.
I see them at the glory hole
in their leather aprons and masks,
emptying their strong lungs

into the shimmering lungs of glass . . .
Choristers, fiddlers, jugglers,
with a taste for the gaudy,
they left behind almost nothing –

a few glass whimsies – dippers, turtles and canes
bits of glass slag gleaming in the dirt,
and a marginal local
increase in transparency.

III

AFTER HEIDEGGER

Lichtung: a clearing;
fire-break or beaver meadow,
Dutch farmer-pioneer meadows, stump-littered and raw;
first harvest ashes; second, Indian corn
tilled with a thorn-bush harrow.

'A man was famous'
the psalm reports, 'according
as he had lifted up axes upon thick trees'.
The trees are still thick, and although you've traded
that king for the secret king

of thought, and exchanged
your axe for a Makita,
it remains a matter of the ground beneath you; first
making it *unverborgen*: unconcealed,
then second, planting your feet.

I've muddled it all
like the old-time dairy-men
in their doggerel of gable and salt-box, their pastures
a garble of ditches. But that's how it is
after *Verfall*. The fallen

tend to a certain
makeshift approach towards life.
Like Kant they know nothing straight has ever been built
from the crooked timber of humanity,
and just keep patching the roof.

Theirs is the kingdom
of God, or at any rate
Dasein. Being here's just a question of having been
elsewhere unhappily long enough to feel
that that was exile, this not.

Tim Parks

EROS

IF BRAHMA IS a more endearing creator than Jehovah, it is because he wasn't pleased with what he had made. He found the world dull and dusty. Death was the answer, suggested Siva. Living forever, people were bored. A time-limit would galvanize, give dignity. But in that case some way of replacing the population would have to be found. Brahma brought together a few trusted fellows and explained what was required. The pleasure took them by surprise. What was that for? To put a fresh shine on the world, they were told. Otherwise it might get dusty again . . .

I'm always taken aback when people talk about the eroticism of food and drink, of sunbathing and massage. This is mere sensuality. Or avoiding the issue. No experience even remotely compares with true eros, with long and lavish love-making. It is perfectly understandable that people should imagine its having been tacked on to creation afterwards, so extravagant is the pleasure it brings, so far beyond what is necessary. Never does the world seem so freshly painted, so brightly enamelled, so new, for heaven's sake, as after the best sex. But, alas, depending on where you're up to in life, it may be full of new complications too. A lesser authority than Brahma's would have issued a health-warning.

Over billiards and beer a friend is explaining why he is leaving his wife and two children. He's playing with unusual speed and precision. His eyes are brighter than the beer could account for. 'And the girl is twenty-three,' he explains. French. So intelligent. 'Intelligently pert breasts?' I enquire,

219

'Perceptively warm thighs?' He laughs. He is deliriously proud, confused, unhappy. 'I feel I was never really in love with my wife,' he says.

Eroticism paints out the past. In this sense it is the most potent myth-making and myth-destroying power we have. How those first encounters are told and re-told, cherished and savoured over and over again. How solid and irreplaceable they begin to seem. I did this, you said that. When your hand first . . . When your mouth . . . Beneath all the structure of domestic economy, in-laws, even children, it is on this bedrock that marriage rests. But only once? Is it never to happen again? Suddenly solid ground is quicksand . . .

'As soon as I'm in the door, I feel suffocated. I married too young.' Thus Franco, potting the black. 'I never experienced real passion.' Before *la jeune fille très intelligente*, he means. And is setting up the table again. He is smoking too this evening. I have never seen him smoke before. 'I feel I will die if I go home,' he says. I ask him if he wants more children. He doesn't. 'Perhaps it's all a terrible mistake,' he says, 'but at least I will have had this passion.' Should I tell him that when we first met years ago he had seemed very passionate about his wife? Who is nothing if not intelligent . . .

Women. Another Indian myth – sexist, if you wish to be offended – has it that when the gods became scared of a man, scared of his developing spiritual powers, they would send him a woman. Or alternatively they might send Indra to seduce his wife and make him jealous. In either case, the turbulent feelings would disperse the power he had accumulated. So Franco, whose expertise once took him round all the capitals of Europe, now finds his life in pieces. Lawyers, quarrels, returns, departures. Then more women too. For if marriage has a way of declining into dusty routine, myth-making likewise can lapse into tawdry chronicle. The third marriage, the fourth. Meantime, my billiards is improving.

Eroticism has this in common with an addictive drug: that there is a coercive element to its pleasure with which part of us is in complicity, and part not. Thus ever since time began men have been trying to enjoy eroticism without being destroyed by it. Societies, religions can be defined in the way they deal with this conundrum. Polygamy, monogamy with repression, monogamy with affairs, monogamy with prostitutes, serial monogamy. Not to mention individual solutions of great ingenuity, or desperation: Victor Hugo with the door knocked through the wall of his office, to let in a girl each afternoon. Auden's flair for finding call-boys in every town. Picasso who simply refused when wife and mistress demanded he choose between them. Then there is always the hair-shirt of course. But perhaps the thing to remember when you wake up with a life full of fresh paint and tortuous complications is that eroticism wasn't invented for you, nor merely for the survival of the species perhaps, but for a divinity's entertainment. Nothing generates so many opportunities for titillation and *schadenfreude* as eroticism. Which is why it lies at the centre of so much narrative. How the gods thronged the balconies of heaven to see the consequences of Helen's betrayal! And your friends are watching too. Your antics have put the shine on many a late-night conversation.

On the borders between mythology and history, that wily survivor Odysseus was the first who learnt to trick the gods. And perhaps his smartest trick of all was that of lashing himself to the mast before the Sirens came in earshot. There are those of course who are happy to stand at the railings, even scan the horizon. Otherwise, choose your mast, find the ropes that suit you: sport, workaholism, celibacy with prayerbook and bell . . . But the kindest and toughest ropes of all are probably to be found in some suburban semi-detached with rowdy children and a woman who never allows the dust to settle for too long.

Robert Crawford
THE ST ANDREWS QUESTION

GETTING HERE ISN'T easy. It never was. Centuries back, you would have come to pay homage to the relics of Scotland's patron saint. The most dangerous part of the journey was by ferry over a sometimes treacherous firth where, from time to time, pilgrims drowned. Scotland's first university was set up here in 1410, its inception greeted with bonfires in the streets, but around the time of the Reformation there were human bonfires in St Andrews. A friar well versed in gunnery had a cannon hauled up one of the cathedral towers so that Protestant forces in the mediaeval castle could be more accurately bombarded. Inside the castle the body of a murdered Cardinal lay packed in its coffin of salt. Later, in the 17th century, an Archbishop was dragged from his horse on a moor near the town and done to death. A bumble-bee flew up out of his tobacco box, indicating complicity with Satan. St Andrews has a rich past, and one bound up with inter-factional violence. A good place to think about national, and inter-national arguments.

In today's newly-devolved Scotland, if you head for St Andrews and take the train north from Edinburgh, you come in along fault-lines of gender. Shortly before your destination the train pauses at a station called Ladybank – unmanned, as its name suggests. Along the platform here, in the early years of the century, battle-lines were drawn up between militant suffragettes and members of the Prime Minister's entourage. Asquith's constituency was in East Fife, and the female attackers at Ladybank knew it was a key site. Their struggles are virtually unrecorded – no blue plaque, nothing in any of the standard history books. Their names are forgotten, but they won.

En route to victory they also torched Leuchars railway station, which, thanks to Lord Beeching, is as close as the railway now gets to St Andrews. When you detrain and catch a bus or a taxi to take you the last five miles into town, go to the Gatty Marine Laboratory, another site of suffragette arson. Along the road a bit Willa Muir, the novelist and proto-feminist thinker, was a student at the University, siding with the suffragettes just before World War I. From the late 19th century onwards many leading men of St Andrews were arguing determinedly over women's rights and education. One of them, the big, spade-bearded former preacher William Knight, espoused a degree programme called the 'Lady Literate in Arts' which attracted students to an international network of out-stations from Adelaide to Cairo, and from Calcutta to Stornoway – all co-ordinated from St Andrews. Most of the LLA students are long dead, and few political parties today regard gender as uppermost in the voter's mind. Yet the new Scottish Parliament, elected on 6 May 1999, and about forty per cent of whose members are female, marks a milestone in politics of gender in the British Isles. 'Gender, gender, gender' may not be the MSPs' priority, but it is a leyline underlying the terrain of modern politics everywhere. The railway to St Andrews, both extant and axed, guides you right along that leyline for miles. Each day, my walk to and from work takes me over what was its dinkiest viaduct.

By car the approach road is clearly party-political. Driving towards the sea down Strathkinness Low Road you pass Rufflets Country House Hotel where, once upon a time, some young St Andrews chappies met in the bar and dreamed up that most seismic of modern British fiscal measures, the Poll Tax. Pride and joy of the Thatcher government, it was trialled first of all in Scotland, and then prescribed for the ills of all the British nations. Defended by the then Scottish Secretary, a St Andrews graduate called Michael Forsyth, the Poll Tax came to emblematize Thatcherite economics, and its St

Andrews inventors went on to play a leading role in a right-wing think-tank, the Adam Smith Institute. Topiaried and hushed, the gardens of Rufflets Hotel seem far removed from the picket lines and Big Bangs of Eighties cultural conflict, but as much as Canary Wharf and Wapping they are part of that Tory story.

Keep driving, though, towards the mediaeval skyline, expansive sandy beaches and golf courses of this small coastal town, and the political landscape gets more complicated. Go as far as you can, until you come to the small ruined Castle surmounted by its glinting, gilded metal flag. Just opposite, in Castle House, is the office of the Scottish poet Douglas Dunn, author of the 1990 pamphlet *Poll Tax: The Fiscal Fake*, a prose and verse denunciation of the 'crude cunning' and 'fraudulence' of that Thatcherite measure. Once dubbed 'Red Dunn', the author of *Barbarians*, who became more recently and more doucely Head of the School of English at St Andrews University, is a reminder that St Andrews bridges ideological crevasses, and not simply those of right and left. For if you stand in front of Castle House and look out over the North Sea, your eyes will soon turn in the direction of the constituency of another celebrated St Andrews graduate, Alex Salmond, 'Smart Alex', leader of the Scottish National Party. Politics of the right and left are changing so fast in Britain now that, from a Scottish, Welsh, or Northern Irish viewpoint, the main division is no longer between Labour and Conservative, but between unionist and non-unionist parties. Three parties in the Edinburgh Parliament – the Scottish National Party, the Green Party, and the Scottish Socialist Party – support independence, while three others (New Labour, the Conservatives, and the Liberal Democrats) oppose it. While in London New Labour seems to have learned a trick or two from old Tories, in Scotland the Conservative Party, which holds 18 seats, has already announced that it will vote with Labour's 56 MSPs in order to help preserve the Union of the United Kingdoms. In this the Tories would be joined by the Liberal Democrats, closely involved with Scottish Labour, who can muster 17 MSPs.

Such a Tory-Labour-Lib-Dem alliance would face its main opposition in the form of the Scottish Nationalists, who hold 35 seats and see devolution as a stepping stone to independence. The SNP's ultimate aim is to keep Scotland within the European Union, but to take it out of the more local British union. Seen from London, British politics still looks left-rightish; viewed from Brussels, British constitutional change may appear to have to do with regional, rather than national matters. Seen from St Andrews, British politics and constitutional change look rather different. They're about Unionism versus independence.

I work in the building next to Castle House. I'm a poet and a Professor of Modern Scottish Literature. In case my bosses want to sack me, I'd better make it clear that I'm writing in a personal capacity. A Glaswegian, I've lived in St Andrews for ten years now. That's not nearly long enough to count as 'local', but it's given me time to tune in to some of the quirkier frequencies. St Andrews is lyrically beautiful, can be a bit smug, and is honeycombed with secret histories. Most days I pass the site of the 'wee house' in Market Street where the newly demobbed Christopher Grieve (better known as the nationalist and communist poet Hugh MacDiarmid) stayed briefly with his wife in 1919 and felt the beginnings of that cultural power-surge known as the Scottish Renaissance. A few hundred yards away MacDiarmid's friend the American bisexual editor and activist James H. Whyte set up his nationalist magazine *The Modern Scot* in the 1930s, mesmerizing the sniffy locals as he swept past them in his gleaming Bugatti. It's easy to get dewy-eyed about all this intricate cultural heritage, or to sentimentalize the way Willa and Edwin Muir felt cold-shouldered when they worked in St Andrews in the late 1930s. What matters is that St Andrews has complex pasts, and that its histories involve issues pertinent not just to 21st century Scotland but to 21st century Britain. How do we come to terms with a shifting political geography in which left and right are being realigned, cut across crucially by politics of nationalism and gender? That's the geography surrounding us now. That's the St Andrews Question.

Over the last decade I've lived not just in this town, but in this question. Though poetry is dream and crystallization, rather than just a play of ideas, my poems in such books as *A Scottish Assembly* (1990) and *Masculinity* (1996) are nourished by this intellectual mulch, as are prose books like *Devolving English Literature* (1992), and the recently controversial *Scottish Invention of English Literature* (1998). For me the landslide British election victory of 1997 and the ensuing 1999 Devolution referenda meant that the virtual stuff of dream and argument was about to become real. There's a great danger of being solipsistic about such matters, grandiosely strutting out as a self-acknowledged poetic legislator for modern Scotland. That way puffery lies, and too much politics risks turning poetry into propaganda, one of the worst things poetry can become. Yet I'd be lying if I said I felt no excitement, even anxiety, when, after several years of imagining which, politically speaking, was oppositional, suddenly I was part of a democratic majority. Living out here, on the margin of a margin that is North East Fife, the question I lived in and walked through has become everybody's. The St Andrews Question is going to be answered.

The process will, and ought to take some time. In Scotland and in Wales on 6 May 1999 Labour won more seats than any other single party; yet in neither of these countries did they win an outright majority. This means that they can only govern through strategic alliances. Even more striking is the fact that in each country the main opposition is the nationalist party, which holds about one third of the seats. This is a huge advance for Scottish and Welsh nationalists who, even in my parents' generation, were regarded as a bunch of crazy poets. At Westminster they were always marginal players. Now they are very much front-of-stage.

If Scotland had suddenly become independent on 6 May 1999, it would have had to ascend a learning curve so steep that the g-forces might have been fatal. Despite keeping its own educational, legal, and ecclesiastical systems distinct for centuries, along with lots of others of its own national institutions, Scotland has got used to not being entirely in charge of itself. If we are going to be self-respectingly independent, better to take a little learning time first. South of the Scottish border, the implications of devolution are emerging only slowly as people realize that England is a nation, but not a state. The state of which they are part, Britain, is developing fresh constitutional patterns in its northern and western sectors – in Wales, Northern Ireland, and Scotland where new parliaments and assemblies now exist – but in London constitutional energy still seems tied up with the feudal system as democratically-elected Westminster MPs attempt to dismantle or reform the House of Lords. More than that, for all the influx of female MPs dubbed Blair's Babes, the lower chamber at Westminster remains very far from a House of Ladies. Londoners can commute to France through the Chunnel, yet waves of Europhobia sweep across their country, and there are signs of anxiety about English identity, on the one hand, and about loss of power from London to Brussels on the other. Over the next few years, the distinct nationalisms of Scotland, Wales, and Northern Ireland may be further complicated by a growth in an anti-European English nationalism, built on a desire to resist rather than participate in, further European integration. While Scottish Nationalists are brandishing the slogan 'Scotland in Europe', English nationalists, sore about devolution and about rule from Brussels, may soon be flaunting the slogan 'England free from Europe'. Forthcoming debates over the Euro could precipitate such a movement, since both of the principal English parties – Labour and Conservative – contain elements opposed to a federal Europe with a unified currency. Scotland has myths, such as that of the Auld Alliance, which let it look to Europe with confidence and affection. North of the border, Rupert Murdoch's *Sunday Times* publishes its Scottish section under the title 'Ecosse'; it is hard to imagine a southern counterpart thriving under a masthead of 'Angleter-re'. It looks as if England needs to learn from its closest European neighbour – Scotland – how to be a little more

European. Yet Scotland, Wales, and Northern Ireland need to learn from England also. Though there are some mutterings to the contrary, England seems on the whole happy to be governed by a Scottish Prime Minister, Scottish Chancellor, Foreign Secretary, Defence Secretary and other prominent North Britons. Not since the resented Bute administration of the 18th century have the Scots wielded so much power in London. Perhaps their strong unionist credentials, and an element of relief at getting beyond the Thatcher era that the Scots so resolutely opposed, gives present-day Scots at Westminster a relatively easy, unprejudiced reception. Some of the leading figures, such as Tony Blair, appear only minimally Scottish, and play with a very British bat. As by far the largest partner in the Union, the English have always been able to be tolerant towards other British minorities in their midst. Westminster now has a small number of black MPs. Worryingly, the new Scottish and Welsh parliaments, which will have to discuss racism in those countries, are all-white and even contain few people who were brought up in England. British society has been rocked by recent high-profile racial scandals such as the murder of the black teenager Stephen Lawrence, though the toleration of Scots, Irish, and Welsh people in England has been markedly generous for centuries. Attitudes towards the English in Scotland, Ireland, and Wales are not always so open-handed.

Here the American-Australian, saltire-painted face of Mel Gibson comes to mind. I watched *Braveheart* the other night for the first time when the BBC, with very little advance publicity, put it on the telly one weekday evening. Perhaps that lack of publicity and the avoidance of a weekend screening were signs of anxiety about the passions the film seems able to ignite. Just as the 18th-century Scottish novelist Tobias Smollett kept his mouth shut in London when news of Culloden excited the mob there, in case someone recognized his accent as Scottish, so English people in Scottish cinemas hunched meekly on the velour as their rampant Scottish neighbours cheered on Mel Gibson's freedom-fighting Franco-phile Scoto-Latinist, William Wallace. Welcomed by at least some in the SNP, and derided by po-faced Scottish historians, the slashing, disembowelling *Braveheart* nonetheless touches several raw nerves in Britain's body politic.

In one way, as a cultural icon, it's the mediaeval counterpart of that other recent Scottish film success, *Trainspotting*. Both films rely on assumptions that the Scots, though they may know Latin and have street-credibility, are somehow more barbaric and macho than their refined southern neighbours. This supposition goes back at least to Tacitus who in his *Agricola* presents the nobly barbarian Scottish warrior chief Calgacus resisting the decadent Roman Empire. When Doctor Johnson remarked that 'Much may be made of a Scotchman, if he be *caught* young,' he too summoned up such a figure of the wild male Scot. This myth, whose incarnations range from Wallace to television's string-vested, bottle-wielding Rab C. Nesbitt, is alive and well in modern Scotland, Britain, and beyond. It has come to be enjoyed by many Scots, who are sophisticated in the ways they play up to it. If the woad-painted Mel looks uncannily like a member of Scotland's rowdily pacific World Cup Tartan Army, that isn't an accident. The myth may be fun, though it's all too easy to put a feminist spin on it. It reinforces the assumption that to be Scottish is to be male (name ten famous Scottish women who didn't have their heads chopped off), and it can have nastier overtones. Imagine yourself as an English public schoolboy surrounded at night in a Scottish town by twenty Rab C. Nesbitts.

To see *Braveheart* as a trivial flash in the pan is to miss the point. In each of the centuries since the 1707 Union of Parliaments the Wallace myth has been a powerful factor in Scottish cultural life. In the 18th century a skilled minor poet, William Hamilton of Gilbertfield, enjoyed a major success with his English-language updating of Blind Hary's late mediaeval Scots poem about Wallace. Hamilton's neo-Wallace was phenomenally popular throughout Scotland, and the poem was devoured by many fledgling writers. Robert Burns recalled it as favourite childhood reading: 'the story of Wallace poured a Scottish prejudice in my veins which will boil along there until the flood-gates of life shut.' 'Scots, wha ha'e with Wallace bled' would become one of Burns's best-known songs. A hundred years later the building of the vast Wallace Monument (Scotland's national phallus) near Stirling became a focal point for Scottish patriotism as well as attracting international attention. Ten years on, the Scottish Home Rule Association emerged; later still, in the 1920s, the decade when the National Party of Scotland was formed, there were public commemorations of Wallace's death. However Hollywoody, *Braveheart* is scarcely a new departure in Scottish cultural life. It recycles energies kept alive by writers as well as by politicians and others in the three centuries of the Union.

Yet what may be most troubling about the *Braveheart* effect is if it suggests to modern audiences that Scottish politics involves continuing feudal pitched battles against the English. Just as England's tabloid nationalism can too readily tap into Eurothreats from the German Menace, as if the EC were straightforwardly a Fourth Reich, so Scottish chauvinism can effortlessly conjure up Bruce and Wallace as models for the modern Scot. Today Scotland's unofficial national anthem, sung on sportsgrounds across the land, is 'Flower of Scotland', with its delight in confronting 'proud Edward's army' and sending the English forces of that Hammer of the Scots 'homewards, to think again'. If English chauvinism still seems pinned down under heavy fire on the Normandy beaches, then velociraptoral Scottish chauvinism takes its reference points from the far remoter middle ages. Scottish mythology is long-memoried, even today when most Brits have forgotten, or politely omit, those lines from the British national anthem which censure proud, rebellious Scots.

Just as England now needs a sense of its own identity which is self-respecting rather than Europhobic and oppositional, so Scotland has to come to see its identity as dynamic rather than static. Earlier waves of 20th-century Scottish nationalism were international in their orientation, but also often anti-English; the poet Hugh MacDiarmid famously listed his recreation in *Who's Who* as 'Anglophobia' and saw aureate mediaevalism as the future of Scottish verse. This Anglophobic strain remains present in contemporary Scotland, and needs to be replaced by an Anglophile Scottish nationalism which is confident about the future and whose confidence is expressed through inclusive generosity. How?

That again involves the St Andrews Question, for it is part of modern Scottish mythology that this small town, whose University attracts a higher than average share of English public-schoolpersons, is something of a South British colonial outpost. Such prejudice is not just class-based, but is bound up with a 'bash-the-English' strain of Little Scotlandism that a mature Scottish democracy needs to move beyond. Scotland should be judged on the way it treats its minorities, not least its English minority. It needs a more confidently pluralist sense of its richly entangled identity. A panoptic survey of mediaeval Scotland would bring to mind that the first great Scottish poet was St Columba, an Irishman, and that Old English, as carved on the Ruthwell Cross in what is now Dumfriesshire, was, along with Latin, Welsh, and Gaelic, then, later, Old Norse, Old French, and Scots, one of the ancient languages of Scotland. Present-day Scotland, like any other contemporary nation, is accidental. Its boundaries might easily have included Berwick or excluded the Orkneys and Shetlands; it so happens that history has left them where they are. Some rather sinister old-style nationalists liked to suggest there was some sort of core, unchanging Scottishness – the same at Bannockburn as it is today – an essence that is always with us. That is the sort of nationalism that is a dangerous religion-substitute. To be a modern nationalist is to accept the accidental 'given' of nationality, and to work with it, not to pretend that it has been constant throughout history, or chosen by God for the sole use of His Elect.

Similarly, to argue for some soundbyte, essentialist 'Scottishness' or 'Englishness' is daft. Any nation that has a simple, one-size-fits-all identity for its inhabitants is likely to end up with ethnic cleansing. 'If you don't fit my definition of Scottishness, line up against that wall' is what naive notions of national identity boil down to. Scots come in different colours, have different religious beliefs, talk different languages. What links them is something closer to Wittgenstein's notion of 'family resemblances' – the way members of a family share some (but not all) similar features and bonds – than any idea of being identical. We may have helped to develop cloning. That doesn't make us all clones. If Scots choose to accent a political definition of themselves according to national boundaries, then they will opt for more independence. If they see it as more important to view themselves in terms of those who live in the Central Belt and those residing outside it, or those who do and do not speak Gaelic, then events will move in a different direction. Whatever happens, rather than speaking in terms of some monolithic Scottishness, it is better to think and imagine in terms of 'Scotlands'. As editor of a magazine called that, and as the inventor of its title, I have a vested interest in the word and in making it common currency. Certainly I would love to see it taken up more as a term of political debate. The term 'Scotlands' is about pluralism, about the many versions of Scotland that exist both inside and beyond the country itself. It's about malleability and possibility. It presents, if you like, identity as envisioned by the Russian thinker Mikhail Bakhtin, who saw national and individual identity not as solitary and fixed entities, but as each dialogic – the self as a conversation rather than a monologue. In the culture that produced Adam Smith, whose *Theory of Moral Sentiments* gave Robert Burns the germ for 'O wad some Pow'r the giftie gie us/To see oursels as others see us', this porous notion of identity as fluid and dialogic, native and foreign at once, seems especially pertinent.

Problems arise when people start to define themselves *only* by means of an identity that is national. Most of the time we think of ourselves in terms of all sorts of other identities – as a postman, or someone overweight, or a thirty-year-old, or a woman, or as working-class, or a speaker of Japanese, or a combination of these – rather than just as a Pole or a Scottish person. When only one identity becomes paramount, as an apparently all-encompassing definition of who and what we are, the resulting narrowness and inflexibility become (sometimes fatally) oppressive. Mobility of identity, which allows one to step forward as a Welsh Tory in some circumstances, allows one in others to be simply a schoolteacher or an artist. The best nationalists are not preoccupied with their nation in some monomaniacal way. Opponents of Scottish nationalism like to imply that nationalism is always a destructive and oppressive force, and point to Adolf Hitler or the British National Party. Scottish nationalism, however, prides itself on a tradition of civic nationalism which looks far more to such models as Norway. No one blames the Norwegians for having their own state.

Whatever happens, Scotland, like Wales, is achieving far more democratic control over its own affairs than it has ever enjoyed. While we may define the years 1707–1999 as an interparliamentary period, a time when Edinburgh lost its parliament to London, we would be daft to assume that Scottish democracy post-1999 is somehow picking up on what was enjoyed pre-1707. To start with, no women, and precious few men, could vote in pre-1707 Scotland. Just before the Act of Union, about 4,000 males out of a Scottish population of one million had the vote. Modern notions of democracy were in their infancy. It's worth remembering that even in post-1945 Britain some individuals still had two votes at General Elections, while most people had one. What devolution means for several areas of Britain, and most acutely for Scotland (present population five million), isn't the restoration of something mediaeval, or even pre-Union; it is very much something new.

That's why, for the moment at least, there's a sense of everything being up for grabs, not just politically but also culturally. Devolution is imaginatively exciting, if only because the nitty-gritty hasn't been worked out yet, or at least hasn't all bedded down. There's a sense of being up in the air, partly buoyed up with elation, and partly, no doubt, with politicians' gassy vapours. I think of the generations of Scottish people – a fair number of them writers – who lived and died without seeing the hope of any measure of self-government realized, and I feel very lucky to be living now. In North Street, St Andrews, I meet the poet Kathleen Jamie, who lives nearby, and we go into a teashop for lunch. She has her baby son with her, and soon we are talking about how we each want to take our young families to Edinburgh at the time when the Scottish parliament opens so that we and they can remember that moment for the rest of our lives. Neither of us wants to stand as an MSP. We're poets who see poetry as something international, yet who have sometimes touched on politics as well as other matters. We're not politicians. We just want to celebrate the poetry of that shared, democratic moment.

Poets like to surf on the energy of language, and language here is changing. Already the word Edinburgh, which used to conjure up for me a beautiful museum city, a locus oddly purposeless, now means in a new sense the capital, the place where parliament is. More interesting is the word 'Holyrood'. For most of my life it has meant a royal palace at the end of the Royal Mile and that ruined abbey which so impressed the Mendelssohn of the Scottish Symphony. But, as a 20th-century person, I was also aware that between the Holyrood of ancient Scotland and that of my childhood there had arisen the too-close-for-comfort rhyme word 'Hollywood', so that one can't see Holyrood today without a twinge of Disney, just as one can't view the monarchy now without a splash of soap-opera. In a world mediated by the media, Holyrood seemed condemned to becoming a tourist-site, a museum of itself.

Then, a couple of years back, the word's meaning changed again, decisively. Headlining the Scottish papers, 'Holyrood' means where the new parliament is being built. Now the media are coming to report and imagine our future, not just our past. We almost got it terribly wrong, and thought about building our parliament in a station car-park at Haymarket. Then, too, there was argument about whether it should be shoehorned into the old Royal High School, seen by the Labour Party as a Nationalist icon (because it was the proposed site for the Scottish Assembly at the time of the

1979 Referendum fiasco), but actually a building which is bound up with the history of British unionism since it educated Sir Walter Scott and got itself 'Royal' approval. Now, though, almost everyone agrees that Holyrood is the place. That word has somehow shrugged off its royal pomp and gone over to the side of the people. The word has strolled across the road from the ruined abbey and splendid palace, scene of eternal garden parties, put on a hard hat, and has given itself to a building site. Here, designed by a controversial Catalan architect, the new Holyrood, the parliament, is going up storey by storey.

Some see the Parliament as symbolically kept in check by the palace over the road. I doubt it. More likely, there will be the new Scotland confronting the old across the way. The symbolic geography of Edinburgh, where the new Scottish Poetry Library is cheek-by-jowl with the new Scottish Parliament, and whose public sculptures mix Eduardo Paolozzi and Walter Scott, is shifting in potent ways. To walk from palace to parliament, from the old Holyrood to the new, is to follow a course of democratic evolution. Even if you don't view the monarchy as Britain's last form of hereditary slavery, it's hard to see its role in modern Edinburgh as other than awkwardly curatorial, part of that museum culture the city for so long lapsed into. Princess Anne is going to live in the palace, apparently. We should welcome her. But the centre of power will be on the other side of the road.

If words like Holyrood and Edinburgh are changing their semantic loading, then so is the word London. I like going to London now. When I worked in Oxford and went 'up' to London, often it felt oppressive. Its ruling echelons were more cosmopolitan (London's more like a country than a capital), but harboured some continuation of that Junior Common Room-cum-High Table world of Fellows and chaps and public schooldom that makes up an absurd percentage of the British establishment. In London I seemed to be walking through the city of *The Waste Land*, a place of Edwardian Empire, for all its postmodern add-ons. Once I strolled by the

Scottish Office buildings in London where in the early morning a black janitor was washing windows. Rightly or wrongly, I felt that he and I were somehow second-class citizens. Now, if I go to London, I feel I'm going to the exciting capital of a foreign country. I enjoy it, and have my own place to go back to. London has a vast capacity for sucking in power (just look at a map of Britain's railways or major roads), but devolution means it has spat some out again. Unless the Scottish Parliament turns into a puppet government, I know I will no longer feel under London's thumb. I can like it, with all its galleries, publishers, bookshops, cafés, libraries, its airports for flying on from, or flying back.

Back, eventually, after bus and train and taxi to St Andrews. Here in an anemometerish town of around fifteen thousand souls, the population oddly ebbs and flows. In the summer golfers from America, Japan, and elsewhere, mix with Scottish families who have come to the beaches. These groups jostle happily, sometimes with a sort of puzzled amusement. No one is small-minded enough to suggest that all the golfers should be Scottish. In the winter and spring semesters when the University is in session the age-profile of the town's inhabitants takes an exhilarating dip. Nearly half the students come from Scotland, about ten per cent from overseas, and the rest from other parts of the UK, many from England, so that the very make-up of the young people thronging the seafront streets poses the St Andrews Question again. An insecurely small-minded Scotland will resent 'English incomers', whether staff or students, seeing them as part of some privileged neocolonial outpost. A more confident Scotland will want to be able to play on an international map, and will take pride in somewhere world-class enough to attract not just golfers but also students from beyond, as well as from within its national borders. 'Scotland small?' asked Hugh MacDiarmid in a famous poem, expecting the answer 'No!' Today we need to ask the question 'Scotland Small-Minded?' and hope that we hear the same reply.

If what devolution produces in Scotland or elsewhere is a

parliament which functions as a sort of parish council, its eyes fixed only on parochial affairs, it will probably be a bad thing. If, however, it generates a much more internationally-minded seat of government, willing to look beyond local boundaries, and to see how Scotland might interact with other nations in Britain and beyond, then it is likely to lead to a more sophisticated and mature outlook. In this regard, a place like St Andrews, marginal and internationally recognized, complex rather than straightforward in its identities, may not only pose some of the key problems concerning devolution, it may also hint at the answers.

One of those answers has to be internationalism. Scotland's major earners and employers, such as tourism and 'knowledge industries', operate on a global playing-field that demands international vision. That key knowledge-word 'epistemology' was invented in St Andrews, but no one thinks of it as belonging to this tiny place; it is part of international currency. The St Andrews that attracts golfers and scholars alike from around the globe is a model of how to be wee need not mean to be small-minded. If the Scottish Parliament wants to be true to some of the social and ethical vision which made Scotland internationally respected, then it will break out of its narrowly domestic terms of reference and will discuss the most important contemporary global issues, such as starvation, third-world debt, and pollution. If it does not do, think, and act in an internationally-minded way, it will encourage the worst kinds of Little Scotlandism. It will be the parliament not of Robert Burns, David Livingstone, or Mary Slessor, but of dour wee buddies.

Little Scotlandism is a danger facing the Unionists as much as the Nationalists. For if the Scottish Parliament is seen to be a mere local talking-shop whose leaders are there to facilitate a puppet government, with Westminster pulling the strings, then Holyrood will be seen as a means of turning a nation into a northern province. It will pat Little Scotland on the head. On the other hand, if the pro-independence parties simply become fixated on flying the lion rampant and bashing London, rather than seeing nationalism and internationalism as indivisible, then they will confirm their opponents' worst fears of small-minded Little Scotlandism. To confound these alarms will take some doing, not least in a country where no major newspaper supports independence, and where the most powerful broadcasting organization, the BBC, is, as its name suggests, profoundly unionist with very little real power devolved. Whatever happens, though, the elections of 6 May 1999 have changed the arguments of British politics. What was once marginal has become central. The British dilemma now is the St Andrews Question.

Alan Warner

LET THE WORMS CARRY US TO HEAVEN

Extract from a novel in progress

In the gulches, in the dry places beyond the outer
outskirts of our city there grows the common fern which
must be sought out on rugged slopes. There the lucky
searcher must sit down to watch how the flowers open
at the first light of dawn upon which the searcher's
desires will be instantly fulfilled.

He murmured, 'The lucky searcher', then coughed. He had
wicked affection for old guidebooks of his city; ones like this,
including bad translations aimed at northern tourists.
Remembering the snakes his father would kill in the gulches,
he thought of their severed heads; the jaws continuing to snap
and never falling still until after moonrise!

Stressing his local accent, Follana said, 'How much for
this?'

Slowly, the Old One took back the guidebook and turned
the rectangular pages, as if the price was related to some
obscure expertise of his. 'Five thousand?'

'Five thousand!' Follana jerked his head up to the balcony
of his mother's empty place, above Town Hall Plaza. 'After
being raised in that apartment, looking down on this market
since I was a kid, you want a local boy's money at tourist
prices?'

'It's a historical document.'

'It's the same age as me! Nineteen sixty four! Am *I* to be
historical now?!' Follana had raised his voice; he touched a
shovelled hand to his jaw and rub-rubbed, leaning in at the

239

smiling Old One. The Old One's trestle table (topped with torn blue felt, obviously from the recently refurbished casino) was like the others beneath the portico: fake Roman, even Phoenician coins, that had been oxidised with a battery and water, for sale among banal postal stamps from the nineteen eighties; and there were the year-old newspapers enfolding foreign pornography magazines, hopelessly rust-clogged flint-locks from shattered hunting muskets, (early 20th century at the oldest) and there were arcane books with titles like *Origin of the Air-Cooled Engine,* and worthless editions of com-memorative coins from the dicatorship, but mostly Follana gazed at endless photographic albums containing deleted currency in coin and note, thinking, *Swapping coins, collect-ing deleted currency; that's become the consuming passion of my city's old men.* Twilight Sundays, holiday Trades too, you saw them: Grandfathers far into evening, trousers too short, visible blood vessels like magnified bacilli on ankles, cheap chewed cigars rolled in teeth, swapping and growling bar-gains over coin and note trays. Follana mused, *It was as if by possessing useless five and ten thousand notes, old men won some unhealthy vengeance back over the tyranny which money had subjected them to all their working lives.*

The Old One stared at Follana, beaming. He said, 'I knew Mrs Follana and your father when they had The Palace.'

Follana just grunted.

'I remember you, just a child at auction when your parents sold up.'

Follana nodded. 'Ah, the great auction.' He spread his arms. 'So, like me, *you* sleep in sheets embroidered with my father's initials?' Follana laughed but the Old One looked worried and slightly hurt.

Follana could remember how he had cried, hidden up in the apartment while all the beds and furniture from the lounges and dining room had been auctioned off in the big salon of the hotel below. Sometimes, far across his city, while grimacing on the way to a bathroom at some dinner party with vague business acquaintances, Follana would come upon a chair from the television salon or an escritoire from one of the sea-facing rooms. The furniture of his youth spread across his city, placed furtively in unknown houses waiting for him, challenging him to re-assemble some lost Eden.

Follana remembered his ex-wife at night murmuring, 'Ever seen moonlight on fish scales?' among her Grandmother's hand-cultivated lavender fields and brightly painted bee-hives; the scent hanging like gauze at her bare-waist-level. Veroña's bone-white winter legs were beneath a mini-skirt, the moonlight along the scales of the dead dogfish, swung like a feather boa round her neck. Then the scooter ride with his hands on her waist and after their cunning sex, at dawn the table with carved elephant heads from room 86 that had held him in fascination as a child, standing on its six legs at the foot of Veroña's single bed, the stinking fish thrown over by the curtains. Sure enough, her Grandma had attended the Palace auction years before. Veroña still has the table up there in the apartment by the tobacco factory with that bore she finally chose. Follana thought, *It's objects alone that survive broken relationships: a table, a butterdish you'd forgotten existed which you discover on a chance visit ten years later and it all leaps up to the fore of your mind. Other men's designs.*

'Your Father: a real gent,' the Old One said.

Follana had taken his hand away from his own jaw, let it linger at his nostrils; he could smell expensive French aftershave. He reached for the guidebook, stood straighter to remove his wallet in the trousers of his suit, took out a five-thousand note and jerked it at the Old One.

'Thank you sir.'

Follana stepped away, holding the guidebook left-handed, caressing with his thumb, his wide, flat finger, so identical to his Father's. He should have asked for a receipt, because he could claim most books as a non-taxable expense. He almost headed back, but imagine the Old One, slowly moving Follana's hesitating Aurora fountain pen over some strip of torn paper! Perhaps the Old One would tear a page to write on from one of those piously concealed skin mags that could later be submitted to Chola Accountancy! That Old One would never have been asked for a receipt before, *So a thousand five goes to the bloody socialists who seem to need more money in life than anyone*, Follana thought and stepped on, deliberately not looking at the guidebook as he moved between municipality workers' parked cars, trying not to touch their dusty bodywork and he crossed to the other Plaza side and beyond the tobacconists at this end.

But the guidebook was a cracking specimen, a real discovery and maybe the jewel of his collection; wide, like a calendar that might fold out. Beneath the Helveca sans-serif lettering of the city name, it read, in Follana's language: IN YOUR HAND then there was a very poor watercolour of the Esplanade: its scallop-like concrete shell of the bandstand; rows of date palms; and the town hall's primary-coloured folding chairs for the Old Ones. There was no way he would get an opportunity to glance at the book from the moment he was in the office. Halfway down Major Street, Follana was looking for a cafe, a cheap one he would never normally go in; those that don't clean the machine well, so the cup of coffee tastes burnt, with little flecks of bean marauding round and round after you've stirred!

Just before traffic lights on the Rambla he saw the crazy guy's cafe opposite the nougat shop. (Each *Walk Now* traffic crossing played an electronic but traditional song to allow the blind of the districts safe crossing and to identify their location!) Follana thought, *The blind of my city navigate by music!* and smiled. The outside cafe chairs were the cheapest sort of white plastic, easy to lift in at night but with no drainage so in a torment, rainwater would gather in the well of the seat. Follana thought, *Or in summer when the African dusts come across the sea or from the inner wastelands blow red rains, the edges of the seat's swiftly evaporated puddles would be reminiscent of those little, ferrous smears of fertilisation you find inside chicken eggs.* Also, you couldn't miss the silvery crescent of saliva spits on the pavement outside the cafe doorway, spat there by regulars so they would not disgrace themselves spitting on the floor inside. Follana stepped through the doorway.

'Ah man!' yelled the crazy bar keeper as he jerked up an arm and yanked at a chain – a whole network of goats' bells strung right around the ceiling rafters began to swing and clang together. 'Yes, yes yes, Sir?'

'Give me a coffee with a cut of milk.' Follana grimaced up at the ceiling; some of the bells were genuine rusted goatherd's but others were shaped like bull testicles. Bullfighting photographs from the 60s and 70s covered all wall space and there was a copy of that photo of the big-headed American writer, Hemingway, in The Terrace of The Palace trying to light a cigarette and really just looking like any old crone down on his luck, thought Follana. Behind the bar was a collection of plaster dildos with grotesque faces painted on them and there were cliché collages of foreign money bills and postcards. Hanging above the bar was a fierce-looking bird cage with a stuffed green parrot inside; a card on the cage read, *All Complaints to The Mayor*. The strangest thing Follana noticed was, apart from bar stools, all of the wooden interior chairs and tables in the cafe were in miniature, as if the crazy bar keeper had bought them second hand from some infant's school. Follana seemed to recall a Fountaineer anecdote about drunken hilarity in this bar; customers so drunk that fat men were trying to squeeze into these seats, all sense of proportion destroyed, wood splintering beneath their wide bottoms in baggy slacks and all the time the crazy owner asphyxiated with laughter.

Two other men further along the bar, sitting on normal metal stools, had the city's morning paper open at the sports section, spread out so both pages almost touched and each man could easily have looked over, read the other's and saved the price, Follana thought. He took the coffee from the crazy owner's hand, over the snack display, walked to the street-opening end of the bar and sat on a normal stool below a dated poster of the city football squad when that Salvador was still in goals. Follana placed down the guidebook and although he'd promised himself to save it till evening, reached into the jacket of his linen-lined suit and removed the hard leather coronation-size cigar holder. He bit off the end of the last cigar, puttered his fingers to his lips in case of any tobacco strands and used a booklet of matches bearing the Gold Cafe logo. When he held the guidebook up, he made sure the cover was displayed so he looked like a tourist too early in the season. The coffee was filthy and Follana only took a single sip, reading pages quick, his smile showing through the lifting degrees of cigar smoke, which was already making his mouth dry. When he looked up from the pages he noticed the cigar smoke was brown, almost orange against the clouds visible in the sky; blue as it sneaked before the dark ceiling:

Our city, in its magnificent and sheltered bay, is situated 38 20 min. and 54 sec. N. latitude and 32 min. and 24 sec. E longitude and has a Mediterranean climate, and an average temperature of 63.6 F. According to the annual statistics, it has 179 days of sunshine, 144 slightly cloudy and only 44 days are cloudy. The rains are very light.

This beautiful city was founded in the third century B.C. by the Carthaginian, Amilcar Barca. True progress began in 1900, beginning with notable improvements to the port. Then the city widened and opened new and large avenues and built their municipal buildings.

Follana skipped a few pages:

A VISIT TO THE CITY

Surrounded by two castles, that of San Fernando with its Children's Park and that of Santa Barbara, ancient Moorish Fort on the heights of Benacantil Mountain, the city is bounded on the East by the sea. All the streets with a West-East direction lead to it. Sea is separated from the city by the Esplanade, a walk-way paved with mosaic the full length of its 500 meters; and its graceful palm-trees which make it a walk-way unique in the world.

He grinned. Here was a good bit:

The Typical District at the foot of Benacantil Mountain with its typical streets adorned with a profusion of potted plants and flowers is very typical and is attractively illuminated by night and provided with many typical taverns.

!

Follana looked at the hand-drawn map and thought of the white doves in the shade of Gabriel Miro Square, where once you could buy the big grain cornets in rolled newspaper from the kiosk man. Just the word 'cornet' brought back to Follana the mauve, marauding shade of the frightening carob trees, the desperate circular scuffling of the white doves with their filthy patches and brown blemishes, scabrous eyes or missing feet among the flitters of thrown grain. Poor Father, bored, reading his newspaper in the grey cashmere overcoat on a bench nearby.

He turned to the English translation. Follana spoke English very well, in a pompous accent and read it even better. The foreign translations were often the source of greatest fun in these guidebooks. He scrutinised pages of the English section, bored by familiar phonetic spelling mistakes, like 'tipical' for 'typical' then suddenly he burst out laughing at three lines:

GASTRONOMY

As a seaport our city offers, to its visitors a great variety of seafoods: Local Rice, Rice of Sea, Sea Rice and Fish Rice are popular savoury rice platters.

Follana looked up and peered around – smiling without wanting to share and it was then the Black came in. There was commotion to his left and, as he turned, the Black had manoeuvred his board through the doorway. All the wares shivered, hissed like a viper mass. 'Hey elephant man!' yelled the crazy one and gave the bells a really terrific jangle. Follana checked the shoulders of his jacket because little flakes of rust were pithering down from the low rafters.

'Good day.'

Follana looked round. A gold-coloured trinket, draped over, hanging in front of a palm, pinked like a medium rare steak in The Dolphin, Follana thought and held up the guide-book so the Black could see its cover.

The Black said, 'You French?'

Follana looked at him, sardonically, also ignoring him.

'You Italian? You like?' he said in English then he said, in Follana's language, 'It's the mode.'

Follana said back, 'No it's not. It's ugly,' and the sports page readers glimpsed along the bar at his local accent. The Black swung the gold-plated trinket at the board he carried. It was a piece of chip-wood, the sheet punched with regular rows of holes. Watches and necklaces, rings, vulgar bracelets, anklets, toe-rings, ostentatious sunglasses and enormously buckled belts were attached with little loops of fuse wire. Follana watched as the Black carefully hung the bracelet on the board then was waving a wrist watch.

'Rolex', he announced flatly. Follana smiled and held out his hand. The Black placed the watch in it.

With real satisfaction, Follana felt its lightness, 'A Rolex?'

'Rolex. Best watch.'

'You're trying to sell me a fake Rolex!' Follana murmured. 'It's like one of the parables. You're assuming I'd be grateful for that and here,' Follana held up his left arm, shook the hand so out the sleeve of his suit, conjured from beneath the all-cotton shirt and tortoiseshell cuff link, the Omega chronometer on Follana's wrist flumped down into view. Follana's gold Omega wrist watch was so heavy it'd bruised his toenail once when he dropped it in the bathroom.

Knowing now he was local, assuming intimacy, the two sports page readers had turned to stare and laughed together at Follana mocking the street trader who said, 'Then give a present for a friend you don't like.'

Follana karked a brief laugh, holding the fake watch out to

him. The Black took it straight back. Follana turned to glance at the two readers, smiled at them but instantly turned again to the street trader in case his look of acknowledgement was mistaken for an appeal. The Black started to speak but then did that thing that they all do, thought Follana: he snapped his head round, looking out to the street. Police maybe or ancestral memories of the bush? Follana squinted at him sceptically, for the morning sun was getting high now and falling down between clouds into this narrowness of Major Street.

The Black had twisted, slung round a leather shoulder bag, definitely a woman's, Follana thought, watching the black fingers with grey nails first undo a securing piece of string then work on the buckle. When they wash their hands they must not seem immediately clean?

'Very special.' Resting the board against his thigh, the Black was holding out a carved chunk of ivory, a short tusk, tailed with a silvery metallic cap, hollowed out with minute carvings of gondoliers.

Follana thought of the table with carved elephants from room 86, for an instant felt Veroña's waist between his palms on the ride through the country, trembling with the scooter vibration, on the farm tracks, said, loudly but too quick to be understood, 'So, some half-savage concept of the Gritti Palace come to me via poachers of the jungle!' Follana placed the ivory on the bar and said, 'Do you know how you test real ivory?'

'This is . . . elephant.'

Follana went on, 'You test by a baptism of fire.' He placed his cigar in the ashtray, took the booklet of matches and struck one, watching the expression on the street trader's face. 'If it's real ivory, it blackens but you can wipe the soot off,' Follana announced, lifted the tusk and raised the wobbling match flame to the curve of ivory carving. The Black looked worried. The flame contoured round each side of the bone and immediately the tusk began to melt, lifting in a welt at the edges as a tremble of oily chemical smoke crawled upward.

'Ay, ay,' called one of the sports readers cheerfully.

The Black snatched the plastic tusk back and frowned seriously at it, 'Hey, you break its face, you pay for it.'

Follana dropped the spent match on the cafe floor, heard one of them behind him say, '"Break his face." They can never speak proper.'

Follana said, 'You told me it was ivory. You want to call the police to discuss this, or my acquaintance, Mr Duranti, at the Trading Standards in the Town Hall there?' The men at the bar were laughing. Angrily, the Black rubbed a finger on the melted plastic. Pointing, Follana announced, scientifically, addressed to no one, 'You can see the joins where the plastic casts have been moulded together,' and re-lit his cigar.

Suddenly the Black kneeled to him. Follana thought he was going to mutter some predictable insults but the Black whispered, 'Sir,' in Follana's language (with a reticence that makes it translate better as 'Mister') then in French he said quick, 'After it was shot I've seen an elephant stand still all day and night, breath heavy in the dark and it would have stood another day, dying, but killing ants crawled up through its trunk and ate out its brain. Next day I saw a blood-soaked child smile out from the ribs of the gutted elephant.' He nodded.

Follana blew smoke without removing the cigar from his mouth; he couldn't follow French, though he liked its sound and said, 'What are you, Senegal?'

The Black ignored him, stood and raised his chin to the crazy bar keeper, 'Any chance of a glass of water?'

'It would cost you two hundred for a bottle.'

'From the . . .' he seemed to think for the word, 'Tap,' said the Black.

'Hey, it's not safe from the tap!' called one of the sports readers.

The Black hoisted the shivering board, said perfectly, 'Thank you. For your interest in my health, Barons.'

Follana laughed and waved at him as the Black swung out, holding the fake tusk in his hand, cheap trinkets shimmering. 'Farewell Hannibal,' called Follana.

'What did he say to you?' asked one of the newspaper readers.

Follana just shrugged.

'Hey,' said the older reader, 'how do you get an African girl pregnant?'

'Don't know,' smiled Follana.

'You come on her thigh and the flies do the rest!' The other men laughed while the crazy cafe owner rang those bells in celebration. Follana grimaced and nodded severely a few times. Then he turned again to the guidebook but his mobile phone began vibrating in his jacket pocket. Follana lifted the mobile out, squinted sceptically then pushed the appropriate button, 'Talk to me.'

'Where are you?'

Follana said, 'Kiko, *you* work for me.'

'Gold Bar already!'

'No, I'm in bed with a woman, smells like yours.'

'It's about time but if it's with her, you have my pity man; look, they phoned about the Pier Development again. Police Commission want a meeting today and how about this, the bingo hall phoned, squeezing their own balls: Old Ones are falling over in the foyer during stampedes and they want some slippery floor signs quick before they get sued!'

'Ask double price then,' Follana snapped into the phone, looking out at nothing.

'It's done.'

'Is Marisa doing it?' said Follana, coughed suddenly then whipped the phone back to his ear.

'Marisa's at the dentist.'

Follana shook his head at the street, thought, *That bingo hall flashes all night, pulsates through its windows mysteriously, like some insane new Stock Exchange far down the pier*. Kiko's voice went at Follana's ear, 'When will you be here?'

'You work for me.' Follana took the mobile from the side of his face and re-pressed the button, sighed and stood up, patting at the sides of his jacket after putting the phone away. Deliberately leaving his coffee cup out of reach, he stepped to the bar. Even though Follana was obviously no tourist, the crazy bar owner seized a cloth and with a piece of white chalk scratched an inverted 300 on the wooden counter in front of Follana so the numeral faced him correctly. Follana looked at the numerals then raised his eyes severely to the owner who seemed to be muttering to himself. Follana edged another five thousand note out of his wallet and placed it in the thin fingers.

'Hallelujah,' the owner yelped. He crossed to the till which was a real old-fashioned mechanical one.

'You'll have trouble converting that to Euros, friend.'

The sports page readers chuckled.

The owner chunged the drawer open, countered it with his belly, flicked out four one thousands and picked at some coin. He laid it all across the chalked numerals on the counter top. Follana removed the notes and placed them in his wallet then carefully lifted up the coins according to denomination so they formed a tube in his palm making it obvious he was leaving no tip. As soon as he lifted the last coin, with a side sweep the crazy cafe owner sliced a wet cloth across the counter surface, obliterating the chalk numerals; the cloth was hot and a few tendrils of steam rose from the wet streak which just as quickly began to evaporate towards the right. Follana slipped the tube of coins into the pocket of his trousers and their weight immediately began to make the linen pull at his belt buckle.

Follana walked away from the counter towards the doorway, paused, then addressed the stuffed parrot, 'The coffee here is expensive, filthy, and the jokes worse.'

'Hallelujah,' yelled the crazy owner and Follana ducked as the bells above began to clatter louder than ever.

Follana left the bells and laughter of the sports readers behind him as he stepped out into Major Street, looked both ways for no reason. Weighing up the bundle of loose change in his pocket, he stepped in the direction of his office as he did every weekday.

After he'd crossed the Rambla, smoking the cigar, Follana

saw a young man begging, sitting against the back wall of the Dolphin Restaurant. Follana sauntered over to the beggar's side of the narrow street.

'Spare anything?'

'You want money off me?'

'Anything you can spare.'

Follana reached into his jacket and removed the folded envelope with 'Young Beggars' written on it in his own hand. He folded up the back of the envelope and peered in teasingly.

The beggar looked up at him enthusiastically.

Follana removed some sort of single sheet, official form and there were three or four more identical forms still folded inside the envelope. Follana passed the form down to the sitting man and he stretched up a thin, tanned arm, the wrist bound in colourful bangles, to take it.

'You're a young man, a young man has no excuse to beg. I can spare this.' Follana walked on, leaving the beggar squinting at the form. It was a Job Application Form for MacDonalds hamburgers who'd just opened a restaurant on the Esplanade.

Two blocks further at Catalina Road there was an old man with one leg and a crutch. He wasn't wearing a shirt and silently held out his hand. Follana gave him all the loose change from his pocket and walked on. A young man begging in today's Europe is a bad sight; an old man is unspeakable, Follana thought and coughed again.

Trezza Azzopardi

THE HIDING PLACE

Extract from a novel in progress

THEY'RE DEFYING GRAVITY.

Nebuchadnezzar, King of the Jews, Bought his Wife a Pair of Shoes . . .

Celesta's hands are plaiting air: the tennis balls skim her palms, fly, beat on the red brick; hand, brick, hand, brick. She is concentrating. If Celesta could only take her eyes off the arc she is weaving, she would see Rose up-ended in a handstand, her scuffed shoes pressed flat against the wall, her fat legs splayed, her black hair hanging like pondweed from beneath the bell of her skirt. Marina's eyes flit from Rose to Celesta and back again, carefully studying the moves. She won't try anything yet: she'll examine every angle first.

Through tartan wool, Rose sees the world the wrong way up. The houses on the street fall out of the sky; a dog trots blithely along the grey cloud of pavement.

Look at me! Celesta! Look!

Celesta twirls and claps and catches; the balls hang in the air just long enough for a spin to the left. She ignores Rose and her blood-rush face.

Rose rights herself, squints at the grit embedded in her palms, spits on both hands and wipes them on her skirt. She inches along the wall, feeling the vibration of each bounce through the brick, and stops. Rose is intent for one minute, then suddenly snatches at a mid-flight ball, interrupting the pattern of hand, air, brick. The ball flies into the gutter. Celesta is patient. She retrieves it, inspects it, and resumes her game.

You, are, a Pain-in-the-Neck, she says, in rhythm.

They all ignore Luca: she is tethered to the pram. The harness is blue and has a lamb frolicking on the front, which Luca has drenched with dribble. Two metal hooks clip on to two rusted rings at either side of the hood. She pulls at the rings, and yells, and smears her face with her sticky fist. Fran has been told to watch her; but Fran has gone Walkabout. She's got a box of England's Glory in her gymslip pocket. Inside are three pink-headed matches. She's heading for The Square.

We live at Number 2 Hodge's Row. Between Number 9 and Number 11 is an alleyway which leads onto a hopeless patch of asphalt called Loudoun Place, but which everyone calls The Square. Fran goes there a lot, sidling along the alleyway until she reaches open space. The Square is a rectangle of nothing. There used to be swings and a see-saw, but now all that's left is an iron climbing frame and a strip of battered grass. Fran explores. She likes it: better than wiping snot from Luca's nose; better than sitting on the low kerb and watching Celesta play that impossible game; better than waiting for Rose to find an excuse to hit her.

There are treasures here, stashed along the edge of The Square where scrub grass ends and gravel begins. Fran studies the ground minutely, her boots marking a careful path between the dog-shit, broken bottles, coils of rusted wire, fluttering chip-papers. The asphalt shimmers with shards of glass; green, blood-brown, clear as ice. She collects the best shapes and places them carefully in the pocket of her gymslip. Today, Fran has the matches. She strikes one and holds it to her face. A rush of phosphorous stings her nose. Crouching now, she strikes another. Fran loves this sweet, burning scent. She licks the sandpaper edge of the matchbox. A tang of spent fire.

Under her bed, Fran keeps a red oblong box. It used to have chocolates in it, and smells like Christmas when she prises off the lid. But now the plastic tray holds all her jewels from the Square: jagged slips of sapphire; worn lumps of emerald; a single marble with a twisted turquoise eye. To mark my arrival, she has begun a secret collection which she stows in a cigar box my father has given her. Not glass this time, but an assortment of cigarette stubs she picks up, when no one is looking, from the pavement outside our house. Tipped or untipped, flaky grey, or smooth menthol white. Some are crushed flat with the weight of a heel, others are perfectly round and lipstick-smeared. Fran holds each butt to her nose before she hides it away.

I'm stuck in the house with my mother: at one month old, I'm sickly and I must be kept warm. My mother brings the chest down from the bedroom and puts me in it, smothers me in layer after layer of mothballed blankets. She drags a bucket of coal from the outhouse to the kitchen, bumping it against her knee until she gets to the hearth, where she pauses for breath. She bends down, rattles at the grate; it looks like an age since a fire was lit in the kitchen: the ash which should be smooth and fine is clogged with stray hairs and clots of dust. Turning the strips of newspaper neatly in her hands, she thinks: Joe's man will call for the rent today, that kindling's a bit damp, bet the chimney needs sweeping. The chest scrapes across the tiles as she pulls it, pulls me in it, nearer to the hearth; two long thin scars, like a tram track, will remain to show what she did. My mother puts me at an angle in front of the fire: the sight of the flames will amuse me. She turns to the table, hacks at a loaf of bread and sings in her sharp, tense voice,

> *Don't you know, Little Fool, you Ne-ver can Win*
> *Use your Men-talitee, Wake up to Re-alitee . . .*

Upstairs, my father is making music too, whistling through his teeth as he pulls a tie off the rail in the wardrobe, catching sight of himself in the mirror as the wardrobe-door widens. He looks Lucky. Today, Frankie's choice is a black tie with a thin seam of gold running through it. He sweeps the length between finger and thumb, smooth and cool as water, then ducks his head, flips the tie around his neck, folds back the stiff white collar of his shirt. He pauses in front of the mirror, pushes the door open to get a better view. It annoys him, this glass; flecked and tarnished with oily orange patches beneath the surface – even in close-up, he can't get a clear reflection. Frankie pauses. He hears my mother downstairs, shouting from the front door.

Celesta! Kids! Dinnertime!

My father pulls on the jacket of his suit, casually stretches out his left arm, then his right, turning the exposed cuffs over the sleeves. A pair of gold cufflinks, embossed with the rising sun, is now the only jewellery he owns. He lifts them from the polished surface of his dressing-table, chinks them in his palm for a second, and then puts them back. He doesn't feel *that* lucky. He takes his hat from the bed-post, pads downstairs, avoids my mother's eyes. She weaves between the children in the kitchen as he makes for the living-room mirror.

I won't tell you again, wash those hands. Will you see Carlotta today, Frankie? Leave that. Eat your dinner. Frankie?

Frankie, mouths my father as he steps up to the glass. Frankie, he goes, flipping one end of the tie into a smart loop, taking up the slack, adjusting the knot, nice and tight.

Do you hear me? shouts my mother.

He's going out, says Celesta, straddling kitchen and living-room doorway and staring at my father. They share the same black eyes, hard as steel, and a stubborn squareness in their faces. Celesta holds a plate of sandwiches high in the air, out of reach of Rose and Marina. My father grins at her in the mirror. She grins back, then suddenly retreats into the kitchen as the clamour rises behind her.

Wash your hands first, Celesta yells, slapping at Rose and Marina as they snatch at the bread. And again,

Mam, tell them to wash their hands.

Wash their hands, says my mother automatically.

It's getting very hot in this kitchen, what with the fire and the heat of my mother's bad mood. She wedges the back door open with a chair, sending a blurt of wind racing through the house. The flames in the fireplace swoon in the draught. A door slams upstairs.

My mother mixes up a bowl of something grey for Luca, rapidly beating milk into powder. Her fury travels down the spoon and into Luca's dinner. I am breast-fed: I get rage straight from the source. My mother's also angry with herself: she needs Carlotta to visit with one of Salvatore's parcels; some corned-beef pie maybe, or a bit of roast chicken. Her words are thrown to anyone who will catch them.

Never thought I'd want to set eyes on her fat face again, she says, thinking of Carlotta as she forces Luca into her high-chair. Celesta laughs, thinks it's a shocking thing to say about your kid, even if it's true.

And where's Fran? asks my mother, an afterthought.

My father moves from the mirror to the sideboard, stops his breath as he pulls open the drawer. His eyes stay on the doorway, watching the shadows on the kitchen wall while his hand slides over bills and chits and a soft bundle of knitting. His promise forgotten now, Frankie thinks only of the Race. His fingers trip along the stitches, the sharp point of the needle, and down to the cool metal surface of the Biscuit Tin. Then his hand inside, and the unmistakable greasy slip of money beneath his touch. Frankie feels the edges of the notes – not much, enough – catches them up fast and folds them over, straight into his pocket. It takes five seconds. With his tongue hot on his lip, he pushes the drawer back into place, and starts up his whistling again.

Do you hear me, Frankie? Will you see Carlotta?
My mother appears at the doorway with one hand on her hip, waving a spoon in the other.

And where do you think *you're* going?
She has noticed his smart suit. And the hat.

Frank?
An accusation.

Out, he says.

*

There are eighteen cafés on Bute Street, and my father doesn't own any of them. Not any more; not since me. My parents argue about whose fault it is. She blames him, he blames me, and I can't blame anyone yet. But I will. I'll lay it all at Joe Medora's door, when I'm ready.

Except Joe Medora has so many doors. He owns nearly everything round here: two boarding-houses on the Terrace, and our home, of course; and four cafés on Bute Street – the latest being The Moonlight.

My mother has to pass the café every day. She's got herself a job at the bakery next to the timber yard. It's a factory more than a bakery, churning out hundreds of thick white loaves which my mother drags from the ovens with a long metal palette. She does the night shift, so whether she's setting off for work or coming home at dawn, she can't pass The Moonlight without noticing that the lights are on and there are people inside. Sometimes, not often, she can smell cooking, and she gets a yearning for one of Salvatore's almond tarts. She hears music too, a lonely voice in the early hours; but mostly she hears the jangle of money rolling over and over in Joe Medora's pocket. She spits a dry curse at the window as she passes.

My father takes the same route now, cutting over the street, down the alley, and across The Square. Fran sees his shape approaching from around the broken fence, his head cocked to one side in the sunshine, and she hides from him. For a second she wonders if he's come to march her back home for dinner, but Fran senses that there's something different about him today. She sees how his hair catches the light, a slice of pure silver dancing on the black, and the hat in his hand beating lightly against his thigh; she hears his whistle wandering on the air. It's like watching a stranger. Fran ducks, crabs along the track of dirt near the railing and crouches behind the hedge.

My father doesn't expect to see her, so he doesn't: his eyes are fixed straight ahead, conjuring the sleek brown frame of the horse he will gamble on. Just one bet, that's all. Court Jester. Two-thirty.

Frankie strolls past the Bute Street cafés, nodding now and again at a familiar face, or raising his hatted hand in a greeting. This is Frankie's Patch. Most of the restaurants and cafés are owned and run by his friends: seamen from the Tramp Trade who came to rest and stopped for good. And my father has also stopped, for now, although like most of the other Maltese, he won't settle in the city – he can't escape the salt-scent of the docks. When he talks about his ship coming in, meaning a winning streak, an odds-on favourite, a dead cert, he also feels, like glitter in his blood, the day when he will take a folded stash of money and simply disappear. This is not that day. This is the day I am burnt.

*

She was sure. She was absolutely certain. But now the money has gone. My mother wrenches the drawer and it slides too quickly, tumbling from her hands onto the floor, and with it falls the spilling mess of paper, magazines, a brass bell, a broken picture-frame, the abandoned knitting in baby-blue. She claws on her knees through the bills while the Tin sits wide open beside her. Perhaps she put it somewhere else. She casts her eyes around the room to the fireplace: two framed photographs, my father's long black comb with its pointed end jutting over the tiled lip, and in the centre of the mantel-piece, a glazed chalk fawn with a mocking smile. The dull orange rent book nestles behind it, thin and empty.

Celesta! she calls, wildly scanning the floor.

Have you been in this sideboard?

Celesta stands over my mother with Luca in her arms and a look of dismay on her face. She drops Luca into the armchair, and crouches down on the floor.

No. It's Him. Again.

As if my mother needs telling. Celesta rises to shunt the empty drawer back in its gaping hole. She gathers the heap of papers from the floor and forces them back.

Use Your Men-talitee, my mother sings suddenly, with a bitter laugh. It frightens Celesta, this noise.

What you gonna do, Mam?

My mother doesn't answer directly. She's listening for the thud of a fist on the door.

Haven't a clue, she says, to the ceiling. Not a clue.

Then to Celesta,

Take the kids out for us, Cel. Get them out of the way for a bit.

Celesta leans over to pull Luca's coat off the chair. She kneels in front of her, pushes one baby hand into the sleeve, pulls the coat around the back, bends Luca's arm into the other.

C'mon, she says to Rose and Marina, Let's go and find Fran.

My mother drags the chair from the back door and sits on it. We both stare into the orange fire. She contemplates the sink, the square table strewn with crusts of bread, the gas cooker with its beckoning oven: she could put her head in there. Instead, she bends, puts her hands between her knees. There's an ache in her leg where the falling drawer had caught her. She stares down at her calf and the rising blue in her flesh.

*

Frankie passes Domino's Resto, then Tony's Top Café, then The Seamen's Mission. He passes the barber's shop with its striped red awning rippling in the breeze. Next to it is The Moonlight, its new neon sign at a right-angle to the wall. It smells of fresh paint here, and sure enough, on the red door there's now a glossy silhouette of a woman in a tight dress and stiletto heels. Frankie doesn't falter, doesn't turn his face to the window: he looks straight ahead towards the black square of shadow like an oil-spill under Bute Street Bridge. Just got time for a soda before meeting Len the Bookie.

*

My sisters go searching for Fran. The sun has gone, whipped away by the sharp wind, and in its place, a bolt of cloud. It scuds over the top of the wall at the end of the street, smearing the last of the blue sky with a hard metallic grey. Rose cradles two of Celesta's tennis balls in the crook of her elbow, dawdles behind the train of pram, Celesta, Marina. She pauses at the corner, watches her sisters cut sideways down the alley, waits, then turns to the wall next to Number 9.

Rose throws hard, first one ball, then the other: she catches the first but not the second, which angles off the brick, rebounds against the door of Number 4, and finally deflects with a clud off the window of Number 1. Home of the Jacksons. It rolls in silence along the pavement and drops into the gutter. Rose stands waiting with her fist wrapped around the other ball and her legs set to run. She runs.

*

Len the Bookie sits in the café with his back to the window: he needn't bother, no one can see in since the glass got smashed six months ago. The proprietor has mended it with a rough square of hardboard. He's written a notice on the side which faces the street:

> *Mikey's Bar*
> *Open Late For Tea's Coffee's Reffershment*

Len's refreshment, depending on who asks, is a lemonade soda. Mikey has tipped in a thimbleful of something which is supposed to be whisky. The tall beaker sits on the table in front of him, pale yellow, lethal, a tart froth breaking slowly on the surface. Len leans slightly to one side now to avoid the wind pushing in around the shifting board at the window. He hears a sudden burst of rain, like horses' hooves, sputter at his back. He reaches inside his pocket for his notebook.

Len is not a noticeable man. He's small and thin as paper, his smooth brown head fringed with remnants of hair. He rests his notebook in his lap: a row of carefully pencilled lines dissect each page; a series of tiny numbers crawl in steady formation from the tip of his pencil. As he writes, his free hand scratches absently at the bristles on his cheek. He has only two remaining digits on this hand; forefinger and middle finger. He managed to save his thumb. He used to gamble himself, but now he's found a safer occupation.

Never Bet with The Syndicate, my friend, is his only piece of advice. He gives it with a wave of his carved fist.

The door of the café bangs open and shut.

Hoy! Lenny! says my father, pinching up the fabric of his trousers as he bends to sit with the man.

Frankie, says Len. Long time no see.

*

My mother stands on the front doorstep with the Tin in her hands and the lid hanging open like a shout. Martineau is collecting today; she shows him that there is no rent to be had this week. They both stare into the shiny inner, Martineau with his heavy lashes cast down like an apology; my mother's reflection distorted into a cold silver fury. My mother wishes Frankie dead. It's not just rent money: it's bills and house-keeping and family allowance; it's debt money; it's her wages. It's everything.

Martineau, soft, holds out his big hands and tries to take it from her, but my mother throws it. It hits the pavement with the sound of an oil-drum being slapped.

Let's go inside, Mary, he says. We'll talk about it. Maybe Joe can wait a week, uh?

He'll have to, won't he? You go and tell him. Tell him to take a running jump.

The wind breathes through the swinging back door, circuits the kitchen. One rush of air is all it takes for the single coal to tip out from the fire, falling to rest on the frayed edge of the runner. It settles: lets out a wisp of smoke, a lick of curling light around the coal, and then a sudden sweep of gorgeous blue. Like the crooked eye of Fran's marble, the flame twists in the draught.

And this same wind moves on to the living-room, escapes past my mother at the front of the house, and blows the door shut behind her. She sways on the step, surprised to feel the wood so solid at her back. She wraps her arms around her body and stands her ground.

I'm all alone now. I'm watching. The blue flame ebbs and flows, ebbs and flows, sneaking along the fringes of the runner, lighting each strand like touchpaper. A bright coil of orange turns, widens, presses itself against the polished wood of the chest. It's so pretty.

Martineau bends to pick up the Tin, and over his stooped back my mother sees Alice Jackson at the window opposite. The woman raps twice on the pane, points her finger at my mother. I want a word with you, she mouths through glass.

Mary, pleads Martineau. We are friends.

We're not – we can't be. Not now you're Joe's flunkey.

The door of Number 1 swings open, and Alice Jackson steps into the street, retrieving the abandoned tennis ball from the gutter outside her house. Alice moves towards my mother with a grim fix on her face. My mother ignores her, turns away; she's trapped now between Martineau and this woman she doesn't know. She moves quickly, forgetting me, forgetting me, pacing up the street ahead of Martineau. The man is crouching; he's trying to make himself smaller. He looks like he's dodging the wind.

Frankie's taken the money, Tino, she says. The words fall out behind her and are lost.

What am I supposed to do?

Mary knows what she *could* do. She could go to Joe herself; she could plead. But the thought of him heats her insides like a swarm of wasps. There is another way.

Alice Jackson stands at our closed front door with her arms folded over her chest. She clutches the tennis ball against her ribs and watches as my mother swings towards and away

from the big man in the sharp suit. Alice Jackson sniffs
something burning on the air. Turns her head to one side,
sniffs again.

*

Frankie stirs his coffee with a long metal spoon, leaning his
elbow on the bar in The Moonlight like he's never been away.
Salvatore hears what he has to say, but he can't look at him,
so he scrapes at the enamel stove with a blunt knife. Stars of
blackened cheese skid away from his touch. Salvatore holds
his tongue until my father has ended his monologue of woe:
then he straightens, launching into the silence.

Okay, so you lose on a horse. Then what you do? You go
home? No. Too sensible for you, eh Frank. Frankie, he don't
want to go home! Frankie want to win, yeah?

Salvatore talks and scrubs, plunging his hand into the bowl
of filmy water, chiselling fiercely with the edge of his blade.
Rainbow bubbles cling to the black hairs on his wrist. He
stops, points the knife at the ceiling above his head,

Joe Medora don't want to see you – I don't want to see
you.

Then waves it in front of my father's eyes.

Take your face somewhere else.

For my father has come to beg. He will beg Salvatore for a
loan, and he will beg Joe Medora for extra time with the rent.
He stays silent, waits for the storm in Salvatore to pass, and
listens to the rain belting off the pavement outside. The going
was too heavy, thinks Frankie, watching a replay of the race
in his mind. It's not monochrome in his head: the racecourse
is green, the horses always chestnut brown, the bobbing
jockeys brilliant in Silks. He puts the race away before he
catches sight of Court Jester loping home in fifth.

Frankie puts his hand in his trouser pocket, pulls out the
chit from Len the Bookie, and slaps it on the counter. He
turns the lining inside-out, catching the debris in the palm of
his hand and depositing it neatly in a gritty mound beside the
crumpled docket. A half-crown rolls away from the flecks of
tobacco and dust.

Go home, my friend, says Salvatore, hearing the lonely clatter of the coin. He gives the money back to my father and wipes the fluff off the counter with the corner of his apron.

It was a sure thing, Sal, says Frankie, pocketing the half-crown.

Sure thing. Sure. *Ciao*, Frankie.

Frankie looks steadily at Salvatore, turns and walks slowly away from the bar.

Frankie – *il cappello*! shouts Salvatore, gesturing to the hat on the counter.

Frankie isn't listening. He winds between the booths, heading not for the exit but for the narrow door marked Private which will lead him up the stairs to his old home, to his old life – to Joe Medora's new office. He'll find out for himself if Joe doesn't want to see him.

Salvatore smooths the felt brim of the hat with his fingers: his eyes track Frankie's footsteps across the ceiling.

*

Our yard door is locked, so to get round the back of the house, you have to climb over the side wall and drop down onto the flags. Those in the know, when they're out slipping the lead off someone else's guttering, use the outhouse roof as a sliding break. A foot on the lintel, one hand gripping the frame, then the other hand, and down with a silent jump. Fran has another way of sneaking in: she pushes aside the fencing at the rear of Number 4, sweeps the slat back into place, and throws her leg over the low chicken-wire that separates our back-yard from theirs. Fran sees the smoke leaking out from under the kitchen door, and stands amazed.

There is a rush of action, shouting in the street. Alerted by their mother, the Jackson boys come bouncing off our outhouse roof like a pair of experts. They knock Fran sideways onto the concrete path. Martineau surfs down after them, slices his palms on the jagged slate, and lands with a crack on his knees. He moves the boys away and puts his shoulder to the hot wood of the kitchen door.

My mother, on the wrong side of the wall, hears her baby burning on the inside.

Our kitchen thick as tar. A sudden suck of air that punctures heat, and the fire becomes fury. Flames spill in a river across the floor; scalding oilcloth, blistering wood, boiling the blankets on my bed. The boys shield their foreheads with their arms and flail about like drunkards, tipping over chairs and shouting. They are devils out of Hell. It is burning burning burning – and then Martineau lifts me with his great scored hand and hauls me out to daylight.

By the time the fire engine arrives, we are all in the alley, the yard door is battered open, and the Jackson boys are the heroes of the hour. They pat each other's shoulders and brush bits of cinder from their clothing. They are all arms now, describing the heat to their friends, pointing to the flames gulping at the window. Martineau bends and grips his mossy knees, breathing in shallow bursts. From under his fringe, he watches my mother. She stands in the pouring rain, her head raised to heaven: she won't look at me. She carries me loosely, this charred little thing, as if I have fallen from the sky. She is sure I am dead. When the ambulance-man holds out his red blanket, she drops me into it like a swathe of kindling. Later, undressing Fran in the back bedroom of Carlotta's house, my mother finds two dingy cigarette butts and a box of spent matches. Her heart turns mad with blackness.

Tinder.

My right hand is fine. There's little damage, and the fingers are quite beautiful, in the ordinary sense of them actually being there, bending, flexing, pointing things out to strangers who stop in their cars and wind down their windows to ask directions.

But the left hand. People who don't know me stare when they see it. They look away, then sidelong at my face in search of further evidence. There are scars there too: if they get close enough they could find them. But not many get that close: an outstretched hand, my left one – it's enough to ward them off.

I lost the fingers. At one month old, a baby's hand is the tiniest, most perfect thing. It makes a fist, it spreads wide, and when it burns, that soft skin is petrol, those bones are tinder, so small, so easily eaten in a flame.

But I think of it as a work of art: a closed white tulip standing in the rain; a cut of creamy marble in the shape of a Saint; a church candle with its tears flowing down the bulb of wrist.

I go back, and try to piece together how it was. I think there must be a design. I can picture Len the Bookie and his bet with The Syndicate (how soon my fist would echo his); the sight of my mother hopeless in the rain; Martineau behind her, clasping his casket like Balthazar. And I think of my father, standing all the while in a room across town, knowing nothing, oblivious: always betting more than he can afford to lose.

Adam Thorpe

MERCENARY

STUART WAS NOT a bold sort, but he had made a good soldier. There was something about his nerve that stayed him even in the chaos of conflict. Those who knew him were aware of a past murky with acts not altogether run-of-the-mill; in fact, it could be said that Stuart had a reputation based wholly on events too far back for anyone who knew him at present to be in any way familiar with, even as rumour. Stuart's past was a closed book in a secret drawer, the salient facts reduced to the knowledge that he had served in Suez, Aden and the Congo, that he had received a wound on the face sufficiently serious to have remained as a scar uniting his mouth with his left ear and giving him a lop-sided look when he smiled (which he did, to his credit, frequently), and that he had killed a man in cold blood.

This last was an item of information, not a rumour; thus unwrapped from rumour's hood and cloak, the item was in no way sinister or particularly remarkable, and was supplied by Stuart himself after a definite number of pints in the Red Lion's bar with a regularity that struck the publican and the various habitués as morbid rather than chilling.

'I've killed a man,' he would say, apropos of nothing in particular, propping his hand on his thigh and swivelling on the stool, elbow stuck out, fixing the eyes of the man nearest to him on his right or left, the other hand remaining around the ceramic tankard kept for him on a hook above the peanuts, and which depicted a stately home no one had yet identified, though several were of the opinion that it was

Chatsworth for no better reason than that they had recently watched a TV film shot there. 'I've killed a man in cold blood. War.'

The last quiet word served, it was thought, to calm the nerves of the listener, who was always a stranger. Stuart's face, though genial, suffered not only from its inability to smile evenly, but also from the setting of the eyes, which lay too deep under the brows for their bluff honest glance to be properly registered. They were green, but they might have been black. No one was quite sure why Stuart, otherwise so guarded about his soldiering past, should (after a precise level of drink) show his hand so crudely and abruptly, with the cold feel to it of a flick-knife. Yet nothing further was ever said on the subject; it retreated back into its sheath and was replaced – however the stranger might probe – by generalised bludgeoning reflections on politics, the need for *force majeur* in the world, curt comments on the young.

Stuart had no friends, a fact suspected rather than known. He had returned from his time in the Congo (where, it was supposed, he had been a mercenary) to find his mother dying and his sister in pod by a man she would not identify. The mother had died, the sister had settled in the far north of Scotland with her child and an oil-rig worker who was not the father, and Stuart had inherited the house. The house stood back from the leafy road, pebble-dashed and modest, behind a low screen of spindly lawsons, and gradually sprouted accoutrements that pointed to days spent fiddling with electronics in the spare bedroom. No one visited Stuart and he rarely stayed elsewhere; yet on Tuesdays, Thursdays and Saturdays he was always to be found in the bar of the nearby Red Lion, treating the immediate world as if it was his bosom, his lifelong companion, his mess-hut.

Those regulars who drank alongside him – he was generous with his wallet – liked him, but only within the confines of the setting. In some ways he was an actor, popular while he remained on stage, mistrusted and even shunned the moment he stepped off. Some of the more reflective among them wondered at the definition of 'cold blood', which was never given, and which no amount of discussion in Stuart's absence could satisfactorily construe – though the publican ventured a theory that Stuart had shot an unarmed 'native' in the Congo, thus confirming for most of those present the essential harmlessness of the act Stuart had long ago committed, whose drama was heightened only by the means by which he purveyed it (or refused to, as the case may be).

What was not known to those in earshot of his warm laugh and stolid conversation was the rigour of his own self-judgement. That he had nightmares stemming from memories of fly-blown bloody limbs, a heap of Hush Puppy children's shoes (still laced – all that remained of a missionary school party fleeing the rebels), and the odd burst of wild fighting between giant wet leaves and steaming pools, was neither here nor there; each of the regulars summoned similar phantoms from even the quietest and most blameless of lives. But the panga that had slit his cheek had been wielded by a man, and he had killed that man with a single bullet to the broad back fleeing through the trees. Stuart's definition of 'cold blood' was simultaneously subtler and broader than any of those tossed about in his absence; he had fired on a man *from behind*. Though that man had sought to kill him, had reduced his mouth to flapping uselessness, Stuart had momentarily considered sparing him. His mind, possibly abandoning the mess of the physical realm in the shock of confrontation and pain, had floated detached from the heat of the action, the terror of the sudden attack, and judged the moment. The smooth muscling back was taking an age to zigzag its way through the thick undergrowth – though it must have been only a matter of seconds before Stuart, weighing the options carefully, pressed the trigger and saw the man's form disappear as if fallen into a leopard-trap. Cold blood had run though Stuart's mind in those seconds as thickly as the hot blood welled about his teeth and mingled with the sweat in his collar-bone.

It was vital to him now, decades later, that no amount of explanation might relieve the frigidity of the moment; his need to state the fact was indulged at least once a week, but to expand further, to illustrate, to explain, would be to rob his hold on his own guilt, to hand it to others to stroke, to meddle with – others around him who had no notion of such things, whose lives had slept through the years he had been away, lives as uneventful as his own mother's.

When the stranger who replied 'So have I' embarked on his story – a complicated one involving some criminal feud and general drunkenness in the stranger's Gorbals youth – Stuart still refused to bite. That was some ten years ago, though the ripple of dismay the stranger's rejoinder set to work inside Stuart's mind seemed to have been felt yesterday, more vivid even than memories of the Congo, in which terror ran through sensations like a dilution of stiffening blood and blurred what still remained of the pictures.

After his evening in the pub, mildly drunk, he would walk steadily home and boil up some packet soup – Knorr's, generally tomato – to which he conceded a knob of butter. With the natter of the bar settling or circling in his head behind his deep-set eyes, he finished the soup and washed up. All of these actions – the walking home, the boiling-up, the spooning to his damaged mouth of the soup, the scouring with the all-but-bald brush his mother must have bought back in the fifties – were performed with a slow and satisfied rhythm. There was an air of triumph to it, as if something again had been conceived and successfully executed.

He had had women but not what he would think of as an affair, let alone a steady relationship. This bothered him only when he watched some domestic, sentimental series on television – and then only as regret, rather than hope. He had no plans to set up with anyone nor even, at sixty-one, to indulge in games. His vigorous twenty-five years as a paid fighting man struck him as price enough for peace; he enjoyed the sunshine through the windows of the sitting-room (not cleaned in his mother's absence), succumbed to the touch of its gold on his face and sat for hours as impassive as a Buddha, much as a cat does on the arm of an easy chair, feeling no guilt. He seldom even walked, as the countryside around the town did not attract him, flat and bald as it was;

preferring to entice the world in, he worked long hours on constructing short-wave radios of various sorts, and erected a huge metal mast in his garden, kept in place with wires and cables, as well as other antennae perched like skeletal birds on the roof. He communicated with other hams now and again, but was more the listening sort – particularly attracted to military planes, which posed a challenge he could rise to, unscrambling their coded intercourse or simply keeping them tracked. The local air-base was close enough to walk to – he had no car – and he hovered regularly in a concealed part of the perimeter fence with a device that enabled him to home in with frightening accuracy on the cockpits of departing and arriving aircraft.

He considered bringing along on one of these expeditions a member of the East Anglian short-wave club to which he belonged, and whose meetings in Norwich he would occasionally attend. The members were mostly much younger than him, young enough to have been his offspring, and he hesitated for some time before asking Rob, a pleasant enough youth, if he would consider a trip that Saturday to the air-base.

Rob was enticed by the illicit air around the enterprise, and agreed with enthusiasm. Thus it was that the two, armed with picnics and receivers, crept up between the fir-trees to a point where the high electrified wire gave a view of the runway, while keeping the observers concealed in shade.

They had an excellent time with the apparatus, eavesdropping on some alarmingly dirty banter between pilots delivered in a US drawl Rob was reasonably skilled in imitating, and fell upon their sandwiches in high spirits. As they chatted on the soft carpet of fir-needles, sharing mostly technical data, Stuart indulged in the fantasy that Rob was his son, receiving in the process a recognition of loss, of what he had lost by certain actions and decisions, that was almost equivalent to a physical blow. He continued the conversation haltingly, all but overwhelmed by the days that still lay in front of him, shorn of satisfaction or triumph. The American fighters roared close over their heads, crushing him further, but he took hold of himself by concentrating on what Rob was now describing.

'It's compact and it's got a range of about eighty yards. You could hear a snail move. They're in more places than you think. They'll have everywhere covered soon, alarms going off every twenty seconds. Deafening, too.'

Rob paused in his talk to pour some tea from his thermos, offering Stuart a cup, and Stuart, chilled by the easterly wind, accepted. This kindly gesture of the young man revived in the older man, there under the whispering fir-trees, a regret that was like a tearing of the solid earth. The wild back was zigzagging again through the trees and involuntarily he jerked his hand, burning the skin with his tea. His yelp of pain was drowned in the roar of the fighter landing beyond the perimeter fence, but Rob saw in his companion's face the lengths it went to to preserve composure, even as the blister rose in its crisp flush.

John Logan

TORTOISES AND BATS

Extract from a novel in progress

AT THE NEW Year it was Stevie and me, standing beside the
pool tables in Farmer's Show Bar with Boney, this guy we'd
known for a couple of years. Boney and I hated each other's
guts but tried not to let on because we shared an interest in
books and films. Like me, he'd been on the dole almost all the
time since leaving school at sixteen. The previous year I'd
been in his living room at Culloden when he'd typed the last
page of the film book he'd been writing for three years. Boney
was staring at me as I guzzled my Guinness. He thought I was
a wanker for going to university and liking it. After a bit he
leaned towards me and went,

'You assume a spiritual gravity you do not possess.'

Later on, after the bells, Boney went to the bog and I was
left to guard Stevie, who had drunk away most of his
conscious identity and was reaching out towards female
bodies as they came towards us through the crowd. I had to
slap away his paw and make quick, good-natured apologies
to stupid young mutts and their boyfriends.

'Happy New Year, mate!' this pumped-up guy went to
Stevie.

'Fuck off.'

'Sorry, mate,' I interceded, 'he's out of it.'

Stevie spotted a girl standing alone and, before I could do
anything, he was off across to her and whispering in her ear. I
watched her face. She looked a bit like Spock from Star Trek.
I had the strong impression that if you lifted away the fair

hair the ears might really be pointed. When she started to look upset I came in and between them.

'Sorry,' I went to her, 'he's really drunk.'

She went off and I asked Stevie what he'd said. He laughed. 'I just said to her, You're *so* ugly!'

'Ah, that's a shame man, the girl was just standing on her own.'

'Ugly,' went Stevie as Boney turned up, back from the bog and not interested when I tried to tell him what Stevie'd been up to.

We got crisps and cans from the garage and walked carefully through the ice and snow that clogged the pavement. I saw her coming the opposite way so I slowed down a bit. She punched Stevie up the side of his head and he landed on his arse in the wet, looking up, stunned. Boney went towards her and she lobbed one at him, too. I saw him slip and almost balance but not quite. He looked up from the pavement, resentfully, not at the girl but at me.

'You fucking ruined my New Year!,' the girl who looked like Spock was screaming in a Geordie accent at Stevie.

'That's the worst New Year of my fucking life, you bastard,' she went and started to walk on through the snow.

Stevie was up and went,

'That girl hit me so hard.'

At the Aviemore church we all stopped for a piss round the side but Boney took longer and got caught by a police van. When he hadn't caught us up we headed back and saw him being questioned. They questioned me and Stevie a bit up the street from Boney and I gave his real name, drunkenly assuming that he had to. I didn't anticipate that he would use the name of a world-famous golfer instead. Boney did a night in the cells and had a new reason to hate me.

Back in Aberdeen I entered the lonely drunkenness again, sitting among the chattering groups of young students, looking around at them. No-one spoke to me and at the end when the bouncers were clearing people out I leaned against a pillar, holding my pint, returning stares. The next day's hangover was more than a hangover. Walking through Seaton Park my vision seemed to have acquired a quality of penetration. Colours were vivid and beautiful, clear light seemed to bathe everything around me. It almost drove me mad, seeing the world like that, and I remembered that years and years before, when I'd been six or so on the farm, I'd seen the material world in the same way. Somehow alcohol and loneliness had stripped away layers from my mind and brought me back to an earlier state. The things I looked at were alive and real again but they also had their alien terror restored. I was too painfully in the present. Drinking tea in cafés returned some sanity so I ordered a ham omelette and walked back up to Hillhead. In Jason's room I tried to tell him about the colours,

'It was like being assaulted, you know? I was petrified of what the next leaf or bit of gravel would look like, or how seeing it would make me feel.'

'And you got that just from a hangover?'

'I don't know. It's just the way things are just now. I mean I came here like it was a homing beacon, you know? Your room. I might have to come here sometimes and talk.'

'You're welcome. OK?'

'Yeah. I don't want to get annoying, though.'

He smiled and shook his head with the long frizzy mane hanging past the shoulders and swaying with its own wild life. Above his head the crow-feathers he'd hung up dangled, musty and raw.

'Hey,' I said, 'what about going through to Aviemore tomorrow and going out with Stevie and that in Farmer's.'

He laughed and nodded the mane.

'OK then,' he went.

The next morning when I went round to his room he was still asleep. As he got up he was holding his hand to the side of his belly, pressing his fingers in.

'My liver hurts, Brian. Bloody whisky.'

He always kept a bottle of whisky in his room.

'Do you still fancy Aviemore, then?' I went.

'Yes, Brian, yes. Just give me half an hour to wake up so that I can drive.'

He took us the Balmoral route and told me to hold on as he got the car up to a hundred.

'This bit of road has a bump like a ramp, Brian,' he went.

The car left the road.

'Aaaaaah!' he went.

When it landed you could tell he'd lost control. We veered towards the big drop on the right and then away again.

'You're mental,' I went, 'you lost it, didn't you?'

He was laughing.

'It was close, Brian, *fucking* close.'

Then he took a hand off the wheel to massage his liver.

'Ooo-oh, Brian. This hurts. It worries me. You know my aunt and uncle always drank wine every night but he drank much, much more. Now she's dying of cirrhosis and he's fine.'

Jason wasn't going to drink so he drove Stevie, Boney and me over to The Wanking Owl that used to be The Winking Owl but someone kept painting the I into an A. In Farmer's the situation wasn't good because Barry, Boney's younger brother, was down from Inverness with three shady guys. They kept glancing over at Jason's long, frizzy mane and Canadian cattleman's coat. We were all at a big table but I only talked to Jason and Stevie. Boney was in both camps sort of, talking to us for a while, then turning away to Barry and the three heavies. You had to shout over the music and the place was packed. Stevie wanted to get closer to the dance floor and check out the pussy. So Boney, Jason and me stood with him, scanning. But I could feel waves of attitude coming off Boney as though talking to the tough-monkeys had botched up his brain. I looked at his eyes and they were like raisins. Stevie was staring at a thigh on the dance floor, his pupils vibrating in sympathy with the female flesh. I exchanged a wee affirmative smile with Jason. Then Boney came close and went in my ear,

'Right . . . give me a fiver and that'll keep the money right for the rounds.' I felt pain in my ear at the pitch of his voice and said back,

'What about Barry and that? Are they in for rounds?'

'Aye,' he nodded, impatient.

'And you're getting fivers from them?'

'Right,' he hissed, the face twisted with acid contempt, 'fuck it! You can get your own drinks.'

I went forward and put my face close to his, emphasising each word, 'Yeah, no problem . . . at . . . all. I'll get my own *fucking* drinks.'

Boney brought up his paws with speed and took hold of my throat. I copy-catted. We were standing among the crowd beside the dance-floor like a pair of duplicate Frankenstein's monsters, choking each other. No-one was interfering. There were so many people the nine bouncers couldn't see us. Even the two standing on chairs with their arms folded beneath the mediaeval shield and sword displays high up the wall.

'Ruu-ggg-hhh!' went Boney.

'Gllll-uuuggg!' I managed to gurgle back.

Then Barry's hard mates got in and separated us expertly. For the couple of hours until closing a tactic of segregation was employed. I was kept with Stevie and Jason at one table. Boney and the rest were at another. The two groups headed out of Farmer's without interaction and stood at a distance. Then Boney came over and we all walked to the taxi queue. On the way to Stevie's house Boney was in the front.

'These guys,' Stevie went to the driver to break the silence, 'are mental. I thought we were just on a quiet night out, then they're strangling each other in the middle of Farmer's.'

The driver shook his head with a rueful look. Stevie popped his head between the seats to get a sight of Boney then sat back and said,

'I don't want any hassle at mine, OK? You two can sort it out somewhere else. I'm not letting you guys in my house if you're going to make trouble.'

'Yes,' went Jason, 'it's not fair to Stevie.'

When I saw the turn-off to Dalfaber I reached up my sleeve and unfastened my watch-strap with one hand. I put it away safely and felt Jason react to the movement but he must have thought I was just putting my hand in my pocket. I gave change for the taxi and got out Jason's door after him. We all walked around the back, through the darkened garden and up to the door. Stevie got his key out and I watched their backs go through the entrance. Lights came on and I turned back into the garden. I took my jacket off and laid it across the mesh fence. I waited a bit then heard Stevie call from inside,

'Mr Miller . . . what are you doing?'

I walked nearer the door so I wouldn't be too loud for Stevie's neighbours and went,

'Boney . . . you manky lump of shite, are you going to fight or not?'

Something like a big bat flew out the door towards me. It blocked the light for a moment. Then it was like being on a ride at the shows, the Big Dipper. I was upside down like landing from a good bounce on an inflated Magic Castle. Then I was pinned down, looking up at Boney.

'Look,' he went, 'just quit it, OK? That's enough.'

'Yeah. OK.'

He got off and walked back inside. I heard him going to Stevie and Jason,

'That's it over now. He's coming in.'

I got up off the grass and felt to see if it was in my hair. At the door I roared in,

'You think it's over you twat? COME OHH-NN!'

I'd learned. Even as I'd screamed I'd started to back-pedal on the damp grass. When the big bat blocked the light again before exploding out the door I was halfway up the garden. I saw the raisins scan and lock onto me. Then I saw him just in front of me, punching me in the head. I lashed out, catching him wee skiffs, while he thudded into me with full choks. I was back on the Big Dipper for a bit. Then I had a go on the Inflatable Castle. Finally I was a rabbit on my dad's farm that had been wounded with a pellet. My dad had taken it and dangled it by its back legs. Then he'd broken its neck with a chop from the edge of his hand. After I'd been the rabbit I was looking up at Boney again. He had me straddled, my arms re-pinned to the earth. I could feel the damp grass through my shirt.

'Have you had enough?' he went.

I tried to lift my head off the ground. I couldn't. So I said, 'Aye.'

Rose Tremain

THE STACK

SHE SAYS TO him, 'On your birthday, McCreedy, what d'you want to do?'

She always calls him McCreedy. You'd have thought by now, after being his wife for so long, she'd have started to call him John, but she never does. He calls her Hilda; she calls him McCreedy, like he was a stranger, like he was a footballer she'd seen on the telly.

'I don't know,' he says. 'What'll we do, then?'

'Forty-six,' she says, 'you'd better think of something.'

'Go out . . . ?' he says.

'Out where?'

The pub, he thinks but doesn't say. With the fellas from work. Get the Guinness down. Tell some old Dublin jokes. Laugh till you can't laugh anymore.

'What'd the kids like?' he says.

She lights a ciggie. Her twentieth or thirtieth that Sunday, he's stopped counting. Smoke pours out of her mouth, thick and blue. 'Never mind the kids, McCreedy,' she says. 'It's your fuckin' birthday.'

'Go back to Ireland,' he says. 'That's what I'd like. Go back there for good.'

She stubs out the ciggie. She's always changing her mind about everything, minute to minute. 'When you've got a sensible answer,' she says, 'let me know what it is.'

And she leaves him, click-clack on her worn-out heels, pats her hair tidy, opens the kitchen door, and lets it slam behind her.

McCreedy stares at the ashtray. Time she was dead, he thinks. Time the smoking killed her.

He goes out into the garden where his nine-year-old daughter, Katy, is playing on her own.

Katy and the garden have something in common: they're both small and it looks like they'll never be beautiful, no matter how hard anyone tries. Because Katy resembles her dad. Short neck. Short sight. Pigeon toes. More's the pity.

Now the two of them are in the neglected garden together with the North London September sun quite warm on them, and McCreedy says to the daughter he tries so hard to love, 'What'll we do on my birthday, then, Katy?'

She's playing with her tarty little dolls that have tits and miniature underwear. She holds them by their shapely legs and their golden tresses wave around like flags. 'Dunno,' she says. 'What?'

He sits on a plastic garden chair and she lays her nymphos side by side in a pram. 'Cindy and Barbie are getting stung,' she whines.

'Who's stinging them, darling?'

'Nettles, of course. Cut 'em down, can't you?'

'Oh no,' he says, looking at where they grow so fiercely, crowding out the roses Hilda planted years ago. 'Saving them, sweetheart.'

'Why?'

'For soup. Nettle soup – to make you beautiful.'

She looks at him gravely. For nine years, she's believed everything he's said. Now she's on the precipice of disbelief, almost ready to fly off the edge.

'Will it?' she says.

'Sure it will. You wait and see.'

Later in the day, when his son Michael comes in, McCreedy stops him before he goes up to his room. He's thirteen. On his white neck is a red mark that looks like a love bite.

'What you staring at?' says Michael.

'Nothing,' says McCreedy.

'What, then?'

'Your mother was wondering what we might all do on me birthday. If you had any thoughts about it . . . ?'

Michael shrugs. It's like he knows he's untouchable, invincible. He's the future. He doesn't have to give the present any attention. 'No,' he says. 'Not specially. How old are you anyway?'

'Forty-five. Or it might be a year more.'

'Which?'

'I don't remember.'

'Fuck off, Dad. Everyone remembers their fuckin' age.'

'Well, I don't. Not since I left Ireland. I used to always know it then, but that's long ago.'

'Ask Mum, then. She'll know.'

And Michael goes on up the stairs, scuffing the carpet with the bulbous smelly shoes he wears. No thoughts. No ideas. Not specially.

And again McCreedy is alone.

But they have to do something. Like Christmas, a birthday is there: an obstacle in the road you can't quite squeeze round.

So McCreedy goes to see his friend Spiros, who runs a little restaurant two streets away, and tells him they'll come early Saturday evening, about seven so Katy won't be too tired, and can Spiros do steaks or cutlets because Hilda won't eat any Greek stews or fish.

'No problem,' says Spiros. 'And we make you a cake, John?'

'No,' says McCreedy, 'no bloody cake. Just do some nice meat.'

Spiros takes down a bottle and pours two thimbles of brandy for him and McCreedy. It's five in the afternoon, and they're alone in the place, sitting on stools under the fishing nets that drape the ceiling.

'Commiserations,' says Spiros.

'Ta,' says McCreedy.

They drink and Spiros pours them another. He's a good

man, thinks McCreedy. Far from home, like me, but making a go of it. Not complaining. And he does lovely chips.

He tells Hilda it's all booked and arranged, she can take it off her mind, and she looks pleased for once. 'All right,' she says. 'Good. But don't go and spoil it by going out first and getting sloshed, will yer?'

'Why would I?' says McCreedy.

And he wouldn't, he thinks, honest to God, if only the presents had been better. But Hilda has no imagination. Where her imagination should be, there's an old tea stain.

Socks, they give him. A Mr Grumpy T-shirt. Tobacco. Katy draws a house in felt-tip, folds it in half, like a card, forgets to write anything in it.

He has to tell someone how pathetic this seems to him, how the T-shirt is grounds for divorce, isn't it?

'Absolutely,' say his mates in the pub. 'Fuckin' socks as well,' they say. 'Socks is grounds.'

They've done the pub up. It feels almost like you're drinking somewhere classy, except it's the same landlord with his face like a dough ball, and the same drinkers, mostly Irish, he's known for fifteen years. And they all, after the first couple of drinks, start to feel comfortable and full of friendliness, and the world outside goes still and quiet. And McCreedy loves this feeling of the quiet outside and the laughter within. It reminds him of something he once had and knows he's lost. It's the best.

He wants to prolong it. Just let everything unwind nice and slowly here. But he tells his mates, 'Kick me out at seven. Make sure I'm gone.'

And they promise. In between pints, they say, 'Plenty of time yet, John, hours of time.' And the pub fills up and starts to get its Saturday-night roar. And a spike-haired girl he's seen before comes up to him for a light and stays by him and he buys her a lager. She smells of leather and her skin's creamy white and she tells him she went to Ireland once and got bitten by a horse. And she shows him the scar of the bite on her shoulder and he touches it and thinks, She's what I'd really like for my birthday.

He's only twenty minutes late at the restaurant. You'd think it was two hours from the look on Hilda's face, and when he says he's sorry she turns her head away, like she can't bear the sight nor smell nor sound of him.

'Well,' he says, 'did you order?'

'Nettle soup,' says Katy, who's wearing a funny little velvet hat. 'I want nettle soup.'

'Fuck off, Katy,' says Michael.

'That's enough, Michael,' Hilda snaps.

She's ordered a gin. She's billowing her smoke out into the room. The menus sit in a pile, pushed aside, like she thinks she isn't going to understand a single thing in them.

McCreedy takes one and opens it. 'Dolmades.' 'Keftedes.' 'Horiatiki.' Excuse me, Spiros. Even the lettering's weird.

'Hey!' he calls, tilting his chair backward and feeling himself almost fall. 'Spiros!'

But Spiros is in the kitchen, as he should have remembered, and it's Elena, Spiros's wife with her mournful face, who comes over with an order pad and McCreedy tells her listen, none of this fancy-sounding stuff, just meat, steak or chops, with chips, O.K., and a pint of Guinness and Coke or something for the kids.

'Lilt,' says Michael.

'Lilt, then, for him,' says McCreedy.

'Which you want?' says Elena.

'One Lilt, one Coke for Katy.'

'Which you want, steak or pork chops, pork kebab?'

'Not pork, do you, Hilda?'

'Steak for me.'

'Steak for her. And me. You want steak, Michael?'

'Yeh.'

'Katy?'

'You said nettle soup would –'

'Not now. Pork or steak?'

She hides under the sad little hat. It's like she's got no neck at all. And now she's going to start crying.

'It's O.K.,' says McCreedy, 'she'll have steak. Small portion.'

'How do you want them – rare, medium, well-done?'

'Well-done,' says Hilda and passes Elena the rest of the menus, like she wants them out of her sight. Then she hands Katy a red paper napkin and the child holds it round her mouth like a gag and her tears are just enough to moisten its edge. She glares at McCreedy over the top of it.

McCreedy can't eat the food. It's a good steak. Large and juicy. But he can't get it down.

It's partly the drink he's had, but it's something else as well. It's what his life looks like across this table. Hatred. Indifference. Love. All three staring him in the eye, waiting for him to respond, to act, to assert himself, to be. And he can't. Not any more. For a long time he could and did. He fought them and held them close. He wept and screamed and tried to think of all the appropriate words of apology and affection. Right up to yesterday. But that's it, over now. They can't see it yet, but he knows it's happened: they've used him up. McCreedy's used up.

He sits in silence while they eat and talk. Katy stares at him under her hat, stuffing chips, one by one. Hilda and Michael blather about Arsenal. Michael snatches Katy's steak and gobbles it down. Hilda sucks the lemon from her gin glass. All McCreedy is doing is waiting for them to finish.

And when they have, he begins gathering up the plates. Dinner plates, knives and forks, side plates, veg dishes. One by one, he reaches across the table and piles them into a stack in front of him. It's a neat stack, like Hilda makes at home, with his own uneaten piece of meat transferred to the top plate, and then he sits back and stares at it.

'McCreedy,' says Hilda. 'This is a restaurant.'

'I know it's a restaurant,' he says. Michael is falling around, giggling, scarlet. 'Dad,' he splutters, 'what the fuck you doing?'

'What does it look like?'

'Pass them round again, McCreedy,' snarls Hilda. 'You'll make us the laughing stock.'

'No,' he says.

'Katy,' says Hilda, 'give out the plates again.'

'There's nothing on them,' McCreedy says, 'except on mine. Why d'you want them?'

'Jesus Christ!' says Hilda. 'Give us back the plates before that woman comes.'

'No,' he says again. Then he picks up his flab of steak in his fingers and lets it dangle above the stack. He takes a breath.

'See this?' he says. 'This is John McCreedy, aged forty-six today. See it? Chewed and left. Stranded. And this is all your stuff, underneath. Cold and hard and messed up. And I'm telling anyone who wants to listen that I want to get down from here, but I don't for the life of me know how.'

They all three stare at him. They don't know what on earth to make of it all, except it frightens them, it's so dramatic and Irish and odd. Hilda opens her mouth to say it must be the Guinness talking, but no words come out. She begins scrabbling in her bag for a new pack of cigarettes. Michael swears under his breath and gets up and slouches off to the toilet. Katy puts her thumb in her mouth. She watches her father drop the meat and she knows what's going to happen next: McCreedy is going to sweep the stack onto the floor, where it will break into a thousand pieces.

But then Spiros is there at the table. He's smiling. He smells of his charcoal fire, and his face is pink and gleaming. And he laughs good-naturedly at the stack and slaps McCreedy's thin shoulder blades, then snaps his fingers for a waitress to take the pile of plates and dishes away.

He waits a fraction of a second until it's safely gone, and then he says, 'O.K. Serious business now. Some champagne on the house for my old friend John McCreedy and his family, and a beautiful dessert for the princess in the hat.'

Michiel Heyns

THE CHILDREN'S DAY

Extract from a novel in progress.

THE MATCHLESS G9

IN COURT THEY called him Johannes Jacobus van der
Westhuizen, but to us he was always Steve. That was how he
introduced – or rather announced – himself to us, as we
gathered around the big black motorbike parked in the dust
of the main street outside Steyl's Café.

'Call me Steve,' he said, less as an invitation to familiarity
than as a rebuke to Kosie Opperman's *Middag Oom* – Good
afternoon uncle, in the indiscriminately familial vocabulary
of the Free State child. And although I had never called a
grown man by his first name, I could see the inappropriate-
ness of the avuncular form for somebody so unlike the uncles
of our acquaintance. In our town, uncles did not wear blue
jeans and tight T-shirts; in fact, in our town nobody wore
blue jeans and tight T-shirts, except the tsotsis who sometimes came from Bloemfontein and even Johannesburg to
visit friends and relatives in the location, and so could not be
said to be part of our town at all. 'Tsotsi clothes' – that was
all the explanation that was needed or given to justify
parental extinction of any subversive sartorial ambitions
amongst the children of Verkeerdespruit. 'But why can't I
have a pink shirt?' 'Tsotsi clothes' – and that would be the
end of that.

Steve did not look like a tsotsi. Apart from the fact that
tsotsis were black and he was white, tsotsis were, in the
received wisdom of childhood lore, quite puny – 'That's why
they go around in gangs' – and Steve was very big, with

forearms thicker than those of Maritz the Butcher. Maritz was reputed to have stunned a runaway bull with one blow of his tremendous fist long ago. Nobody knew exactly how: the majority opinion was that he had hit the bull between the eyes, but a strong minority favoured a chop on the back of the neck. Louis van Niekerk, challenged to ask Maritz himself, did so once, with all of us watching from outside the shop. We saw Maritz look at Louis impassively, then roll up his sleeves; Louis turned tail and ran and so did we all, to come to a halt breathlessly outside Dominee Claassen's pastorie, which we regarded as a sanctuary from any evil not perpetrated by ourselves. 'What did he say?' we demanded from the panting Louis van Niekerk. 'I asked him how he had stunned the bull and he said – he said he – he would show me.'

Steve, though as powerful as Maritz, instilled no such terror. On his first memorable appearance, roaring down the Saturday-afternoon-deserted winter-dusty main street, he had seemed like a creature of another essence, too marvellous to correspond to any of our categories of fear; and thereafter, though not overtly friendly, and when cruising slowly past up Voortrekker Street not deigning to notice us as we ceased our games or conversations or squabbles to look at the big man on the big motorbike, he seemed nevertheless to enjoy answering our many questions when he parked outside Steyl's for a Coke, of which he had about ten a day. 'My mother says Coke is bad for your teeth,' I volunteered once, not knowing enough about motorbikes to ask a convincing question. I now knew, like everybody else, that the gleaming machine was a Matchless G9, but to my untechnical mind this offered no opening to conversation. 'Your *mother*!' Kosie Opperman jeered, and looked at Steve to corroborate his contempt for such unmanly talk; but Steve looked at me attentively and said 'That's only while you're still growing. When you're big your teeth settle.' He tapped his front teeth with a long finger nail. 'See? I've got thirty-two of them, and they're all strong enough to bite off your fingers.' Without warning, he took my hand and put my fingers in his mouth and bit them, quite hard but not so that it hurt. 'Feel that?' he asked. 'Sharp, eh?' and showed most of his thirty-two teeth in a mock-savage grimace. Kosie and Louis laughed mirthlessly, slightly resentful of the attention I was getting but not wanting to ignore Steve's comic intent, and I could feel myself blushing, not with embarrassment, but with an unfamiliar kind of pleasure. At a loss for words, I examined the light indentations left by his teeth in my flesh.

Fanie van den Bergh, who was watching in his usual taciturn way, did not laugh with the others, merely stared at Steve with the unfathomable gaze of the simple-minded. Then Steve winked at him – not an absentminded flicker such as Mr Osrin bestowed upon us from behind his counter as he weighed off groceries for a customer, but a slow conspiratorial wink which seemed to recognise Fanie as an equal and accomplice, combined somehow against the rest of us.

'I bet you don't know what Matchless means,' I said to Fanie. He transferred his heavy gaze to me, frowned slightly, then looked at Steve, who was watching him with a little smile. 'It means – it means without equal,' Fanie said, flatly and factually, his eyes still on Steve, whose smile now broadened into a grin. 'That's right,' I conceded magnanimously. 'Steve must have told you.' But Steve said 'Fanie knows more than you think – not so Fanie?' Fanie continued to look solemnly at Steve, then shook his head and went and stood next to the Matchless and stroked the saddle.

Steve's arrival made more of a difference to Verkeerdespruit than even he could have imagined – not that he was modest, because he wasn't. But the swagger with which he got off the bike and flicked back the curl from his forehead, totally conscious of the gaze of the contingent of children gathered on the sidewalk, was more prodigious even than his vanity could conceive: how could Steve have known what it was for a child in Verkeerdespruit to see every day, actually living in Verkeerdespruit, an order of apparition that until then had manifested itself only in some thrillingly fearful Big City of the imagination? The TJ registration number gleamed at us like a mantra, calling up a different state of existence.

When Kosie Opperman's mother issued a ban on his association with 'that white tsotsi', it lent to the privilege of Steve's company the added allure of illegitimacy.

Having had the protected childhood that was the only kind possible in Verkeerdespruit, I was used to piecing together my understanding of the great world from literature in the broadest sense, that is, almost anything that I could find to read in an unliterary community. Steve, I learnt from old copies of *Die Huisgenoot* in Mr Welthagen's barber's shop where I reluctantly went once a month to have my head scraped with his blunt clipper, was not unique. 'He's a ducktail,' I announced one day as we were standing around outside Steyl's café hoping Steve would arrive. 'You can see it from the way he combs his hair.'

'What's a ducktail?' Louis challenged in a truculent tone intended to neutralise the humiliation of having to admit ignorance.

'They're people who drive around on motorbikes and comb their hair like Steve's,' I said, conscious of a certain circularity of definition, which was not lost on Louis. 'Big deal,' he said. 'So what?'

'They live in Johannesburg,' I added, 'and they have Sheilas. The Sheilas are women who smoke.'

Louis wasn't going to be trapped into another admission of ignorance. 'Then where's Steve's *Sheila*?' he demanded, and to myself I had to concede that Louis had seized the initiative. To him I said 'In Johannesburg, I suppose. Sheilas live on the streets.'

'So? There are streets here, aren't there?' and Louis gesticulated indignantly towards the dusty waste of Voortrekker Street.

I laughed scornfully. 'And what do you think a Sheila would do on Voortrekker Street?'

'Just what she does on the Johannesburg streets, I suppose,' Louis countered. 'A street's a street, isn't it?'

Looking at Voortrekker Street in the meagre light of an unexuberant spring, its one café and two shops, its petrol pump and its hotel, its ragged eucalyptus trees, I shook my head. 'No. A street's not a street,' I said, though without quite understanding what it was that I was trying to say. 'No Sheila could live on this street.'

The next time we were all congregated around the Matchless, Louis had his revenge. 'Where's your Sheila?' he asked Steve abruptly, in the middle of a general discussion of cylinder heads. When Steve looked at him quizzically, he faltered slightly. 'He –' gesturing towards me – 'he says he read that all ducktails have a Sheila.'

There was a shocked silence. Nobody else had thought actually to confront Steve on the ducktail question: though ignorant of the exact implications of the label, we guessed that it was applied to people by other people rather than by themselves. Steve was looking at me in what I uncomfortably suspected was amusement. Before I could extricate myself from my embarrassment, Fanie made one of his rare contributions. 'Steve doesn't have a Sheila,' he announced flatly and heavily.

I turned on him. 'How do *you* . . .' and then desisted. It was hopeless trying to get anything out of Fanie.

'That's right,' Steve said. 'I don't have a Sheila.'

'Then not all ducktails have Sheilas?' Louis persisted, looking at me triumphantly.

'What's a ducktail?' Steve asked mildly. Louis looked at me in some consternation, but I left him to wriggle on the consequences of his own audacity.

'They ride around on motorbikes and . . . have Sheilas,' he said somewhat lamely.

Kosie Opperman, who was defying his mother's ban because she had one of her migraines and was lying in a darkened room, intervened authoritatively. 'Well, then, stupid, Steve can't be a ducktail, can he?'

We were all still warily considering the logic of this when Steve got onto his bike, and kicked it into life with that nonchalant energy that always reminded me of the way Gene Autrey leapt onto his horse. 'Don't believe everything you read,' he said to me as he putted off. Then he stopped. 'Are you coming, Fanie?' he asked, and to communal amazement Fanie got onto the back of the Matchless and disappeared in a cloud of dust, clinging to the back of Steve's black leather jacket. Later I realised that by this time – 1963 – Steve's carefully groomed image must have been as out of date as everything else that ended up in Verkeerdespruit. But to us he seemed as modern as the passenger planes that flew high over our town, and as dangerous as the hidden blade of the flick knife he once displayed to us. 'It's against the law to carry one of these,' he said, and Louis van Niekerk and I looked at each other in silent acknowledgement of a force superior to our fathers' judicial authority. Steve was the decline of urban youth brought to Verkeerdespruit, the worst imaginings of *Die Landstem* and *Die Huisgenoot* made flesh. No matter that we had only the most generalised notion of the enormities of evil that we ascribed to him, or that he had taken lodgings with the ferociously respectable Mrs Maree: to us he was the sinister stranger who rides into town on a black horse – except that he was on our side, fighting against the adult world of duty and obedience that we didn't have the initiative to defy.

'What's Jo'burg like?' I asked Steve one day. We had taken to calling it Jo'burg because that was how Steve always referred to it, with an easy familiarity I couldn't quite match.

'It's big,' he shrugged, 'and the people are rich.'

'And the Communists?' I asked. Johannesburg had recently been revealed to harbour a nest of Communists plotting to overthrow the government, and the city now loomed in my imagination as a centre of conspiracy and subversion in addition to its more traditional turpitudes.

'What about the Communists?' Steve asked.

'Are they . . . are there lots of them?' I asked inadequately, realising that I knew little about them other than their name.

'Sure,' he said. 'There are lots of everything in Jo'burg.'

Louis van Niekerk chipped in 'My father says the Communists want to take over the country and give it to the kaffirs.' Steve shrugged again. 'They don't bother me, long as they leave me alone.'

In the lurid light of the press reports of the time, Steve's nonchalance seemed brave to the point of sedition. Though I was by no means so emancipated from my class and time as to feel anything but horror for *Umkhonto we Sizwe*, Steve's indifference to their dire plots paradoxically struck me as very fine. To the glamour of his general demeanour was now added the thrill of recklessness, even lawlessness.

One evening at supper my mother asked me 'Have you also been hanging around with that man with the motorbike?'

I was chewing a slice of bread and under cover of emptying my mouth I considered a non-committal reply. 'I . . . I have seen him around,' I said.

'Have you spoken to him?' she demanded.

'A few times,' I admitted.

'And what kind of thing does he discuss with you?'

'Motorbikes,' I said, probably slightly too patly to reassure my mother.

'I didn't know you knew about motorbikes,' she said with a slight frown.

'His motorbike has 500 cc's and eight grease nipples,' I said, hoping that my mother would not ask what that meant. But she only said 'I can't see why a grown man would want to stand around discussing nipples with a group of boys. Doesn't he have friends his own age?'

'I don't know,' I said dumbly.

'I don't think there are any men his age in Verkeerdespruit,' my father contributed.

'There are plenty of girls his age,' said my mother.

'Who?' my father asked.

'Well, there's Miss Jordaan – she's about his age. Give or take five years.'

'Steve says he asked her out and she said she didn't want to be seen on the back of a motorbike in case she got a reputation.' I hoped my mother would tell me what a reputation was, but all she said was 'It's odd, the things you can get a reputation for in this town.' For a while we ate in silence and then she said 'Well, then there's Betty the Exchange.'

'I think he does know Betty the Exchange,' I said carefully. One morning on my way to Sunday school I had seen Steve's motorbike in front of the house where Betty had a room with Steyl the café owner and his wife.

'The poor girl,' my mother said somewhat inconsequentially, and then turned to my father. 'I don't think it's a good thing that he hangs around our streets,' she said. 'Can't he be stopped?'

'I don't see how anyone can do that, my dear,' he said mildly. 'He isn't doing anything wrong.'

'I think he's a bad influence,' she said.

'What's a bad influence?' I asked.

Uncharacteristically, my mother got impatient with my questioning. 'Never mind what it is,' she said. 'I'm telling you he's a bad influence, 500 grease nipples or not. Why doesn't he get a job?'

'Eight. And he does have a job,' I volunteered. 'He helps Mr Deyssel at the garage.' Deyssel's Garage and Service Station was the sole source of petrol in Verkeerdespruit, and the only centre of mechanical expertise. People with new cars took them to Bloemfontein to be serviced, but for emergency repairs and for old cars Mr Deyssel was deemed adequate. His business, though not exactly thriving, had survived quite steadily on this grudging clientele for as long as I could remember.

'I hope he can teach Deyssel the difference between a carburettor and a petrol cap,' was all my father said, which I took as some sort of endorsement of Steve's usefulness in the community.

One Saturday morning I was walking down Voortrekker Street on my way to Steyl's Café with my dog Dumbo snuffling along as usual when the great roar of the Matchless announced to Verkeerdespruit that Steve had emerged for the day. It was the first sunny day after an unusually good bout of spring rains; the night before, a thunder storm had descended on us with such violence that Dumbo had sought refuge in my bed from the noise and the light, and from the deluge that followed. The normally morose landscape was responding brilliantly to the freshness and the warmth, and was sharp with the smell of vegetation. In the crisp air Steve's machine sounded deafening as it approached; then, unexpectedly, it decelerated and throbbed to a pause next to me.

'Hi,' Steve grinned at me. 'Want to come for a spin?'

If Steve had asked me whether I wanted to fly to the moon I couldn't have been more at a loss. It's all very well to be offered a *spin* as if one had one every day, but I literally didn't know how to get onto the back of a motorbike, and once there what to do with myself. Besides, after my mother's mutterings about Steve, I suspected that a spin on the back of his motorbike would count as a bad influence, not to mention the *reputation* which according to Miss Jordaan one could incur as a consequence.

'What's the matter?' Steve said 'Don't you want to come?'

'No – I mean yes,' I said. 'Yes, I want to come.' It was as simple as that. Even getting onto the huge motorbike proved to be easier than I anticipated, and once I was seated behind Steve, he turned around and said, 'Just put your arms around my waist if you're scared you're going to fall off.'

So I held on tightly and the machine leapt forward, leaving behind, it felt, my heart and bowels – along with a reproachful Dumbo, who stared after us dolefully for a moment and then turned back home. I shrugged off my guilt and surrendered to the roar of the bike. Voortrekker Street streaked past suffused with a glamour I had not thought it capable of, the shop fronts glistening in the clean air, the eucalyptus trees sparkling with raindrops and sunshine. I was subliminally aware of Mrs Opperman coming out of Osrin's and looking after us as we sped past out on to the Bloemfontein road, the only strip of tarred road in the area. Once we were on the open road, Steve turned his head back to me, and said 'Hold on tight' and accelerated and once again part of me was left behind as we leapt forward. I only seemed to catch up with myself again as the machine settled to a steady roar. I was sheltered from the wind by Steve's big back, and resting my cheek against him I could see the landscape, transformed by speed and noise, reeling past, itself released from earthbound immobility. The power of the machine shook my whole body, but feeling the strength of Steve's body responding with the movement, I was secure in being at one with the source of power and speed: the swerving of the machine, so terrifying to watch from the side of the road, was the smooth tilting of a single axle around a still point at the centre of which I was fused with Steve.

We rushed through the morning. I wanted it to go on and on, never to return to Verkeerdespruit and its pedestrian existence, always to speed through an empty landscape contained in noise and movement with Steve. But the machine started to counter its own momentum as Steve cut the throttle, and we glided to a halt. We were next to the bridge over the Modder River. For once the river had water in it rather than the mud it was named for or the dust to which the mud was invariably reduced.

Steve turned round to me. 'Hop off,' he said.

For a moment I thought he was going to abandon me there, but he smiled at me encouragingly and I got off the bike slightly less clumsily than I had feared. He pulled the machine up on its stand and got off.

'It's warm when you get off,' he said, and lit a Texan.

It was also very quiet on the deserted road. My body was still tingling with the vibration of the machine, and I felt out of breath. I looked at the blue sky, and felt the sunshine on my skin, and said 'Yes, it is,' and that seemed enough, that and the prospect of going back again on the magic machine.

He pulled at his cigarette. 'Fancy a goof?' he asked.

'Goof . . . ?'

'Swim.'

'You mean here?' I asked.

'Sure, where else? There's a lekker swimming hole just under the bridge,' he said. 'I've come out here before.'

'I . . . I can't swim,' I confessed. Not many Verkeerdespruit children could, for the simple reason that there was no large body of water available for long enough to enable us to get over our native fear of the foreign element.

''S okay,' he said. 'I'll piggy-back you.'

While I was still wondering over this novel form of transportation, he flicked away his cigarette and extended his hand and said 'Come on,' and helped me down the bank.

Under the bridge he took off his T-shirt and boots and jeans and I noticed that he did not wear underpants. My mother said only common people went without underpants; when I said that none of the boys in my class wore underpants, she said 'Exactly.' Steve said 'Come on, get them off, there's nothing to be worried about. Nobody can see us down here under the bridge.'

I took off my khaki shirt and shorts, and then my underpants. I didn't know what to do with my clothes, but he took them from me, folded them and put them on top of his. He glanced at me. 'You're thin,' he said, but I couldn't think of anything to say.

'Come on,' he said again, and turned his back to me. 'Get onto my back.'

He went and stood below me so that I could reach around his neck, then he gripped my legs in his arms and walked into the water. He was slightly unsteady, because the bottom of the river was very rocky, and there was a weak current. Towards the middle of the river the bank sloped down and he let go of my legs and started swimming what I recognised as breast stroke, from the Esther Williams movies that came to the town hall. I could feel the rhythmical contracting and relaxing of his back and shoulder muscles under me, and my belly rubbed against the skin of his back. It was a bit like sitting behind him on the motorbike, except that instead of the throbbing engine there was only the water washing over us, resisting us and yet sustaining us, Steve and I moving as a single unit of force escaping from the pull of the earth.

'You can help us by kicking your legs,' said Steve over his shoulder and I started churning up the water behind us, happy in the knowledge that I was contributing to our progress. The Modder River is not a very wide river and we were soon on the other side.

'Okay?' he asked, and I nodded and said 'Okay.' Then I asked what I'd been wondering. 'Where did you learn to swim?'

'The place I work at has a swimming pool for the workers,' he replied.

'In Jo'burg?' I asked, and he nodded, but he didn't seem to want to talk about it, so I dropped the topic.

'Ready to go back?' he asked.

'You mean to Verkeerdespruit?' I asked, disappointed.

'No, back to the other side of the river.'

'Yes,' I said, although I wished I could say something that would delay our return.

'This time I'll swim on my back and pull you along,' Steve said. 'Come and stand in front of me and just lie back.' I did so, and he put his arms loosely around my body and kicked with his feet so that we moved backward slowly. It went less smoothly than the first time, and we got water in our mouths and noses. Coughing and spluttering and laughing we got to the other side. He pulled me out of the water.

I looked down at my streaming body. 'I'm wet,' I said.

He laughed. 'Of course you're wet. That's what happens when you get into the water. We'll dry out in the sun.'

He found his crumpled packet of Texans, lit one carefully so as not to get it wet, and sat down on a sandy ledge. 'Come and sit next to me,' he said, and patted the ledge.

I sat next to him, half-leaning against his side. He put his left arm on my shoulder. 'Next time I'll teach you to swim,' he said.

'Really?' I asked, thrilled as much by the idea of a next time as by the promise.

The sun was warm on our bodies, and apart from the sound of a bird making a fuss in a *soetdoring* tree next to us, it was absolutely quiet. Steve's smoke drifted in the still air in front of us, the sweetish smell of the tobacco mingling with the scent of the first yellow flowers on the tree. He blew a smoke ring and we watched it hover in front of us before it gradually dispersed.

'Blow another,' I said, and he did. The insubstantial ring drifting in front of us seemed to me the most perfect thing I had ever seen, but I was too shy to say so.

We sat for a while and then he threw away his cigarette, rubbed his hand across his stomach, and said, 'I'm just about dry, how about you?'

'I'm quite dry,' I said.

''Course you are. There's much less of you to get dry,' and he ran his hand down my side. Then he got up from the ledge and stretched himself in the sun. I had never seen a grown man without clothes before, and I looked at the hair on his body and wondered why men got hair there. I wondered what it felt like and I put out my hand and touched the hair on his chest. It was rougher than ordinary hair.

Steve said 'You'll have some of that too one day. Plenty of time.' But I looked at Steve's body, the broad shoulders and thick arms, the strong legs, and shook my head. I knew that my body would never look like that.

'Yes, you will,' he said, misinterpreting my headshake. 'It happens to everybody. It's natural.'

I thought of Mr Viljoen and Mr Deyssel and Dominee Claassen and somehow I couldn't imagine that they had hair on their bodies, or that if they did it looked like Steve's. 'It looks nice on you,' I said, then blushed.

'Of course it does,' he said, and put his hand behind my neck and pressed my head against his shoulder. 'Time to go,' he said. 'Your old folks will get worried.'

As we pulled on our clothes there was the sound of a car approaching, not very fast. As it got to the bridge it slowed down and stopped. A car door opened and slammed, and my mother shouted 'Simon? Are you there?'

'Your old lady?' Steve asked.

'Yes,' I said. 'I don't know how she knew I was here.'

'Simon!' my mother shouted, sounding half-angry, half-worried. I fastened the snake clasp on the buckle of my belt and clambered halfway up the bank to the road, and said, 'Yes mom, I'm here.'

'What on earth are you doing there?' she asked.

'I'm here with Steve,' I said, thinking that the presence of an adult would make it all right.

'Yes I know *that*,' she said, but it didn't sound as if this made things any better. 'Where is . . . he?'

'Right here, madam,' said Steve behind me and he passed me and pulled me up the last bit of the bank. My mother was standing next to the car with a scarf around her head. I could see that her hair was in curlers, which meant that she must have left home in a hurry. My mother said it was common to appear in public in curlers. My mother wore a hat to go to town, except when she was just going to Osrin's quickly to buy groceries.

Mrs Opperman was sitting in the car staring straight ahead, as if she would be turned into stone if she cast an eye on Steve or me. Dumbo was in the back seat, uncritically overjoyed to see me.

'Mr . . .' my mother began, and hesitated.

'Call me Steve,' he said, in the same languid way he had introduced himself to us upon his arrival in Verkeerdespruit.

'Steve,' my mother said, though I could see she didn't really want to call him Steve, 'You can't just go off with our sons on the back of that thing.'

'Why not?' he asked, as if he really wanted to know. 'I bring them back, don't I?'

'Yes, but it . . . it's dangerous,' my mother said. 'They could fall off.'

'No chance,' he said. 'I tell them to hold on tight and they hold on tight.'

'Anyway,' my mother said, and I could see she was coming to her real point, 'I don't think it's right for a grown man to drive around with little children.'

'Why not?' he asked again. 'I like little children.'

At this Mrs Opperman could no longer keep her countenance. She turned down her window all the way – it had been open just far enough for her to hear what was happening –

put her head out, and hissed at Steve 'Pervert!' Dumbo jumped on top of her and leapt out of the window to get to me. Since Jumbo was a large dog this demonstration detracted from her dignity.

Steve looked at Mrs Opperman, looked at me, shrugged, and said 'You know what the old lady's on about?' but Mrs Opperman, having uttered her incantation, had closed her window again.

'Get into the car,' my mother said to me.

'But I want to go back with Steve,' I protested, devastated at the prospect of losing the trip back on the motorbike, and quite prepared to betray once again the affection of the forgiving Dumbo.

'Listen to me,' my mother said in a tone which she used very seldom, and which did not allow for argument, 'and get into that car immediately.' She opened the back door so imperatively that Dumbo jumped in in a cowed sort of way and licked the back of Mrs Opperman's neck. She screamed and slapped at Dumbo; she missed and he nipped her hand playfully. I also got in, trying to catch Steve's eye; somehow I wanted to tell him I was sorry for having brought this punitive expedition down upon him. But he was looking at my mother, who was saying 'It's very irresponsible of you to take children away. I was very worried when the dog came home on its own. If Mrs Opperman hadn't seen you leave with Simon and come to tell me I wouldn't have known where he was.'

''S right,' Steve said, 'and he'd have been back before you knew it.'

'In any case,' my mother said, 'I'm warning you to stay away from my son. If you don't, I'll report you to the police.'

'Suit yourself,' said Steve. 'But why don't you ask your son's opinion?'

'I don't ask my son's opinion on such matters and you know very well why,' snapped my mother and got into the car.

As we drove off I looked back and Steve gave me a thumbs up sign. I waved at him. After a minute or two the Matchless roared past our car. There was infinite contempt in the easy way it swerved to pass us and then cut in in front of us and left us behind.

There was silence in the car for a while. I scratched Dumbo's ears and he nestled up against me happily.

'But what did he do with you under the bridge?' Mrs Opperman demanded suddenly.

'He didn't do anything with me,' I said, sensing obscure horrors lurking in her question. 'We swam in the river.'

'You *swam*?' my mother exclaimed. 'Where are your swimming trunks?' I had an old pair of swimming trunks for our annual trips to the sea.

'I didn't wear trunks,' I said.

'Then what did you wear?' my mother demanded.

'Nothing,' I said.

Mrs Opperman turned round to me. She looked as if she'd seen a snake. 'You mean you were *naked*?' she exclaimed.

I nodded. Then, with a dim intention of warding off the wrath and revulsion facing me, I said, 'But Steve was also . . . naked.' The word was a violation.

Mrs Opperman said 'I think I've got a migraine coming on,' and my mother asked me, very gently: 'Simon, did this er . . . Steve touch you at all?'

Again I heard a world of adult anxieties in the question, and an unfamiliar instinct warned me not to tell the truth. So I lied to my mother for the first time I could remember, and yet it was not really a lie either, for I knew that what my mother meant was not what Steve had done. 'No,' I said. 'He didn't touch me.'

After this Mrs Opperman visited all our parents and most of them forbade their children to talk to Steve. Jesserina Schoeman giggled when she told us that her father had said she was not allowed to talk to 'the ducktail'. 'I told him that I wished I could, but that Steve only talked to the boys, and he said worse and worse,' she told us. 'What did he mean?'

'I think he meant that Steve is a pervert,' I replied, remembering the term Mrs Opperman had spat at Steve.

'What's that?' demanded Louis van Niekerk.

'I don't know,' I confessed. 'It's what adults call Steve.'

So when Louis was angry with me for not allowing him to copy my homework, he told Steve that I had said he was a pervert, and reported to me that Steve had replied 'Well, bugger him then,' and Steve stopped even waving at me when he drove past.

After a while the only boy who was still allowed to talk to Steve was Fanie van den Bergh. Kosie Opperman reported that his mother had been to see Mrs van den Bergh but that, unexpectedly for such a mild and tractable person, she'd refused. 'As long as it makes the boy happy,' she'd said, and when Mrs Opperman had threatened to report her to the OVV, had said to her 'Mind your own business,' which Mrs Opperman said nobody had ever said to her. When I told my mother this, she said that she could see Mrs van den Bergh's point, even though of course Mrs Opperman was quite right.

As in a sense the cause of all this activity I was the object of some curiosity at school. From Mrs Opperman's reaction I knew that what I had done was open to disapproval, but by and large the other children were too envious to be censorious. Mr de Wet, our teacher that year, made a comment about children who risked their lives and futures by consorting with strangers, but his formulation did not accord with any recognisable reality, and was ignored as the kind of thing adults had to say as token of their authority.

Around this time Steve disappeared from our streets, to the consternation of the children and the relief of the adults. It was just starting to seem that the problem of Steve had been solved when he reappeared one day, a week later, as nonchalant as ever. But now the *Oranje Vrouevereniging*, or OVV, of which my mother was the secretary and Mrs Opperman the president, took it upon itself to rid the community of 'the threat to the children of Verkeerdespruit', as Steve was described in the circular Mrs Opperman composed and my mother sent out, announcing a special meeting in our sitting room. This fortunately took place on a Wednesday afternoon when I was at home. Having opened in advance the little window in the corner of our sitting room which my mother said the builder had put in because he had a window left over from building the police station, I could listen to the proceedings by crouching in the flower bed outside, hidden from view by a large aloe which my mother had planted to obscure the little window.

It was an uncomfortable position and the aloe was not a congenial kind of shelter, but I was rewarded for my endurance by hearing an unedited version of a meeting that I knew I would have been given only a very partial account of.

The meeting was opened, like everything in Verkeerde-spruit from cattle auctions to baby shows, with scripture and prayer, in this instance conducted by the Dominee's wife, on the principle perhaps that being married to the Lord's anointed she would have privileged access to Him. She read from Ezekiel what she called a message of comfort to the Lord's flock in times of peril: 'And they shall no more be a prey to the heathen, neither shall the beast of the land devour them; but they shall dwell safely, and none shall make them afraid.' She thanked the Lord for sending us shepherds who were dealing so fearlessly with the onslaught of communism and other foreign elements. Perhaps judging that in dealing with an Omniscient power it was indelicate to call things by their name, she referred to 'the wise measures recently introduced', in acknowledgement of God's part in the passing of the Ninety-day Act, and asked Him to avert also 'this new onslaught from the heathen and the beast dwelling in our midst'.

Clearly, though, the job was not going to be left to God's unaided efforts, and the rest of the meeting was devoted to a somewhat unstructured consideration of ways to rid the community of Steve. Discussion was lively, the majority of women apparently favouring the simple expedient of driving him from their midst. I had visions of Steve on his motor-bike, pursued out of town by stick-wielding members of the OVV. My mother pointed out that there were no legal grounds for driving anybody from one's midst without that person's consent.

'What about the Bantu?' Mrs van Onselen demanded. 'They're being moved all the time, and some of them are quite respectable.'

'Yes,' my mother said. 'but that's because they're black. There's no law to move a white person from anywhere.'

'Yes,' Mrs van Niekerk confirmed. 'Piet says the police can't do anything to him until he's done something wrong.'

'So must we sit around and wait for him to commit . . . some atrocity before we can get rid of him?' asked Mrs van Onselen. 'I must say, I don't understand the law.'

'Dominee says' – Dominee Claassen's wife always referred to her husband as 'Dominee' – 'that the church can't do anything to this man because he doesn't belong to the Dutch Reformed Church.'

'But,' said Mrs Opperman, 'we can make it impossible for him to stay here if we deny him a place to live and work.'

'How will we do that?' asked my mother.

'Well fortunately we have both Mrs Maree and Mrs Deyssel here,' said Mrs Opperman.

There was a silence. Mrs Maree, Steve's landlady, was not a person who took kindly to being prescribed to by anybody. Then in her emphatic, precise way she said: 'Steve pays me ten rand a month for his room and anybody who wants me to get rid of him will have to pay me ten rand a month. And Skollie likes him.'

'Must our dogs choose our children's companions?' asked Mrs Price, the English hairdresser, who was not really a member of the OVV but who was attending because her son Desmond had asked her if he could have a motorbike when he turned eighteen, which request she ascribed to Steve's influence.

'Not if it's a useless ball of cotton wool,' said Mrs Maree, in pointed reference to Mrs Price's Maltese poodle Fifi, which, much bathed and perfumed, graced her hairdressing salon, *Chez Boutique*. Once when Mrs Maree had taken her dog with her for her wash and set, an enraged Fifi had pursued the thoroughly cowed Skollie down Voortrekker Street. I knew this, because Mary, the wife of our gardener Jim, worked for Mrs Price.

'Order please, ladies,' said Mrs Opperman. 'Obviously we can't force Mrs Maree to give up such a lucrative arrangement. We must consider other ways of persuading this man to leave our town. Now Mrs Deyssel . . . your husband employs him.'

'I'm sure Fred didn't know he was a . . . heathen and a beast when he took him on,' said Mrs Deyssel, a meek and not very enterprising woman.

'Nobody's blaming Mr Deyssel; the point is, now that this man has shown himself to be a millstone and a stumbling-block, don't you think Mr Deyssel would consider terminating his employment?'

'You mean Fred must sack Steve?' Mrs Deyssel asked.

'Yes.'

'I don't know,' said Mrs Deyssel. 'Fred says the man knows about engines. He says that nobody else could get that van of Vermaas's going.'

'What is more important, the safety of our children or the mobility of Mr Vermaas's van?' demanded Mrs Opperman.

'I'm sure I don't know,' said Mrs Deyssel in a depressed tone.

'Well, I know,' said Mrs Opperman, 'and I think you should talk to your husband.'

'I can talk to him,' said Mrs Deyssel, 'but I don't know if it will do any good. Last year I talked to him about washing his hands when he came in from the garage because he was getting my new lounge suite full of oil, but he said a man is master in his own house and doesn't have to take orders from his wife. So now I've put loose covers on the lounge suite so that I can put them in the wash when they get dirty.'

'That was a good solution to that problem,' my mother said, 'but loose covers are not going to do us any good with this Steve man.'

'No, I was just saying about talking,' said Mrs Deyssel, but she had lost the floor. Mrs Dominee interrupted her.

'Mr Deyssel is an elder on the church council, isn't he?'

'Yes,' said Mrs Deyssel. 'He says he was chosen because they hoped he would service the Dominee's car for free.' A grateful congregation had given the Dominee a Mercedes Benz the year before, in recognition of his initiative in organising a day of prayer for rain, to such good effect that the Verkeerdespruit came down in flood and washed away half the location. Two people and a cow were drowned. The owner of the cow tried to sue the church but couldn't find a lawyer to take his case.

'Dominee has his car serviced in Bloemfontein,' said Mrs Dominee. 'But what I wanted to say is that although this Steve is not subject to church discipline, Mr Deyssel is, and perhaps if Dominee spoke to him and impressed it upon him that it was his duty to the community to get rid of this man . . .'

'I don't much like it,' said my mother. 'It sounds like intimidation.'

'Well,' said Mrs Opperman, 'if you'd rather have your son gallivanting in the nude with this man on his motorbike . . .'

'My son went for a swim with this man; there's nothing wrong with that.'

'Then why are we having this meeting?'

'I agree that it's a potentially undesirable situation . . .'

'I should think it's a potentially undesirable situation. I shudder to think what would have happened if I hadn't seen the man sneaking out of town with your son on the back of his motorbike.'

'And I'm very grateful to you for informing me so promptly; I'm just saying that there's a difference between swimming and . . . gallivanting in the nude on a motorbike.'

'Ladies,' Mrs Dominee intervened. 'Is it agreed then that I should talk to Dominee and ask him to talk to Mr Deyssel about employing this man?'

There were mutters and murmurs and reservations, but eventually, when tea time arrived, the ladies of the OVV agreed: Steve would have to go, and the way to achieve this

307

was to deprive him of a means of livelihood. The heathen was about to be driven from the land.

The next day, on my way from school, I saw Fanie walking ahead of me. I walked slightly faster and joined him without any preamble. Preliminaries were never necessary with Fanie, whose command of social graces had not yet extended to the most rudimentary forms of greeting.

'Did you hear that Steve's going away?' I asked.

I'd counted on a reaction, and I was not disappointed. He stopped dead and looked at me uncomprehendingly with his light-blue eyes.

'Who . . . who says so?' he stuttered.

'My mother,' I said blithely. 'The OVV thinks he's a bad influence.'

Fanie didn't ask me what a bad influence was, though he couldn't have known. Nor did he question the power of the OVV, having, as an officially underprivileged epileptic, been subject to the whims of official, semi-official and amateur busybody organisations all his life. The Poor Whites were a much looked-after segment of our society.

'When?' he asked.

'When what?' I replied.

'When's he leaving?'

'Oh, I don't know. I don't think they've decided.'

Fanie looked at me like a dog in pain, and didn't say anything more.

Two days after, Fanie came to me where I was sitting on the playground frying ants with a magnifying glass.

'Steve says they can't kick him out,' he blurted out.

'Oh really?' Since I suspected he was right, I took refuge in sarcasm.

'Yes. He says he's got as much right to be here as any – bloody old bitch.'

'I'm going to tell Mr Viljoen you've been swearing,' I said.

'I'm not swearing. That's what Steve said.'

'Well, he'll discover his mistake,' I said in the tone that my mother employed when talking about the bad service she got from Osrin. 'He'll be out of here before . . . before he can drain his sump.' I had learnt something after all from the technical discussions next to the motorbike.

'I'm going with him,' Fanie announced in his flat dull way.

'Then he is leaving?'

'Yes, he says it's not as if it's a pleasure living in a dump like this.'

'And where to?' I taunted. 'To Jo'burg?'

'No. To Winburg. His parents live there.'

'Winburg?' I screeched. 'Steve's parents live in Winburg?' It was like being told that Gene Autrey's parents lived in Bloemfontein; in fact the idea of Steve having parents was unthinkable.

'Yes,' he said. 'He says I can be his brother.' And Fanie smiled, and I realised that I'd never seen him smile before.

'Why should he want you as his brother?' I asked, taken aback.

'I don't know,' he said humbly and walked away.

'You can't be somebody's brother if you have different parents . . .' I called after him, but I don't think he was listening.

Fanie's absence from school was at first not commented on. He stayed away periodically, partly because of his health, partly I suspect because Mr de Wet, our current teacher, terrified Fanie even more than the rest of us. I think I was the only one who noticed that Fanie's absence coincided with Steve's second disappearance from our village. The latter event in any case absorbed too much of everybody's attention to leave any of it for Fanie's absence from school. Steve's first disappearance had been part of his fascinating unpredictability; a second seemed premeditated, final. Children who until recently had vied for Steve's attention now all had an anecdote relating to what had become established as his bad influence. Nasie Grundlingh said that Steve had offered him a cigarette, but since Nasie was suspected of being a secret smoker anyway, this did not seem like bad influence as much as generosity. Annette Loubser said that she had seen Steve talk to two Bantus next to the road.

Kosie Opperman informed us that his mother took credit for Steve's disappearance, on the grounds that Dominee would never have gone to talk to Mr Deyssel if she hadn't called the special meeting of the OVV. Apparently Mr Deyssel, though initially reluctant to lose the only competent mechanic he had ever had, had eventually come round to seeing his duty as citizen of Verkeerdespruit and elder of the Church, and had told Steve he could no longer employ him. Mrs Maree was considering suing the church for loss of income.

So, what with the speculation and perturbation around Steve's departure, it was only after three days that Mr de Wet sent a note to Mrs van den Bergh to ask where Fanie was. I was used as messenger, I suspect because Mr de Wet guessed, correctly, that my ten-year-old sensibilities and snobberies would find a visit to Mrs van den Bergh's slovenly home particularly trying.

I knocked at the unprepossessing front door of the van den Bergh home and waited. There was a forlorn peach tree at the front door which had optimistically formed a few blossoms at the beginning of spring and now seemed to be dying of drought. There was, surprisingly given the general lack of amenities, a door mat; it was made of Coca Cola bottle-tops nailed to a plank. I wondered whether Fanie had made it. At length the mournful face of Mrs van den Bergh appeared around the door.

'Yes?' she asked with that total absence of curiosity which she had bequeathed to her only son.

'I've brought a note from Mr de Wet at the school,' I announced.

'Oh,' she said, wiping her hands and taking the letter hesitantly. She opened it, frowned at it for about thirty seconds, then handed it back to me and said 'Can you read it for me?'

I guessed that Mrs van den Bergh couldn't read.

'Yes,' I said, and opening the little note, read. 'Dear Mrs

van den Bergh; Your son Fanie has not been in school for three days. I hope he is not seriously ill, but if so please let me know by return of post. Yours faithfully, B. de Wet (Class teacher).'

'Oh,' said Mrs van den Bergh. 'Fanie's not here.'

'Where is he?' I asked.

'I don't know,' she said. 'He went away.'

'But where to?'

'I don't know,' she persisted. 'He's done it before. He did it when we were living in Ficksburg too. That time he went to visit my sister in Ventersdorp. She lives on a plot with her husband Derek.' And she looked at me as if that explained it all. 'My husband will give him a hiding when he gets back,' she reassured me.

The police came to ask us all questions. When Mr de Wet asked if anybody knew anything that might help the police in their investigations – the constable standing next to him looked slightly alarmed – I put up my hand.

'Fanie said something last week . . . '

'Last week? Why didn't you tell anybody?' asked Mr de Wet.

'I didn't believe him. He said he was going with Steve.'

There was a rumble of speculation in the class, and Mr de Wet and the constable looked at each other.

'I think . . . if this boy can come with me to make a statement . . . ?' he said to Mr de Wet, who nodded. I left a profoundly hushed class behind me.

'And you're sure he said Winburg?' Captain van Niekerk asked me.

'Yes oom,' I said.

'And this Steve – what's his full name?'

'I don't know oom. But Fanie said they were going to stay with Steve's parents.'

'Should be easy,' Captain van Niekerk said to the constable. 'There can't be many motorbikes in Winburg. Go and find the fucker.'

MICHIEL HEYNS

Fanie was brought back the next day. There was a general consciousness of an enormity, derived as much from the cryptic mutterings of grown-ups as from our own uninformed speculations. As son of the man in charge of the processes of retribution, Louis van Niekerk was much in demand. 'My father says he should be hanged,' he said.

'My mother says hanging is too good for him,' said Kosie Opperman.

'Captain van Niekerk says Steve should be hanged,' I told my father.

He looked at me pensively. 'Fortunately Captain van Niekerk is not the magistrate,' he said.

My father, though, *was* the magistrate, and had to pronounce sentence. I read the report in *The Friend*. The magistrate had said that there were extenuating circumstances, and that the accused had apparently not 'interfered' with the child. He sentenced Steve to three years in prison for abducting a minor. Asked why he had left home, the accused replied that he had felt restless. Asked why he had taken the minor with him, he said that he liked children.

So Steve disappeared from our midst, and I might not have heard of him again had it not been for the *Landstem*, a national weekly which specialised in 'human interest' stories. My parents did not read it – my mother said it was common and my father said it exploited the misery of the few and the boredom of the many – but on Saturdays, when I read magazines in Steyl's café, I sometimes stealthily perused an alluring item in the *Landstem*. And there, a week or two after the trial, was a photograph of Steve; also a photograph of a woman in a beehive hairdo, pointing at a deep-freeze. 'A Wife's Grief' the headline shouted, '"My husband left me for a motorbike."' It appeared from the story that Steve had worked as a mechanic on a gold mine in Welkom. His wife, Mrs Soekie van der Westhuizen, said she had forgiven him for abandoning her, but was hurt that he had pawned the wedding ring she had bought him, and exchanged their new deep-freeze for a motorbike belonging to Mr Stoffel Lemmer, a next-door neighbour. Mr Lemmer was also interviewed,

312

and said he wanted his Matchless back because his wife, Mrs Sarie Lemmer, had effected the exchange without his permission when he went back to Johannesburg 'for personal reasons' soon after they moved to Welkom; now that he had returned to his wife he should have his rightful property restored to him. In this he was supported by Mrs van der Westhuizen, who wanted the deep-freeze back, but Mrs Lemmer refused to return it, on the grounds that it had been a legitimate exchange, and besides, her husband had come back to her only because his Jo'burg girl friend had kicked him out when he ran out of money.

I did not have the money or the courage to buy the *Landstem*, but I cut the report from the *Friend* once my mother had thrown it on the heap of things to be burnt on Thursday mornings by Jim, and showed it to Louis and Kosie at break on the playground, on the rockery, where it was accepted that serious discussions took place. Their fathers got the *Volksblad*, which had not seen fit to cover the trial. Louis' father, though at times more than prepared to share his views on the proper conduct of justice with his own family, more often assumed an air of professional discretion which maddened his wife and frustrated Louis.

'What's *interfered with*?' asked Kosie.

I was reluctant to admit that I had no idea. 'It means that he didn't steal anything from Fanie,' I said.

'What's Fanie got to steal anyway?' asked Louis.

'Nothing. That's why Steve didn't steal anything,' I explained, hoping that they weren't going to ask me what extenuating circumstances were.

'What's extenuating circumstances?' asked Louis.

For a moment I thought I might bluff that one out too, but the expression on Kosie's face told me that he was not convinced on *interfered with* and was going to be tough on *extenuating circumstances*. So I said 'How should I know?'

'Why didn't you ask your father?'

I could in fact probably have asked him, but I didn't want my parents to know that I had read the report on Steve's trial.

'Let's ask Fanie,' I suggested, more to divert attention from

313

my lapses and because he happened to be walking past at that moment than because I thought there was much point to it.

'Hey! Fanie!' shouted Kosie, and Fanie looked up with the unsurprised air with which he met all overtures.

'Come here,' said Louis, with the ring of authority which he at times assumed as appropriate to his father's position and rank. Fanie obediently enough shambled over to where we were sitting on the school rockery, and looked at us with as much interest as if we were outcrops of the rockery.

'What . . . ?' started Kosie, and then seemed to run out of nerve, so I had to step in.

'The newspaper says Steve didn't interfere with you,' I said bluntly. He looked at me expressionlessly. Then he said 'Yes.'

'What does it mean?'

Kosie looked at me as if to say I thought you knew.

'I don't know,' said Fanie.

'Of course he doesn't know,' said Louis under his breath.

'But what . . . what is it that he didn't do?'

'Nothing,' said Fanie.

'He didn't do nothing?'

'Yes . . . no.'

'What do you mean no?'

'He did nothing.'

'Did he or didn't he do nothing?'

'No.'

'Did he . . . okay, what did he do with you?'

'Nothing.'

'Where did he take you?'

'To Winburg.'

'And what did you do there?'

'Nothing.'

'Then why did they put him in jail?'

Fanie looked at me. 'Did they put him in jail?'

For the first time it occurred to me that nobody had seen fit to tell Fanie what had happened to Steve.

'Yes. Didn't you know?'

'No.'

Then he looked at us. 'Why?'

'Why what?'

'Why did they put him in jail?'

'Because of what he did to you.'

'But he . . . can they put you in jail for that?'

Louis and I pounced simultaneously. 'For what?' he demanded, and 'Then he did something to you?' I asked.

He shook his head. 'No. He . . . he . . .'

'If you don't tell us I'll tell my father,' said Louis.

'He . . .' Fanie got that fixed expression which by now I recognised. But he didn't have a fit. He stared in front of him; then absent-mindedly he bit the side of his hand, and said 'He kissed me.'

'Kissed you?' I exclaimed in incredulous disappointment. My mother and father kissed me at bedtime, and when they were going to Bloemfontein for the day, and my uncles and aunts kissed me when they came to visit; I had never considered it to be something which one might do voluntarily or because it gave anybody any pleasure. People did kiss in movies, but people in movies also did any number of things which people in Verkeerdespruit or even Winburg wouldn't dream of doing, like bursting into song in mid-conversation or dying for their beliefs.

'Kissed you?' I repeated, and he nodded, clearly still lost in his own thoughts. 'Where was he going?'

'Nowhere.'

'Then why did he kiss you?' Something in me rebelled against the idea of Steve's kissing Fanie, rebelled against anybody's kissing Fanie, and Steve's kissing anybody. I looked at Kosie and Louis; they were looking at me hesitantly, clearly expecting me to clear up the mystery.

'Why did he kiss you?' I repeated.

Fanie thought for a moment; then 'Because he liked me,' he said, and smiled for the second time since I had known him.

A few months later *The Friend* reported that Johannes Jacobus van der Westhuizen, 'the convicted child molester', had been killed by his cell-mate in Bloemfontein prison. I asked my father why.

'I don't really know,' he said. 'Strange things happen in prison. But they're often very hard on child molesters.'

'What's a child molester?'

'Oh. Somebody who interferes with children.'

'But you . . . the newspaper said that Steve didn't interfere with Fanie.'

'Well no. Not technically. But you see, that's not the way his cell-mate would have seen it. To him what Steve did would be molesting.'

I thought for a moment. 'Fanie said . . . Steve kissed him.'

My father looked at me enquiringly, but didn't say anything, so I carried on. 'Is that what molesting means?'

My father seemed vaguely surprised. 'Yes,' he said, 'I suppose that would count as molesting.'

'So Steve was killed because he kissed Fanie?' I pursued.

My father thought for a moment, then shrugged slightly and said 'Yes. I suppose that's what it amounts to.'

When I told Fanie this, he said nothing, only looked at me in that dumb way of his.

MACULAR DEGENERATION

At the end of Standard Two we moved to a new class, which although ostensibly a rung up the ladder, entailed a demotion from lording it over the Standard Ones to being lorded over by the Standard Fours. But it was more than the loss of caste that made us dread the transition: it was the knowledge that we were moving into Mr de Wet's class.

Mr de Wet was odd, even by the standards of a school that had to accept such teachers as were desperate enough to apply to Verkeerdespruit, and odd beyond even the oddness that children ascribe to anybody not conforming in every respect to their idea of normal humanity. His short body, though powerful and broad-shouldered, seemed to be warped somewhere: not quite a hunchback, not quite a limp, more a list to one side. It was probably a minor hip defect, but at the time his oblique scuttle was part of the mystery and menace of the man. His face was very square, his jaw set very tight, and his head would have been impressive in a monumental bust carved into rock; but it was too big to match his squat body, and being carried at a slight angle, seemed forever on the point of toppling off its precarious perch. His speech, like his body, was not quite deformed and yet not quite normal either: it was really no more than extreme sibilance, but again the elusive nature of the disability made it more sinister than a straightforward impediment would have been. But Mr de Wet's most fabled and feared attribute was an ophthalmic peculiarity which inclined him to focus some twenty degrees to the right of where he seemed to be looking. It owed its notoriety partly to the fact that it was a deviation that could be demonstrated only in action, as it were: to look at Mr de Wet looking, he seemed merely to have a slightly more intense stare than other people. Without actual experience of this obliquity, it was in fact difficult to see why previous generations of Standard Threes had evinced such horror at what seemed to be at most a slightly disconcerting peculiarity. 'Just you wait,' they said when questioned on the point, 'just you wait.'

Mr de Wet was known as Ssscorpion, in reference to his sibilance and his mode of motion. Years later, in training camp, I saw a group of recruits pitting a scorpion and a spider against each other in an ammunition case, and I recognised then the accuracy of the unkind genius who had first discerned the similarity between Mr de Wet's progress through his class and the nervous scamper of the scorpion, its sting poised like a vicious standard.

After the slightly gushy sweet nature of Miss Jordaan, Ssscorpion came as a shock, and knew it. 'We've got a fresh crop today,' he said on the first day, grinning conspiratorially at the Standard Fours, who, relieved to have graduated from the position of victims to that of collaborators in Mr de Wet's humour, grinned back grimly, no doubt recalling their own terror the year before. We stood mutely; there seemed to be

no way of averting a wrath as irrational and unpredictable as
Mr de Wet's.

'You've all been ssspoilt,' he hissed at us. 'You've been
treated like sssugar mice. Well', he said, pausing for effect, 'I
have sssugar mice for breakfassst.'

The Standard Fours tittered obligingly and we looked at
Mr de Wet, all trying as hard as possible not to look like a
sugar mouse. 'Sssome of you,' he said ominously, 'think
you're very clever.' He directed this observation at Fanie, who
once again had the desk next to mine. 'Well,' he said, still to
Fanie, 'you're going to find out your missstake. You're going
to find out that you're not half as clever as you've been
allowed to think you are.'

Fanie stared at Mr de Wet, presumably as mystified as the
rest of us, except that Fanie registered mystification no more
vividly than any other emotion. There was something so
grotesque in Fanie's being accused of intellectual presumption
that I choked back a giggle.

Mr de Wet came walking towards me, his eyes still fixed on
Fanie. 'Why are you sniggering?' he demanded, and I looked
at Fanie in perplexity; he was not known to snigger.

'Don't look away when I'm ssspeaking to you,' Mr de Wet
hissed, and slapped me on the side of the head. Then he sidled
back to the front of the class. 'I'll teach you sssome respect
for authority,' he said. 'Classs sssit.' As I slid into my seat
rubbing my cheek I recollected Ssscorpion's famous obliquity
of vision and ruefully reflected that half had not been told me;
he had so *obviously* been looking at Fanie.

What made this such an insidious deviation was that in
order to allow for the defects of Mr de Wet's vision one had
to distrust one's own; no matter how often one had
mistakenly interpreted the direction of his gaze, one always
made the same mistake again, because it was so hard to
believe that Mr de Wet did not see what he seemed so
obviously to be looking at. In any case, it would have taken
more confidence in our own powers of geometry than any of
us possessed to have calculated the degree of error and
compensated for it. Not long ago, while having my eyes

examined, I asked the ophthalmologist 'Is it possible to have a deviation that makes it look as if you're looking at something you're not looking at?'

'Yes', he said, deftly juggling his little lenses. 'Macular degeneration. No sign of it here. Now – which is the sharper, one or two?'

It seems strange now that we so unquestioningly accepted not only Mr de Wet's authority but also the apparent hatred of us which that authority gave him licence to express. We never asked each other why he should seem to hate us; we simply accepted that he did and hoped that somebody else would be selected that day. His favourite method of terrorism was to place himself straight in front of his victim, so that, whatever the direction of his gaze, the victim knew for once that he – or even she – had been selected. Then Mr de Wet would pose whatever question he had thought up for the day, stand back and wait for the mumbled 'I don't know, sir,' which was the invariable response. 'I can't hear you,' he would say in a quiet voice. 'Don't mumble and don't look down and ANSWER ME!' The moment the panic-stricken victim started speaking, Mr de Wet would close his fist lightly with the thumb resting upward on top of the other fingers, and bring the hand thus armed swiftly and sharply under the chin of the stuttering child. When well timed, this manoeuvre caught you with your tongue between your slack jaws, causing you to bite your own tongue with some violence.

'Bitten your tongue, have you?' he would say with feigned concern. 'You shouldn't mumble like that,' and away he would sidle, looking almost human in the glow of his pleasure. If, on the other hand, the blow was ill-timed and the victim managed to escape unbitten, Mr de Wet would sourly retreat to his desk and inflict various refinements of torture on us for the rest of the day.

Nobody thought of complaining to some figure of authority, the principal, a parent, about this treatment: to us, Ssscorpion *was* authority, or its representative in our midst. A system of education based on the belief that all authority is derived from God does not encourage its victims to complain about the treatment meted out to them. We accepted Mr de Wet as our doom for the next two years, and it is likely that this is what our parents would have advised us to do in any case if we had complained to them; my mother, though suspicious of authority and scornful of our teachers, did not believe in intervening on her children's behalf, on the grounds that this simply caused the children to be victimised. Mr de Wet himself assured us periodically, when he was moved to admiration of his own methods of education, that he was acting purely from a concern for our education and moral welfare: 'Love without dissscipline is sssentimentality,' he would say, 'and dissscipline without love is tyranny; but love with dissscipline is the nourishment of the sssoul.' Those sitting in the front row had learnt to close their exercise books during these eulogies, so as not to get them blotted with the liquid sibilance of Mr de Wet's enthusiasm. Children had been punished – by Mr de Wet – for blots on their exercise books caused by his wet sputter.

For Mr de Wet's delight in inflicting torment was coupled, and I now believe intimately connected, with a simpering and yet bullying sentimentality. Not that we recognised it as that: we merely cringed away from his effusions as we did from the slaps and jeers that so often followed them. Nothing served so well these two impulses of Mr de Wet's soul as the business of essay-writing, which enabled him to set us the most impossibly exalted topics and humiliate us most basely for failing to live up to the nobility of the theme. One particularly successful topic was announced simply as 'Something I love'.

'Use your imaginations, children,' he said. 'Free your ssstarved little sssouls from their tiny prisons inside those dirty little bodies and for once let them breathe and sssspeak.'

Our souls failed to rise to the occasion. The class sat in dumb despair for the hour allowed for the release of their souls and produced, in most instances, a few pathetic lines of insincere gush on a subject on which the writer had obviously never before wasted a thought, not to mention a stirring of the soul. The delightful part of the exercise for Mr de Wet was in then obliging us to read our fraudulent little raptures to a giggling and yet terrified class, while he himself hovered around the reader, right hand at the ready.

Jesserina was the first victim. 'Something I love,' she read, and then started giggling.

'What's the matter, Jessss-erina?' asked Mr de Wet, scuttling up to her. 'You were sssupposed to write on sssomething you love not sssomething that amusesss you. Now carry on.' He went and stood next to her and stared attentively at a spot twenty degrees to the right of her face.

Jesserina desperately gulped down her hysteria and started again in a quavering voice. 'Something I love,' she read as fast as possible, 'is the sound of rain on the roof after a drought and the smell of the raindrops on the dusty ground and the sight of the sunset over the veld.' She stopped abruptly and said 'That's all.'

'Mmm,' said Ssscorpion, in a tone which we had learnt to recognise with relief as the hum of a frustrated urge to inflict punishment. 'Your sssoul hasn't travelled very far from home, has it?' He scuttled on. 'Now Tjaart,' he said, fixing his gaze on Japie Dreyer, 'you tell us what you love.'

There was a nervous titter in the class. Our terror could not altogether dispel our sense of the incongruity of Tjaart Bothma's loving anything other than the rugby ball which he took everywhere with him as if hoping to hatch it. He got to his feet heavily and read haltingly in the deep voice which had earned him the prominence he normally enjoyed amongst our squeaky trebles. 'Something I love. Something I love is my mother and father and sisters and brothers and all our cows.' The titters turned into giggles. Tjaart's father, old Koot Bothma, was about the most unlovable human being in the district of Verkeerdespruit, with the possible exception of his wife Ralie, who had once concussed her husband by throwing the telephone at him. Telephones in those regions were heavy and wooden and fixed to the wall. My mother said it wasn't nice to damage government property but she could see Ralie Bothma's point. As for their cows, Koot Bothma's dairy had two years earlier brought a particularly nasty epidemic of brucellosis upon Verkeerdespruit and its neighbours as far as Clocolan, not counting the tractor salesman from Pretoria who had drunk a glass of milk at breakfast in Loubser's Hotel, to dilute the hangover incurred the night before in an attempt to liven up a Tuesday evening in Verkeerdespruit. The *Landstem* had reported the incident under the headline 'Hangover cure almost kills man: victim vows to keep to brandy.'

'Sssilence!' hissed Mr de Wet. 'Tjaart, just because you've grown up with cattle doesn't mean we want to listen to cow dung.' We roared with the laughter of pent-up fear, knowing that this was allowed, indeed expected, whenever Mr de Wet's jokes were at the expense of one of us. 'Sssilence!' he hissed again, but with a pleased sort of sibilance, like a snake trying to purr.

It was my turn next. So intimidated was I by authority that I deferred even to as perverted a representative of it as Mr de Wet; and I never quite lost an absurd hope of after all pleasing this man whose pleasure lay in the pain of others. So I had taken the topic seriously and had earnestly reflected on something I loved. This proved to be unexpectedly difficult, like writing an essay on the smell of snow or the taste of persimmons. I had heard of love, of course, but mainly as something which parents felt as a matter of course for their children and which children were duty bound to feel back. It did not seem to be the stuff essays were made of. In Sunday school I had learnt that love was unselfish and put the happiness of others before its own, like Jesus getting crucified or little Racheltjie de Beer freezing to death trying to keep her younger brother warm in the ant-hill. It seemed an impractical sort of emotion, and I couldn't remember ever experiencing it, until I thought of Dumbo. After all, I almost never forgot to feed him, even when it was inconvenient for me, and when I went out in the afternoons I usually took him along even if it did mean walking rather than cycling. This seemed incontrovertible evidence as defined by the best authorities. 'Something I love,' I read. 'Something I love is my dog Dumbo. He is called Dumbo because when he was small he looked so much like an elephant and . . .'

'Jumbo,' said Mr de Wet.

I looked at him enquiringly. 'Dumbo,' I said.

'Jumbo,' he repeated. 'Elephants are called Jumbo.'

'But . . . ' I began. One did not lightly contradict Mr de Wet; it was so obviously what he wanted. But he had sniffed the heady smell of insubordination needing to be corrected.

'But what, Sssimon?' he asked in his most reasonable tone, the one that we knew to herald the lightning strike of the clenched hand.

'But my dog is called Dumbo,' I said, except it came out as Ut my og is alled Umbo, as I tried to keep my tongue clear of my teeth.

'That I do not doubt,' he said sweetly. 'But then he is not called after an elephant. Perhaps he is called Dumbo because he is very dumb?' he suggested helpfully, the lightly clenched hand swaying by his side. The class tittered obligingly.

'Dumbo was the name of an elephant in a film,' I explained, even while knowing that Mr de Wet did not want an explanation. He wanted a disagreement.

'Are you sssaying I am wrong?' he asked.

'No,' I said desperately, and then did not know how to continue. 'No,' I repeated lamely.

'If I'm not wrong I must be right, not ssso?'

'Yes Mr de Wet.'

'Then your dog was not called after an elephant after all?'

'No, Mr de Wet.'

'Then why did you say it was?'

'I don't know, Mr de Wet.'

'SSSit down SSSimon. If that's the best you can do for something you love I advise you to give up love as sssoon as posssible.'

I was relieved to escape without physical injury, but my dignity was rather bruised; and when I went home that afternoon I felt somehow disloyal to Dumbo when he bounded up to me, boisterously unaware of my treachery. I was sure that this was the effect that Mr de Wet had calculated, with his preternatural sense of how to inflict pain; what I couldn't understand was why he would go to such elaborate lengths to do so. Most children accepted unquestioningly that Mr de Wet's methods were simply his methods, and as such did not require any explanation. I, however, was puzzled, not so much at the unprovoked violence of his general demeanour as at the unmistakable targeting of myself. Used as I was to being the teacher's favourite, the best reader, the quickest at mental arithmetic, and probably also the cleanest child in class (I had been the only one to escape the ringworm epidemic the previous year), I was unpleasantly surprised to meet a teacher who not only seemed not to appreciate my superiority but actually treated me as if I were the class dunce deviously trying to pass myself off as the star pupil. There was no point in discussing the puzzle with my friends, because they were merely amused. 'Serves you right for always sucking up,' said Louis van Niekerk, and even Fanie smiled faintly at the justice of it. Nothing was more of a mystery to Fanie than anything else.

So I discussed the matter with one of the few adults who wouldn't regard it as her duty to reconcile me to the privileges of authority, Betty the Exchange. In one of our Saturday afternoon sessions in Steyl's Café I asked her 'Do you know Mr de Wet?'

'Ben de Wet at the school?' she asked. 'Yes. He phones his mother in Hopetown every afternoon from the tickey box in the hostel.'

This was new light on Mr de Wet. 'Oh,' I said. 'Well, I think he's . . . strange.'

'You bet he's strange,' Betty said flatly. 'He calls her *Mammie-lief*.' This was one of the few times I heard Betty repeat any of the conversations she must have overheard regularly from her lonely listening-post in the post office. The idea of Ssscorpion calling his mother *Mummy dear* was grotesque, but I was too preoccupied with my own mystification to spare a thought for Mr de Wet's filial devotion.

'Yes, but I don't mean like that,' I tried to explain. 'He's different to other teachers. He says I'm stupid.' Saying it, I realised why I was telling Betty this: she wouldn't regard it as her duty to assure me that perhaps I *was* stupid and I shouldn't be arrogant. Instead she said quite factually 'Yes. He's jealous.'

'Jealous?' I asked blankly. I could see no relation between Ssscorpion and me that merited jealousy.

'Yes. Because of Ariana Jordaan.' Betty and Miss Jordaan were known to be 'best friends', which, as just about the only two unmarried white women in town, they had little chance of avoiding.

'But . . .' I started.

'Yes,' she repeated. 'Didn't you know that he was in love with her?'

'I knew he took her out a few times.' He had brought her to the Saturday night movie in the Town Hall once, causing so much whispering and craning of necks that the projectionist had stopped his machine and told us to behave ourselves.

'Yes. Well, he asked her to marry him and she said no. In fact she said that he gave her the creeps. That is, I'm sure she didn't put it like that, but that's what she meant and that's what he understood. He said that she'd *mortified his pride.*'

'But . . .' I interjected, but Betty was now in full spate.

'Yes. You mean what does this have to do with you. Well you must know that you were Ariana's favourite pupil.'

'Yes,' I said.

'And teachers tend to discuss their pupils with each other.'

'Do they?' I asked, less interested in the conversational opportunities of teachers than in my unexpected prominence in the intrigue.

'You bet they do. It can be very boring being trapped with a bunch of teachers. Well, Ariana told Ben about you while he was still courting her, and he came to see you as in some way specially favoured by her. So that when he was rejected by her, you see, he took it out on you.'

'How do you know?' I asked, in awe at Betty's omniscience.

'I don't *know,*' she said, 'but I'm not a fool, and that's

what I think. Ben de Wet sees you as Ariana's favourite. And
he's still in love with her.'

'But that's unfair,' I protested.

'You bet it's unfair,' said Betty laconically. 'But how else
can he get back at her?'

Betty's explanation helped me as much as explanations of the
inevitable ever can: it gave me a vantage point from which to
survey my own helplessness. Since I now knew that Ssscorpion's displeasure had nothing to do with my efforts or
abilities, I did not feel seriously challenged by his slights.
Besides, apart from the initial slap, he limited his assaults
upon me to verbal sallies, ridicule, and sarcasm, which,
though unpleasant, lost some of their sting with familiarity.
And so it might have remained had I not been emboldened by
the knowledge of my special status in Ssscorpion's emotional
world to test my own power to vex.

At the end of the previous year I had sent a Christmas card
to Miss Jordaan, all the way to Calvinia where her parents
lived. To my great joy I received a card in return, a gaudy and
obviously home-made but to me beautiful confection of holly
and sparkling snow. The latter was pasted onto the card, and
shed glitter all over our lounge carpet when I hung the card
on the string strung annually for the purpose. But more
precious to me even than the tinsel glamour was the
inscription inside: 'To Simon, with love from (Miss) Ariana
Jordaan.' It was written on a slip of paper pasted inside the
card, and Louis van Niekerk said that it was obviously a used
card which Miss Jordaan had recycled, but my mother said
she'd probably just made a mistake writing the inscription the
first time and hadn't wanted to scratch it out.

Once a week we had to hand in our classwork books to Mr
de Wet for inspection. The idea of the classwork book was
that we could work in rough before copying the correct
version into a neatwork book, but Mr de Wet insisted that
our classwork books should also be neat, and was hard on
transgressions. So receiving back the classwork books was
always an anxious business; after he had examined the books

in his own time, he handed them out, commenting on individual messiness or general obstreperousness as best suited his mood. At best it was an opportunity for him to exercise his sense of humour; at worst it turned into a full-scale torture session.

It occurred to me that it might be an interesting experiment to leave Miss Jordaan's card in my book as if as a bookmark. What I hoped to achieve by this I have no idea; I think I simply wanted to see what Mr de Wet would do. I realised that this was unlikely to be anything very pleasant, but I reassured myself that since I was not supposed to know about his attachment to Miss Jordaan, my act could not be interpreted as deliberate. I counted also on his reluctance to admit publicly to his rejection; by and large I probably thought that by mortifying his soul a bit more I might avenge some small portion of the suffering he'd wrought upon us.

When the handing-out ritual came round again, Ssscorpion returned my classwork book to me without comment, usually a sign that he could not find anything to criticise or ridicule. I soon noticed, though, that the card was missing, and from the way Ssscorpion hovered around my desk while handing out the other books I surmised that he was waiting for me to comment on its absence – which of course I could not do without forfeiting the pretence that I had absent-mindedly left the card in the book. So I reconciled myself to the loss of my card as the price of my experiment.

But I should have known that Ssscorpion's displeasure was not to be bought off so cheaply. He had finished handing out the books and was walking past my desk as if on his way back to the front of the class. Suddenly he paused, as if in mid-stride.

'What's that?' he asked, and pointed at my desk as if there were a particularly vile substance smeared over it. At first I could see nothing, and he said 'Are you going to answer me?' still pointing.

I shook my head dumbly. I knew by now that Mr de Wet's questions were never rhetorical: he expected an answer, if only so that he could ridicule or punish its inadequacy. So I took refuge in the flimsy all-purpose shelter of the tormented scholar, and said 'I don't know.'

'You don't know?' he asked. 'Your desk is covered in the stuff and you *don't know* what it is?'

He extended a finger and pressed it on a particle of glitter that had sifted out of the book.

'Get up when I'm talking to you!' he said. Dumbly I obeyed, and he took up my book again.

'It ssseems to be coming out of your book,' he said, and took my book by one page so that it flapped open downwards like a dead chicken. Silver glitter sifted down.

'Look classs, a sssnowstorm,' he hissed. 'Sssimon's book has produced a sssnowstorm.' There were dutiful chuckles, feebly hoping to propitiate or deflect the malice about to be released upon the class; but Ssscorpion was wise to the wiles of the terrified, and rounded on the rest of the class. 'If Sssimon can't tell us where the sssnow comes from, you'll have to help him,' he said, and we knew an interrogation was in progress. 'Sssit down, Sssimon.' Keeping my book dangling down in his left hand, he dragged himself around the class, picking victims at random, calling upon them to name the mystery substance. It was the old tongue-biting trick, presented as the consequence of my refusal to identify the offending substance. Since glitter was not a feature of the lives of Verkeerdespruit children, none of them knew what it was, although Bettie du Plooy did venture a guess that it could be cake decoration.

'Cake decoration?' Ssscorpion exclaimed. 'Simon, have you been eating cake in your classwork book?'

'No, Mr de Wet,' I said.

'No, Bettie,' he said. 'Sssimon says no. Try again.'

The terrified Bettie shook her head. 'What was that?' he said politely, leaning forward. 'I didn't hear what you said?'

'I said . . .' Bettie began, and Ssscorpion's hand shot out like a snake striking. She squealed slightly as she bit her tongue.

'Sit down,' he said, and moved on in his relentless progress through the class. He stopped in front of Fanie's desk, next to where I was sitting mutely awaiting what I now realised was a reckoning.

'Fanie,' he said, in his most pleasant tone. 'Can you help us?'

Fanie got to his feet. I could see that he was trembling.

'Come on Fanie,' he said, 'I'm waiting for an answer.'

Fanie started perspiring slightly. He licked his lips and prepared to say something, then his courage abandoned him and he stared down at his desk.

'Look at me when I'm talking to you,' said Mr de Wet, and Fanie lifted his clouded blue eyes at him. 'Sssuch a sssimple question,' Mr de Wet continued. 'What is this ssstuff that Sssimon has in his book?' and he opened the book at the spot where the card had nestled, leaving behind a particularly rich crop of glitter.

Fanie looked at the book and then looked at me in dumb anguish, and I slowly got to my feet. Ssscorpion shifted his gaze twenty degrees to the right of me.

'And why are you getting up?' he asked in his most reasonable tones.

'Because I can answer your question,' I said.

'You've had your chance,' he said. 'It's Fanie's turn now. Sssit down,' and the eyes swivelled back.

'The shiny stuff is glitter from a Christmas card,' I persisted. 'I used the card as a bookmark.'

Ssscorpion had moved very quickly to stand in front in me. 'And why did you not say so when I asked you?' he demanded.

'Because the card was from Miss Jordaan and was my own special card and you stole it,' I rattled off desperately, but not fast enough to escape the lightly clenched hand. Except that this time it was not lightly clenched and seemed to be aimed at the side of my face. Or perhaps I ducked my head in an attempt to avoid the blow under the chin; it happened much too quickly for me to be aware of much except the astonishing pain in my jaw before I passed out. So I missed the excitement, and had to be told about it by Louis van Niekerk when he came to visit me at home where I was resting with a wired-up jaw. Apparently I collapsed forward on top of Mr de Wet, Jesserina Schoeman got hysterical, and Fanie had another fit, cutting his temple against the side of her desk as he fell.

There was no explaining away my broken jaw, otherwise I do believe the school would have tried to do so. But this time they were up against my mother, who insisted that 'something' had to be done. She agreed not to lay a criminal charge of assault only on condition that Mr de Wet was reported to the provincial authorities in Bloemfontein. The school committee wrote a report and submitted it to the authorities. The authorities instructed the school committee to investigate the incident more fully and make a recommendation. 'And I suppose the school committee will refer the matter back to Mr de Wet and ask him to make a recommendation,' my mother said.

'Not quite,' said my father, who was on the school committee. 'They'll try to avoid scandal, but I imagine they'll take a serious view of the offence.'

'What will happen to Mr de Wet?' I asked.

'I don't know. It's for the school committee to decide.'

'But you're on the school committee.'

'Well yes, but I can't decide for them. I'll tell you after the meeting.'

A week later my father announced at table: 'The school committee has decided to recommend that Mr de Wet be transferred to another school.'

'To go and break somebody else's jaw?' my mother demanded.

'Well, they thought that perhaps there were special circumstances in this particular class . . .'

'You mean they think Simon deserved to have his jaw broken?'

'No, but the headmaster said that sometimes a particular teacher just has a difficult relationship with a particular class, and that a different environment might be better adapted to

Mr de Wet's teaching methods. It seems it's a matter of pedagogical dynamics.'

'And the school committee bought that?'

'Well, Dominee Claassen said that the Bible teaches us to turn the other cheek . . .'

'Turn the other cheek!' my mother exploded. 'Look at the boy sitting there with his jaw wired up! Does the Bible say what you have to do if your jaw gets broken the first time round?'

'I did suggest that it was perhaps an unfortunate metaphor under the circumstances and that the man might not be fit to deal with children, but I couldn't very well push too hard, or people might think I wasn't objective, what with Simon being my son.'

'I should have thought that it had been quite objectively enough established that your son's jaw was broken by this man. What do they want – an x-ray?'

'Well, nobody actually *said* anything, it was just an unspoken implication. In the end majority opinion was that he should be given another chance elsewhere.'

'Majority opinion my foot!' my mother said. 'The majority of the school committee, perhaps, but did they think of consulting the children who had to put up with this man's *teaching methods*?'

This seemed like an opening for me to interrupt, so I asked 'Then Mr de Wet won't appear in court?'

'No,' my father said.

'Why not?'

'Well, he didn't commit a crime, you see.'

'So he didn't . . . molest me?'

He looked half puzzled, half amused, and asked: 'Why do you want to know?'

'Because – because they sent Steve to prison for molesting Fanie.'

'I see. No, what Mr de Wet did wasn't molesting.'

'But . . .'

'Yes?'

'Why is it molesting for Steve to kiss Fanie but not for Mr de Wet to break my jaw?'

My father looked at my mother, but she just shrugged and said 'You explain it.'

'Well,' said my father. 'It's all a matter of definition, don't you see?'

'No.'

'Oh. Do you know what I mean by a matter of definition?'

'No.'

'Oh. Well, if I say something is a matter a definition I mean that a word means something because it's been decided that that's what it means.'

'Like the Sabotage Act,' my mother said.

'Yes,' my father said, 'I suppose like the Sabotage Act. Have you heard of the Sabotage Act?'

'I've seen it in the papers.' The Sabotage Act had been passed the year before.

'Well, then, sabotage used to mean planting a bomb and blowing up something; but the Sabotage Act now defines sabotage in such a way that it can mean well, lots of other things.'

'Anything that the government regards as a threat to itself,' my mother interjected.

My father carried on. 'So sabotage is now, as I was saying, a matter of definition.'

'And who makes the definitions?'

'The people in charge, the people who make the laws. In the case of the Sabotage Act, the law defines certain acts as sabotage and punishes them accordingly; in Fanie's case, the law defines a grown-up man kissing a boy that he's not related to as molesting and sends the man to prison.'

'But why?'

'Well, as punishment for the crime, and to protect other people.'

'You mean because he may kiss other people too?'

My father looked at my mother and sighed. 'Not quite. Let's just say for an adult to . . . be too fond of children is not . . . natural.'

'Is it natural for an adult to hit children?'

'Well not *natural*, perhaps, but it may be necessary if the adult is in a position of authority.'

'I'm sorry,' my mother broke in. She didn't normally contradict my father in front of me. 'But you're not going to convince me that it was necessary for that man to break Simon's jaw. He's a sadist and he should be removed from his position of authority.'

'Well, yes,' my father said. 'I agree with you, if the man is a sadist he must be removed from office. But by the committee's definition he isn't a sadist.'

'Then the committee should have its definitions shaken up. What's the point of being a magistrate if you can't see to it that justice is done?'

'Well, I don't have jurisdiction outside the court.'

'And soon you won't have jurisdiction inside the court either, the way things are going.'

'That's not really the point, is it?' asked my father.

'I don't know,' my mother said. 'Perhaps that's the real point.'

At the end of that year Mr de Wet was transferred to Bantu Education, and disappeared from our lives. I saw him again years later. I was in my uniform in Pretoria; he was waiting for a bus on Church Square. He looked older, of course, but when the bus arrived he scuttled towards it with the same fierce energy that had so terrified us in that stifling classroom. Seeing that mad little scurry, I moved forward on an impulse of sudden hatred, and blocked his path. All the things I had felt as a child came back to me with a clarity I had not known at the time; I now knew the injustices he had wrought upon us and could name to his face the distortions of his spirit. I could confront the man with his own misshapen soul and bring him to account for the terror he had inflicted upon trembling children. I was considerably taller than the hunched figure of Mr de Wet and I gave him time to take me in before I spoke. But as he lifted his head, he seemed oblivious of my presence, for all that I was standing right in front of him: he was reading an advertisement on the side of the bus. Short of grabbing him by the throat there seemed to be no way of claiming his attention. And then I remembered. Allowing for a deviation of twenty degrees, he must have been looking straight at me. Indeed, he was waiting for me to speak, with that air of polite attentiveness which had so terrified us, and instinctively I glanced down at his hand for the dreaded half-clenched fist. But the hand that used to shoot out so swiftly was dangling by his side motionlessly, except for the tell-tale tremor of Parkinson's disease. He put out his hand with the uncertain movement of a blind person and I realised that indeed he could not see me, or see more of me than a vague outline, that his macular degeneration had run its course.

Looking down at the half-blind, trembling, misshapen man, I could not pronounce my flaming curses, my indictment of my childhood and this man's part in it. What did come to me was almost as surprising to me as it must have been to him. 'Ben de Wet,' I said, leaning forward so that my face filled whatever vision he had left, 'Ariana Jordaan will never send you a Christmas card now.'

Simon Armitage

FLYPAPER

IT WAS AN age like today, when people were busy but had
time on their hands, time to be interested in many things.
Accordingly, after years as a minor figure with a cult
following, an installation artist had suddenly achieved fame
on a grand scale. Overnight, it seemed, he'd become a
household name, and ordinary people mentioned him, just as
they might talk about a decent brand of coffee, or the best
route to the airport.

His art was a kind of graffiti, usually in the form of an
indentation or outline left in concrete or cement before the
substance had set. Sometimes this might be a simple hand-
print or a line of footsteps, or a life-mask of the artist's face
pressed into a pavement or wall. But some of his more
ambitious work incorporated other materials, such as the pair
of iron gates erected at the top of the new motorway slip-
road one night, with the tread from the tyre of a monocycle
disappearing along the freshly laid tarmac. Or another piece
on a beach, in which the artist appeared to have emerged
slithering from the ocean, then propelled himself over several
miles on all fours, before the hand and footprints ended at the
base of a fifty-foot oak tree, planted in the sand. Every
installation was finished off with his trademark signature – a
blob of red wax with the fingerprint of his right thumb
pressed into it. It was the seal of authenticity, the mark of a
genius.

The art world had been the first to recognise the artist's
unique talent, embracing the work because of its complex

relationship with commerce, construction and the human figure. Books had been written and monographs published. The impromptu indentation of his buttocks in front of the main entrance of the New National Gallery of Sculpture had met with some private irritation, but for the main part, his work had become richly praised and highly prized, even if it wasn't clear who the pieces actually belonged to. All of the artwork appeared in public spaces or on private land. Not only did this make many of his actions illegal, it also prevented him from selling the work, or even owning it. Profit, of which there was plenty to be had, would go to the owner of whichever site or venue the artist chose for his project. The word would go round, queues would form, money would be made. Some pieces were removed, inch by inch, sold on for a fortune and reconstructed in more convenient locations. This, said the art world, was one more irony, made pertinent by the blob of wax imitating the red dots stuck on paintings at previews and exhibitions, indicating a sale.

Because the artist's activities almost always involved the breaking of laws, he remained anonymous and mysterious. Some said he was a high-born gentleman with nothing better to do. Some said he was a vagrant living rough on the streets, killing time. Others suspected an already established artist, moonlighting between less fashionable work such as portraiture or prospect painting. He was a man – they could tell from the thumbprint, but that was all they could tell.

It was this kind of speculation that caught the attention of the media, beginning with the popular press, who condemned the artist as a public nuisance and a vandal. Longer, more thoughtful articles appeared in the broadsheets, and magazines from *House and Garden* to *The Commune* featured photographs of the installations, presenting them as anything from decorative chic to statements of revolution. A chat-show host put up a sum of money for anyone unmasking the artist, and the sum was doubled by one of the tabloids, hoping to be the first to catch and expose him.

With a price on his head, the artist carried on, apparently

undaunted or unaware. A peculiar-looking fossil was handed in to the British Museum, which when tapped open revealed a cast of the artist's clenched fist with the tell-tale red wax like a thimble over his thumb. And when a new flag was hoisted over Government House on Citizens' Day, it unfurled in the wind, revealing the cut-out shape of a human form, with an outstretched hand and an upright thumb, like a cocked trigger. Imposters came forward to claim the reward. Others were falsely accused, but no one could match the thumbprint that was now held on police files as well as in the trophy cupboards of art collectors and behind glass in the more important galleries. And while the country grew excited and impatient, greedy for news, desperate to put a name and face to the invisible man, the artist carried on regardless, striking wherever he pleased, going about his work. Under cover of darkness, some new installation would emerge, more daring and enigmatic than the last. By first light, journalists and film crews would be crawling all over the site, filing copy for the next edition.

In a small town in the north of England, council leader Perry gave a back-heel to his office door, causing it to slam violently and his nameplate to come loose and swing from the one remaining nail. He studied the fax in his hand again – popularity ratings from the latest opinion poll, with his name half-way down the list – then screwed it into a tight ball and lobbed it towards the bin in the corner of the room. Perry picked up the phone, lighting a cigarette at the same time.

'Plan B,' he said, blowing smoke towards the sprinkler valve on the ceiling. 'Yes, bring the drawings.'

For the next two hours, Perry and his chief architect, Rossiter, bent over a blueprint diagram rolled open across Perry's heavy, antique desk, staked out with one overflowing ashtray and three half-empty coffee cups. As Perry talked, ash fell on to the plans, which Rossiter blew away with small, delicate puffs of breath. When Perry stood up from the drawing he left two, sweaty handprints, blotted on to the paper. Finally, they carried the plans over to the window and peered down into the town square, pointing at the half-derelict fountain and paddling pool, then at the surrounding gardens and walls in various states of repair, then looking back at the plans.

'What about a skate-park, for skateboards?' asked Rossiter.

'Whatever. Just get it nodded through.'

They stared again into the square, then again at the plans.

'How do you know he'll come?'

'He's got two chances,' said Perry. He let a thick trail of smoke rise from his lips, drawing it up through his nose then blowing back out of his mouth. 'But if he does, we're in clover. They'll be flocking here from Timbuktu. I'll be the donkey's bollocks, and you'll still have a job, so keep your mouth shut, your thumb up your arse and your fingers crossed.'

Rossiter shook the remaining ash from the plans, rolled them up and fastened them with a rubber band from around his wrist.

'When?' asked Perry.

'Monday,' said Rossiter. 'Tuesday latest.'

On his way out he picked up the screwed-up ball of paper from the floor.

'Do you need this?' he said.

But Perry had gone outside on to the balcony with a cup of cold coffee and another cigarette.

'We'll nail that cunt,' he said to nobody whatsoever, as Rossiter left the office, closing the door carefully, sticking back Perry's nameplate with the blob of blu-tack he always carried with him, just in case.

It was Wednesday by the time the bulldozers moved in to demolish the fountain, and Friday before the earth-movers could begin, scooping out tons of soil and rubble with their massive yellow claws, churning up the dirt with their tank-tracks, sending great plumes of diesel fumes into the air.

Wagons queued at the gates to shunt the unwanted stone and earth to a landfill site on the edge of town, and muddy tyre-marks ran through the streets, out towards the ring-road. By Monday when the three diggers were carried away on the back of a low-loading transporter, the site looked like a bomb crater, a shapeless hole about fifty feet in diameter and some twenty feet deep at its centre. On his balcony, in his best suit with the big lapels and hand-carved buttons, council leader Perry entertained journalists from the evening paper and a film crew from the local news.

'Yes, but the years go by,' he said, leaning towards the microphone in its fluffy windsock.

'Yesterday's square is tomorrow's circle. We must move with the times.'

'Wasn't it a bit rash, flattening the old fountain without any real plans for its future use?' asked one reporter, holding out a dictaphone towards Perry's mouth.

'Not rash, no. We felt we had to take the initiative. There are too many people . . .'

'Haven't you demolished a piece of history?' interrupted a woman from the television crew.

Perry smiled.

'We are making history,' he said, firmly. 'Tomorrow they'll fill it in, concrete it over. Then we can start again with a level playing field and a blank sheet.'

The camera panned towards the great hole as a man in a council donkey-jacket ran a length of orange tape around the remaining trees, cordoning off the area.

With what seemed like an afterthought, Perry added: 'That artist. What's-his-name. He'd have a field day if he got loose in this.' Then he laughed.

It was a remark he repeated several times during the day to the dozen or so reporters who called at his office, helping themselves to the free Bulgarian wine and sausage rolls.

The cement-mixers arrived in a convoy, and for two days poured load after load of creamy white slurry into the hole, until the area was flat, and a film of chalky water sat on top of the concrete, reflecting the sky. The wagons left with their great mixers still churning and their orange lights flashing against the walls of buildings. It was Wednesday night. A good week's work by anyone's measure, thought Perry, as he rocked back in his chair and watched the sun going down behind the bank on the far side of the square. He held a walkie-talkie in one hand, and in the other a cigarette.

Some time not long after midnight, a figure entered the square. There were no streetlights left standing, but a full moon gave a bright, silvery glow, and the figure circled the calm, concrete swamp three or four times before disappearing into a side-street. The square was deserted, roped off to the public, and the buildings to each side were closed down for the night, or vacant. Ten minutes later the figure reappeared, and Perry watched from behind the smoked glass of his office window.

'Bingo,' he said to himself, under his breath.

The figure was carrying a rucksack on his back. Sometimes in silhouette and sometimes as a shadow, he again circled the concrete before producing a rope from the bag and tossing it up over the branch of a tree, then pulling it tight. He walked around to the opposite side, feeding out the rope along the ground, then threw it into another tree, and hauled at it until it became taut. It formed a kind of tightrope ten or fifteen foot high across the widest stretch of the concrete, and water dripped from where it had trailed in the wet. Perry now watched from binoculars, as the figure walked back to the first tree, shinned up to the branch and attached a pulley or some sort of wheel to the rope, then dropped to the ground. It was hard to make out what was happening, through the darkness and at such distance, but Perry thought he could see the man stripping off, undressing under the tree, and when he emerged into the moonlight he was wearing nothing more than a loose rag around his waist, or a loin cloth. The walkie-talkie squawked into life. It was Rossiter.

'It's him isn't it?'

'It's him all right,' said Perry.

'Right on cue,' said Rossiter. 'That concrete's on the turn. Another hour and it'll be rock hard. Just like you said.'

'Just like I said,' said Perry.

'Shall we move in then?' asked Rossiter.

'Where are you?'

'In the doorway of the bank, ready to go. Shall we move in?'

'No,' said Perry. 'Let him do his stuff. We'll nab him afterwards. Then we'll have the baby *and* the bathwater. Now keep quiet.'

The figure in the square had climbed the tree again, and was now setting out along the rope, hanging from the axle of the wheel, which served as a handle. As the wheel rolled forward, the man was transported out to the centre of the concrete, to the point where the rope sagged in the middle, letting him dangle just a foot or so above the surface. Perry could now see that the man was tall and thin, very slender and fit-looking, and that he wore on his head a kind of crown made of a single strand or loop. By re-focusing the binoculars, he could tell that it was barbed wire.

In total silence, and with what looked like practised ease, the figure then dropped from the rope, and in the next second was lying on his back in the drying concrete, his arms outstretched, level with the line of his shoulders, one leg crossed over the other at the ankles. Perry was quiet and still as he watched, and jumped when Rossiter's voice crackled on the radio.

'Now?'

'Wait,' said Perry. The rope still dithered with the vibration of being released, and the wheel danced on it, several feet above the man's face. Perry thought he could see the figure sinking further into the concrete, could even feel the cold, damp substance against his back, rising around his ribs and thighs, between his legs, under his armpits, behind his head.

Rossiter's loud whisper made him jump again.

'Now?' he hissed.

Perry gazed down at the man spread out beneath the sky, lying under the full glare of the moon which now stood exactly above, picking out every detail, making the whole picture like a image cast on a coin or a medal, or a scene reflected in a pool. Making it all perfect.

'Now,' replied Perry.

From high up in the branches of several trees, powerful lights shone down on to the square, and six or seven men in hard-hats and luminous jackets ran to the perimeter of the concrete. One of them, Rossiter, had sprinted to the base of one of the trees, and with a pair of long-handled bolt cutters, reached up and snipped the rope. The lights burned down on the white concrete, making it dazzle and shimmer. Perry, out on the balcony now, held the binoculars tight against his face, and thought he saw the man in the middle lift and turn his head slightly before easing it back into its mould. There was silence, and a moment or so of inaction, before Perry barked into his walkie-talkie. 'Get him out,' he ordered.

Down in the square there were hurried conversations between the men, before Rossiter picked up the loose end of the rope, and flicked and shook and whipped it, until part of it skipped over the concrete and rested against the artist's hand. But he made no movement. In fact, as Perry looked on, he could see that the concrete was rising around him, and had actually covered his ankles and his neck, making islands of his feet and his head, and was rising still further around the rest of his body. Rossiter was yelling at the man to stand up, to move, to get hold of the rope, but with his eyes closed and with a look of peaceful concentration on his face, he seemed content to lie there, inert and untroubled, sinking deeper and deeper, second by second, inch by inch.

'Get out there and grab him,' screamed Perry from his balcony, having given up on the walkie-talkie. Tentatively, with his suit trousers tucked into green wellington boots, Rossiter began wading into the concrete, holding the hand of another man for support, who held the hand of another, until four of them made a human chain, with Rossiter getting only ten or twelve feet into the creamy mush before it rose above

342

his knees, then suddenly to his middle. The four men fell over, but finally made it back to firm ground, covered in the thick white mud. As Perry bawled from up in his building, Rossiter tried again with the rope, then again with the human chain from seven or eight places around the circle, and sometimes made it to within five yards or so of the sinking man before the concrete took hold, like quicksand, and they scrambled back to shore. Eventually they collapsed under the trees, exhausted, their clothes heavy, clagged with the weight of the concrete setting on their clothes and boots. It was like porridge, porridge made from stone.

Out in the middle, the man was no more than a face now, then just a forehead, nose and lips, then just a hole where his open mouth took in air, then not even a hole. Apart from the still, smooth centre where the man had disappeared, the rest of the area looked like a patch of old snow – sliced, disfigured, smudged, ugly and used.

Rossiter called into the walkie-talkie for instructions, but there was no reply. Perry had left the balcony and closed and locked the doors. Inside his darkened room, the intense and intermittent glow of a cigarette was the only light. Just now he wanted to fill his whole body with smoke, breathe in until it filled every inch of him, until it smothered every sense and every thought, until he was too dizzy to think. Then hold it there for as long as he could.

Toby Litt

A SMALL MATTER
FOR YOUR ATTENTION

I APOLOGISE, HOME SECRETARY , for intruding once again upon your hour of private meditation. It is fully apparent to me how precious, and yet how necessary, these few quiet moments are to you. However, I am afraid that there are some burdens of state whose assumption can be deferred no longer. If I might, perhaps, first make a suggestion: I believe the proximity of a desk would undoubtedly make these matters a mite easier to transact. And so, if we *were* able to relocate ourselves from the recreation room, splendidly comfortable as it is, to the official offices of state . . . Only a short walk, Home Secretary . . . I am most obliged . . . Oh, indeed, sir, my wife is more than well . . . And the children? *My* children? . . . Ah, yes . . . My wife assures me that they are thriving. The country air, don't you know . . . You are too kind for asking. I am touched that the Home Secretary troubles himself so to remember their names – it's more than I myself can do, at times, I assure you . . . Here we are. What a magnificent blotter you have! Antique, I shouldn't doubt . . . Really? Belonged to . . . What an *historical* mind you have, Home Secretary . . . If you would allow me one moment to get the papers in order. Yes, it is indeed 'a bit of a mountain', Home Secretary. However, in this case, Mohammed will not be necessary – my humble self will be the unmoved mover. Ahem . . . Forgive me . . . Where to start? Ah, well, I should – what was that phrase I learnt during that seminar the department was kind enough to send me on – I shall 'bring you up to speed' on the salient issues. Not, I may say, that the

Home Secretary's velocity has ever been in doubt . . . Yes, I am afraid that this *is* the matter that you have been avoiding – for reasons which bespeak your humanity quite plainly . . . All of this distasteful business has, of course, been conducted through our usual agents. William Morris Jr himself, no less, has taken a personal interest in negotiating some of the trickier paragraphs. If you had the time, Home Secretary, I'm sure you'd appreciate the bravura work on sub-section six, dealing with copyright. *Alors. On commence* . . . If the Home Secretary could just sign here, here, here and here; and initial wherever I've put a cross. Then, if you could sign at the end here. This? This here is, let me just have a look, . . . ah, yes, this is for television rights. In the end we've plumped for the BBC – they're going to employ an 'in-house' producer. I hear he's *very* good. He covered last year's Grand National, so he has experience of live broadcasting. There was some debate as to whether we shouldn't move to one of the other channels. To remain with the BBC was, perhaps, a trifle conservative. But, whatever else you may say about them (and their record on your own administration is hardly untarnished), they *do* know how to do royalty. It'll be the usual tried-and-tested format: ominous music, sombre voice-over. We don't want anything too graphic, either. The blood-on-the-lens episode will not soon be forgotten . . . Are you quite all right, Home Secretary? A glass of water, perhaps? . . . I could always come back later . . . Oh, sir, you are a true Stakhanovite of bureaucracy . . . Of course, the Tower is an absolute gift of a location. We've had directors literally coming to physical blows over the chance to get a shot at this thing. America is doing pay-per-view, as usual. That's your signature here. And, ahem, here. We've decided to hold off on the Japanese – they're always a trifle tardy, I find. But they have a tendency to 'come in big' at the eleventh hour. Anyway . . . My, we are getting through this very rapidly aren't we? . . . If you could just initial here and here . . . Beheadings, you know, have a certain rarity value these days. Of course, the Saudis did try to flood the market a couple of years ago. But, honestly, who wants to see another dusky adulteress spilling her life-blood on the dusty square? (That's flooding the market in quite another sense.) It's the romance people want. The combination of high treason and low cunning, modern technology and ancient ritual . . . All the radio stations will be covering it, as usual – though I don't really see the point . . . Has the Home Secretary ever heard one of their Execution Specials? Quite extraordinary . . . They use football commentators, for the most part. The beheading is referred to the whole way through as if it were a penalty shoot-out. ('He places the prisoner's head on the block, takes two slow paces back. Does he look nervous to you, Bob?' 'Well, Jim, in five years at this game, he's got a 95% kill-rate on the first chop.' 'That's world-class isn't it, Bob?' Etcetera, etcetera.) One of the commercial stations actually calls their show, 'The Ultimate Penalty.' Oh, now we come on to the subcontract for the Executioner. There's a flat fee for the job. His agent did try to up that quite considerably, this time. The Executioner – or Mr Ex, as the tabloids call him – has become something of a minor celebrity since taking over the position. He puts himself about a bit – opening supermarkets and village fêtes, that sort of thing. I've heard that he places the red ribbon across a chopping-block and then severs it with a blow from the ceremonial axe. (Not the actual axe, Home Secretary, I must assure you. That is kept locked within a special safe at the Tower.) Mr Ex's whole performance is very theatrical . . . Why, the Home Secretary looks quite green about the gills. Are you sure I can't fetch something? . . . Still on the Executioner's contract. These clauses, here and here, deal with insurance – in case, for example, he injures his back during the decapitation itself. There's an invoice, too, for the employment of one Executioner's Assistant. He's a keen lad. On one of your Work Experience schemes, I hear . . . Plus, of course, there are the usual waivers. We can't have the administration open to accusations of amateur butchery, now can we? A certified medical practitioner will be on hand to declare the Condemned officially dead. We've had some difficulty filling this position – the tabloids' Doctor Death tag has rather a tendency to stick, and there's also some technicality to do with the Hippocratic Oath. If the Condemned weren't dead (hardly likely after having fifty kilos of finest Sheffield stainless steel slicing through his spinal column) the medic would apparently have to try and save his life. But we've located an amenable, if rather – ahem – dissolute General Practitioner . . . Next are the Condemned-Related contracts. I expect you know the form by now – dietician, aerobics instructor, representative of religious denomination of choice. This particular Condemned has requested a Catholic Priest. In terms of television rights, this has certainly helped – demographically – in Spain, Italy, Poland and Latin America. Even Ireland's a territory not to be scoffed at. We've made a small killing there . . . Oh, Home Secretary, please believe me – that was entirely accidental. I realise that humour is entirely inappropriate at such a juncture . . . This here insures us against loss of revenue if the Condemned somehow manages to commit suicide before the day of the execution (which will be, let me see . . . November the 1st . . . All Saints, if I'm not mistaken). He *has* made threats. But please don't concern yourself over this: the man is under constant video surveillance 24 hours a day. The cash cow can't be allowed to cash its chips in quite so easily as all that – if you'll pardon the figure . . . What next? Oh, the hairdresser – of course. We've gone back to Vidal Sassoon – there were a few complaints last time that the long fringe Toni & Guy opted for got in the way. The classic prisoner's crew-cut seems due for a revival soon, but who can anticipate the whims of coiffeurish fashion? . . . Yves Saint Laurent has retained the costume contract – we feel a certain amount of continuity is desirable in this area. Black, well-cut, flattering – getting the basics right is what's important. People shouldn't be distracted from the matter in hand by admiring or execrating the cut of a garment . . . The traditional 'last meal' has proven a little tricky. However, we've kept these petty matters to ourselves – they are far beneath your compass, Home Secretary. If I might summarise: the Condemned, at first, requested his mother's Irish stew. But when it was made clear to him that

this was an impossibility, he agreed to have the Chef from
Maison Les Quatre Saisons ... Now, what's his name. I
never can remember. Anyway, he will be preparing the dish
from the Condemned's mother's recipe ... There was the
expected competition over Last Cigarette rights. Thank God
this one's a smoker, that's all I can say. The last three were a
dead loss as far as that was concerned. I mean, as if it's going
to make any difference to them! They might be a little more
considerate of other people, don't you think? In the end, we
forced Marlboro to pay at least half as much again as they
wanted. However, there are a few tricksy clauses in there that
I'd rather we'd got rid of. They are demanding a reduction in
costs if the Condemned smokes less than 50% of the entire
length of the cigarette. What they say is that this, if it
happens, reflects badly upon their product. I don't think I'm
misquoting their Chairman when he said, 'If all the time
you've got left in the world is the time you're smoking a
Marlboro Light, then you're going to damn well suck that
bitch like a Taiwanese ladyboy sucks his pimp's dick.' Excuse
me, Home Secretary, I don't know what came over me. I can't
apologise enough. However, those were his actual words ...
Then there are the normal spin-offs: video, merchandising. I'll
come to those a little later ... We've had about ten thousand
requests for handkerchiefs. The dipping, as usual, will be
taken care of after the public ceremony is over. The requisite
Certification of Authenticity will be sold along with each
hanky – a DNA printout, blood-type, photograph of the
corpse. The BBC, no doubt, will show a single handkerchief
being dipped – hopefully from the neck rather than the torso.
I think that has a certain necessary *éclat*, don't you? Our
handkerchiefs are particularly big in China, for some reason.
I've heard that they believe it somehow increases the chance
of conceiving a male child. Superstitious nonsense. The
original handkerchief will, as usual, be handed over to the
Victoria and Albert Museum for display ... My, it sounds
like the Home Secretary is coming down with a painful
cough. Perhaps we should call for the doctor? Are you
certain? ... Not *too* many more to do now, Home Secretary

. . . I do hope the Home Secretary isn't overfatigued by these petty matters. How heavy must weigh the fardels of authority . . . This is the Death Warrant itself. It always stands out, I must say, amongst all these computerised and photocopied sheets. The heavy paper. The calligraphy. The black border. This, one feels, is how the whole thing should be done. A certain formality. A sense of history. A basic English decency. That's what we've lost in all this execrable ballyhoo of promotion and publicity. But one must bow to the will of the masses, especially the global masses. And it's hardly practical to fax through the royal seal, now is it? Such a wonderful hand the King has, don't you think? So full of true majesty . . . He'll be attending, of course. Along with the little ones, bless their dear hearts. I've heard they're all of them quite desperate to be present. There was some debate about it being too far past their official bedtime. (We do have to fit in with Transatlantic schedules, though.) The Royal Nanny's a complete Tartar as far as having them tucked up by seven thirty's concerned. But she's been bought off with the promise of a front row seat and a handkerchief. The producer's said he may even cut to her for a close-up at some point during proceedings. (She's secretly a little star-struck.) Not at the climax, of course. The Home Secretary's rôle will, of course, be pivotal at that juncture. But I weary you . . . We will have to go through the usual charade *vis-à-vis* the judicial process. We must keep the certainty of the execution completely hush-hush until the day itself. Please, no hints – even to your closest advisors. We stand to lose out terribly if any of this is discovered. Expectations must be built through the strategic placement of hints to influential journalists – will clemency occur, will mercy be shown, etcetera etcetera, or will the full wrath of English justice be seen yet again to bear down upon the miserable wretch that dared threaten the life of the beloved monarch . . . The Condemned, I believe, uttered his vile threats during the course of an argument in a pub called, believe it or not, The King's Head. Now there's an irony for you if ever there was one. Not that I would presume to point such things out to the Home Secretary. I'm sure there are nuances here imperceptible to myself that your eagle eye has already perceived – even on this short acquaintance with the material . . . Only a very few more signatures needed, now. Merchandising – and, in particular, children's toys. I know there has been a great deal of resistance on this issue heretofore. I believe that you yourself have had grave reservations. However, considering the fact that the execution takes place during the run-up to Christmas, it was decided this time that something in reasonable taste might be attempted. We've decided to go with the good, old-fashioned Action Man doll. There will be two models, sold as a set or separately: Action Man Executioner and Action Man Condemned with Detachable Head and Replaceable Fake-Blood Capsules. The revenue will be quite considerable. There has already been some private speculation as to which of the models will sell best. My money, were I a betting man, would be on the Condemned with Detachable Head – children being the blood-thirsty little monsters they are. (Your own delightful progeny of course excepted. How is Phabia's chicken pox? Quite cleared up, I hope. And, though it might have been irksome for little Trent, it's always best to get that kind of thing out of the way.) . . . Here are the release forms for all the other merchandise. T-shirts. Posters. Key-rings. Snowglobes – in red, don't you know. Commemorative mugs. (There was an article on these in last week's *Independent*. The whole set is now worth quite a deal of money, for those who've been canny enough to start collecting from day one.) . . . Which brings us penultimately to betting rights. There's the usual speculation as to the Condemned's last words. Someone even dared suggest that he might have been got-at by a Malaysian gambling ring. The rumour was that they'd promised to keep his mother in Guinness, and a whole lot more, for the rest of her natural life. No truth to it, at all. She's been under surveillance ever since the trial, and no one has been observed to have contacted her . . . And finally, the *coup de grâce*, if I may so put it – here's the Official Death Certificate. Well, Home Secretary, we ought as well get everything out of the way at once, oughtn't we?

Neil Stewart

PEOPLE WE WANT

CONSIDERING THE SCHOOL was about fifty miles from home, it was always easier to board than to commute. The difference is that I used to go home at the weekends; in Sixth Year it just seemed like too much effort, particularly as my parents already had enough problems without me wandering around the place being seventeen and hormonal.

Sixth Year was quite cool: killing time, really. I already had my place at Glasgow Uni to read English, so I spent a year wasting the school English department's time doing an array of purposeless modules called things like 'Communications', which involved onerous tasks such as learning about job application letters and how to speak to people on the telephone. The Art department grew tired of the sight of me as I turned up day in day out for my Foundation classes, in which I valiantly struggled to draw shoes and glass bottles, making up for my lack of notable improvement over the year with an enthusiasm which grew even as my teachers' own waned. '*Vincent*,' said Mrs O'Reilly one day, 'that *photocopier* has more artistic talent than you do. *It* can *copy* things.' She squinted at my latest masterpiece. 'What is *that* meant to *be*?'

'It's Adam's schoolbag,' I said, then added cleverly: 'It's Surrealist.'

'It's *scrappy*,' said Mrs O'Reilly. It was the worst insult in her vocabulary. I felt honoured.

My eighteenth birthday came and went. Some of the other boys somehow managed to get a hold of my room key – we boarders all had individual cells in Sixth Year – and when I came back after classes that afternoon it was to find Alicia Ferdinand asleep in my bed wearing Playboy-bunny ears and not a lot more. My friend Chris later explained that the idea had been for her to leap out of the bed on my return and give me a birthday gift to remember, whatever that was supposed to mean; sadly Alicia had been rather too busy with one of her other boyfriends the previous night to get much sleep. She had simply dozed off in my bed while waiting for me to return from my daily mission to annoy the teachers into medical care.

There was a mental hospital just down the road from the school, incidentally, and ours were the only two buildings for miles around. To get to Bellshaugh Hall you had to take a train out to Bellshaugh station and hope that the battered white school minibus hadn't already left without you, since it only visited the station once a week. If it had gone, you were facing the choice between a five or six mile hike across spoiled fields, or a week sleeping on one of the rusty metal benches on the train-station platform, where you risked being graffiti'd in the middle of the night by local vandals.

When we were younger, of course, we found endless amusement in the idea that our teaching staff might be former patients at that hospital.

As it happened, with my teachers just as frustrated with me as I was with them, and no real outlet for my increasing sense of aggravation – I couldn't very well go home and shout at my parents, as by November they were living at separate addresses and I imagine it would have taken rather more than just a returning son to get them in the same room at once – I instead found something else to satisfy me. Wednesday afternoon was PE afternoon. I spent November falling in grey mud on the rugby field while the other players desperately tried to avoid passing the ball to me. I was the opposition's best weapon at indoor football in winter, being so ineffectual a goalkeeper that it became quite common for games to end up with scores like 18–1 against. When the weather got better Mr McKay, whose job as Head of PE was to devise ever more elaborate ways to get rid of us all for as long as possible, made us do things like run the perimeter of the sports field twenty times, or spend hours in the gym doing press-ups until we passed out.

I adored Wednesdays. I threw myself, sometimes literally, into all the activities on offer – even the stultifying games of cricket which stretched out over endless summer-term days, and that's not endless in a good way – with the same enthusiasm as I did in my Foundation Art classes, and the same absolute lack of expertise.

Monday 3rd February 1997

'Is McKay shagging Cowan, do you think?'

I laughed. 'What, McKay sleeping with a woman who can't be deflated and stored in a shoebox? Doubt it.' The lump in the lining of my blazer turned out to be an unopened packet of cigarettes.

'Well, I saw them the other day in town and they looked pretty friendly.'

'If they weren't actually getting it on in broad daylight, I simply refuse to believe it.' I peeled off the clear wrapper and offered Simon Jones the packet. 'Fag?'

Si gave me one of his long-lasting deadpan looks until I started laughing and nearly crushed the packet in my hand. He didn't even have to say anything: it was just this totally even way he would look at you which was so much more eloquent than any punchline.

'If you're quite finished,' he said, snatching the packet from my hand and helping himself to a couple of Marlboros, one of which he stuck behind his ear like you always see builders doing with pencils.

A Monday afternoon, and watery spring sunshine beating down on my bare arms as I sat on the front steps of the school, having decided a couple of hours horsing around with Si was much preferable even to running rings around Mrs Cowan, the long-suffering English mistress.

'Haven't you noticed the way she acts all girlish around

him?' A younger girl scuttled past us warily into the main building. Si craned round and bellowed 'Goerssaywhat!'

'What?' squeaked the panicked girl, her face flaring red. It set me off again and I nearly fell off the steps. I lit a fag with one trembling hand and took a calming breath of cold smoke.

'Anyway,' I said, trying and failing to make smoke rings, something at which Si was enviably proficient, 'McKay's as bent as a nine-pound note. Only queers grow moustaches like that.'

Si Jones tucked a strand of dark hair behind his other ear and just went 'Hmm.'

Wednesday 16th April 1997
The problems must have begun at roughly, oh, quarter past three that afternoon? A Wednesday, as I say: the first PE afternoon of the summer term. It had been raining for about a week, but that morning the sun had finally dared shine. With his customary disregard for his class's comfort and security, Mr McKay declared pitch conditions were perfect for a game of rugby. *Why?* I remember thinking, aghast. We *never* played rugby in the summer. Summer meant whites, the *klok* sound of leather on willow or whatever it is. Cricket days. Rounders, at the very least.

Nobody dared argue with McKay, who had assumed a strange aura of power and unapproachability ever since Jill Harris from Third Year had spotted him in the photocopying cupboard with Madame, the two teachers snogging as though their lives both depended on it. Jill Harris, granted rare entry into the Sixth Year common room to tell her tale to us all, related the incident in frankly unnecessary detail. 'She had her left hand in his pants,' she reported wide-eyed, 'and she seemed to be *squeezing*,' at which point about half her rapt audience went 'Eew' in disgust and the other half swapped knowing looks.

'I always said Madame would be a goer,' said Si Jones, sounding disappointed. 'She has to be. She is French after all.'

The news spread through school quicker than something medical: my simile. Like the time we all gave each other measles, nobody remained unaffected by this news. And like that time, while nobody was irrevocably injured as a result of the outbreak, it did make things pretty uncomfortable for some of us.

For a start, it made things a bit difficult for me and Si. I didn't like the way he seemed to have developed this crush on the ever-aloof Madame. It made me feel insecure. I disagreed when he seemed to assume it was okay to be thinking about the French ice queen like that even as he and I were embarking on a romance of our own.

Wednesday March 19th 1997

I don't really know how it started. Well, I say that. I can be fairly sure it started that day during the Easter break in his cell when we were in bed together. The thing is, I can't say exactly why I felt the need to comfort Si in his time of need by actually crawling under the covers with him.

I'd already had the flu, which was an absolute bugger: it made your head feel as though it was filled with digging machines, and the general area of your ribcage feel like someone had been marching up and down on it in high-heeled boots. Si was one of the few boys who was staying at Bellshaugh Hall over the Easter holiday, and almost the only one I could even bear to spend time with. He was kind of like my best friend, although in general I got on better with the girls in the class, who seemed to admire the way I did my best to wind up all my teachers.

Anyway, I was in Si's room while he was lying in bed. I was recovering from the flu just as he was coming down with it – I'd probably given it to him, right enough – and the warden, Mr Arthurs, suggested I keep an eye on the invalid. Fetch him drinks of water, plump up his pillows, take him to the bathroom if he felt the need to vomit. It probably goes without saying that this was meant to be the warden's job, but I didn't mind really. I'd heard the warden's illegally-kept dog Martin, which was named after the headmaster and turned out not to be male after all, had just unexpectedly given birth to puppies. Mr Arthurs had enough to occupy him.

Si was dozing fitfully in the throes of his illness, and I was doing pretty much the same over an antique edition of *Jane Eyre*. Mrs Cowan had suggested I read it now as I'd no doubt go on to study it at Uni; the school's library had a copy which apparently hadn't been checked out since 1962 and which was printed on paper so thin that turning a page became an operation fraught with danger. I had just got to the bit where Jane, picked upon by her grotesque relatives, goes off to boarding school and gains a friend as close as a sibling. I could draw lazy parallels with my own life, casting Si as my fantasy relative.

I set down the book at a particularly prophetic point, where Jane's school is riddled with tuberculosis, surely the world's most unpleasantly-named disease, and went to mop Si's brow with a damp cloth. I rearranged the scratchy bedclothes around him – he was curled into a foetal position, and you could tell he was asleep from the constant flickering beneath his closed eyelids, as he dreamed something untellable. I noticed his body was trembling slightly, with the kind of internal shivers you get when you are feverish.

I'd like to say the only reason I undressed and slipped into his bed wearing only a pair of briefs and a faded Daffy Duck t-shirt was out of pure selfless concern for my fellow man, and I curled myself around his crunched-up body simply to comfort and relax him. And yeah, that was the main reason. But really, when I was rearranging the sheets I caught sight of his monstrous hard-on, and I can't deny that I just wanted to fold myself around someone who could maintain *that* even while delirious and red with fever.

I know what you're thinking. You think this kind of thing happens all the time in boarding schools. You have this tabloid idea that public schoolboys spend about an hour a week in lessons and the rest of the time in the communal showers making a big play of dropping the soap. Well, it didn't work like that at Bellshaugh, in any case. Si and me, we were the only 'same-sex couple' – sorry – that I ever knew about, and even we weren't very sexual. We kept things quiet. Never in all my time at Bellshaugh did I see naked young men chasing each other about the dorms, or offering outlandish favours in exchange for lunch tokens. And we were a fairly close-knit bunch, our school, small and self-contained, so I'd probably have known if anything like that was actually going on. I might even say we lived in each other's pockets, if it weren't such an obvious double entendre.

Wednesday 16th April 1997

So anyway, as I was saying, we were out meant to be playing rugby on a pitch which comprised approximately, oh, one hundred percent mud? Mr McKay actually made it down to the field to 'supervise' us, which was a bit of an innovation. Tempting him out from his little cubbyhole in the department usually took nothing less than a flick of Madame's skirt or the promise he could take full credit for any success his pupils had in sports – not that he had much call for that.

'Mark your man, Jeffries!' barked Mr McKay, less insincerely than usual. He was in a foul mood for some reason. 'McNamara, get out on that field! *Connor*! Put that fag out or I'll come over there and knock it down your throat!' He sounded genuinely angry with me, which was strange as he often sloped over to me during PE and tried to cadge a smoke off me. I threw the cigarette into the grey mud and ground it beneath my cheap rugby shoe, which seemed to be letting in the mud to such a degree I was getting seriously worried about trench-foot.

'Come on, Vince!' yelled Si Jones, charging out the rugby pavilion in rugby kit so clean it positively glittered in the watery sunlight. He pounded up the field, throwing up great splashes of thick mud as he ran. He had found a half-decent rugby ball in the pavilion and contrived to throw it up and catch it even while he was running.

'That's the spirit!' called Mr McKay, confused.

I turned my back, then jogged off after Si, rather less enthusiastically, wondering what he was up to. Normally he was one for trying to skive PE. I remember I once saw a book in his cell with a title like *Horrific Medical Conditions*, and I wondered if that was what he used as a source for the increasingly outrageous excuses for avoiding PE. Once, magnificently, he claimed he had contracted yellow fever and Mr McKay, who obviously didn't know what it really was but didn't like the sound of it, hurriedly excused him.

I had lost sight of Si; the sun was in my eyes. I decided to track him by the deep gouges he'd left in the mud. I followed the path right up to the old oak tree up at the top of the field. I kicked my feet against the tree, dislodging great clumps of sticky mud from my boots, and looked around for Si. I couldn't see him. Where had he gone? Under the tree the ground was less muddy and his tracks vanished. I took a few steps forward, looking around and wondering how much of a twat I looked, when I heard a crackle of dry branches and had a sudden premonition of what was about to happen.

The rugby ball fell out the sky. I looked at it stupidly.

'CATCH!' bellowed Si Jones, throwing himself out the oak tree onto my shoulders. I fell forwards into the mud, but managed to roll onto my back so that Si was pinned underneath me. He grabbed me in a crushing bear-hug, hands locked around my waist, and started rolling us around. The mud squelched and spurted sickeningly around us. He had winded me; I was trying to breathe and watery mud was going into my nose and mouth. I was seized with a terrible fear, which was quickly replaced by a terrible anger

'You bastard!' I tried to say, just as my face hit the mud again. 'You absolute fucking –'

'Language,' chided Si, scooping up a handful of mud and apparently stuffing it down the front of his rugby shirt, which no longer glittered in the same way. 'I'm doing this for your own good!' He managed to get to his feet and grabbed the rugby ball, starting away from me. I scrambled to my feet, took a few hasty steps, skidded terrifyingly on a long streak of mud and fell back down again.

Mr McKay came pounding up to us, lips clamped around his referee's whistle, his face puce. The whistle turned his breath into comical little *peep*ing sounds. He let the whistle drop from his mouth and bristled down at me. '*Jones!*' he yelled, apparently at me. I was about to correct him when Si came running back to him. I got up and made a rather pathetic attempt to brush some of the glutinous mud off me. McKay ignored me and trained his moustache on Si, who stood there with his head on one side as though trying to place who the PE teacher actually was. 'Jones!' yelled McKay again. 'What the blazes do you think you're playing at?'

I had to bite my lip. I just knew, I *knew*, what he was going to say.

Si stared at Mr McKay, timing his deadpan silence just right. Eventually, easily, condescendingly, he shrugged and said: 'We were playing at *rugby*, sir.'

I can't remember what Mr McKay said exactly, but it's fair to say he pretty much exploded. I for one had never heard a teacher swear before, except Madame when she got flustered and cursed us for lazy *salauds*. Some of the words Mr McKay employed, and I was quite impressed by the range of his vocabulary, were 'irresponsible – immature – not one *iota* of common sense – clowns – reckless –' and ultimately, and most impressively I thought, 'capricious', which I'm absolutely certain Mr McKay didn't know the meaning of.

And through it all Si just stood there, managing to be insolent without so much as blinking. If he'd had a cigarette, he would have blown stale smoke into McKay's livid face.

'Go back to the school, clean yourselves up, get changed and go straight to your rooms. *Separately*,' McKay stormed, unimpressively. 'Your behaviour today was disgraceful. The headmaster will get to hear about this. Have – no – doubt – about – that.' Someone had obviously told Mr McKay that the best way to underscore a point was to pretend to be a Dalek.

'Yes, sir,' said Si contritely, once Mr McKay had finished. McKay turned his back on us as though we weren't worth his attention and jogged away down the pitch to the pavilion where a record number of pupils were smoking.

I looked at Si. 'I'm cold,' I said. 'I'm freezing and soaked through and – would you listen to that? My teeth actually are chattering. What the fuck *are* you playing at?'

'You heard the man,' replied Si, who infuriatingly somehow still looked the picture of health. 'We're going to go back early from Games, just the two of us, and shower together with no one to interrupt us. We're going to clean ourselves up. Do you see?' He grinned hugely, teeth bright white in his muddy face, then looked down, as if surprised by something. 'Would you look at that?' he exclaimed, as though talking to himself. 'There's mud in my pants.'

I raced him up the road to the school.

I quite like the notion that I cured Si of his fever that time we slept curled up together in his cell. When we woke up he seemed to have recovered totally from the flu and miraculously I hadn't picked it up again.

I ought to stress again that this half-naked-boys-in-bed routine was new to us. We didn't mention it to anyone else, and that next day spent most of our time in our separate cells. I pressed on with *Jane Eyre*, rather glad my charge hadn't died as I slept with my arms around his neck; Si claimed he had Maths and Physics exams to study for. He was far more science-minded than me, and less of a nuisance to the school since he was doing proper Sixth Year Studies in this final year. I was still dossing around trying to piss people off, probably because I thought that was appropriate training for going to Uni later in the year. I had an Art class exam coming up, in which I was intending to paint huge, childish caricatures of my long-suffering teachers hacking each other with large knives, just to see what their reaction would be. I liked to think these tentative real-life experiments were just as useful as the little robots Si built in his Physics class. The best one not only bent down to lift small metal objects to a magnet on its 'face', it would also trundle happily about the table-top, halting when it came to an edge and turning to continue on its way. It just kept on doing it, carrying a paperclip back and forth across a lab worktop for hours and hours, until Si got bored and tried putting things in its path to annoy it.

It could have ended disastrously much quicker, it later occurred to me: that night we'd slept with Si's cell door unlocked. Mr Arthurs could have come in at any time. After his problems with Martin's surprise puppies, I imagine witnessing another gender-bending incident might have driven the old man right over the edge.

Si hadn't said anything but I wondered if I'd really offended him, if he'd been shocked and disgusted to wake up with me draped over him, probably snoring, possibly even drooling. I know I'd have been rather surprised if it had been me in his place. Still, he must have suspected I had a bit of a thing for him. Not only were we best mates, not only did I share my cigarettes with him, but on the rare occasions he actually made it out on a Wednesday afternoon, I vacated the post-PE showers as soon as he entered. He must have noticed that. I was scared my animal instincts would take over at the sight of his tall naked body gleaming with sweat and the tepid water of the showers. I remember the way we all used to taunt mercilessly any boy embarrassed by an uncalled-for erection at changing time.

And the final thing of course was the day in January he and I had gone into town together with the express intention of buying a supply of pornography to keep us amused for the spring term and after much deliberation and tentative questioning of one another, were both relieved to find we preferred *Playgirl* to *Playboy*.

Anyway, the night after Si's miraculous recovery, I was lying in bed in my own cell, browsing a copy of *Boyz*. I had *Jane Eyre* close to hand, just in case Mr Arthurs the warden turned up and I had to pretend to be an intellectual rather than a schoolboy. I shoved *Boyz* under the mattress when I heard the knock at the door and picked up *Jane Eyre*, opening at random and trying to look studious. 'Enter!' I called imperiously.

It wasn't Mr Arthurs the warden after all. It was Si Jones, in a bright red and green striped dressing gown that did funny things to my eyes. 'Is it safe to come in?' he asked. It was perhaps the only time I'd ever seen him nervous.

'Of course,' I said, magnanimously. I chucked *Jane Eyre* across the room and, with unerring precision, into the sink in the corner. 'Oops.' Si retrieved the book and slotted it neatly back into my bookcase. 'Ta.'

I can't remember what it was he pretended he wanted to talk about. He perched on the edge of my desk and we chatted lazily for a bit. Si was always very demonstrative. He waved his hands illustratively and made huge billowing patterns across the ceiling in the weak orange lamplight.

After a while, conversation trailed off a bit. Si's dressing gown had fallen open to his waist. His body was honey-coloured, a hint of muscle tone on his stomach. He seemed to be waiting for something. I really wanted to know if he was naked under the dressing gown but I couldn't think of a polite way to ask. The silence between us grew thick and slightly menacing until I felt I was about to burst with the tension. 'Well?' I said eventually, desperately. 'Are you going to get into bed or not?'

He was wearing grey jockey shorts under his dressing gown, it turned out. We curled up together under the cover. I reached over to switch the light out just as Si turned his face to mine and kissed my mouth with dry lips. 'Good night, Vince,' he murmured, his eyes already closed.

'Night,' I whispered. I switched out the light.

We had a very chaste relationship, Si and me. We kissed a bit – he was rather more keen on that than me, I can't say why – and sometimes had a bit of a clumsy feel of each other under the bedsheets with the lights out, which was how he preferred it. I'd quite have liked another look at that monstrous erection I'd glimpsed before, but Si really wasn't keen on seeing my cock, as he told me rather disarmingly over breakfast one morning in early April. We sometimes went to sleep with our hands locked around one another's erections, which I was quite fond of. We never fucked. I never even got a taste of him, which was what actually disappointed me the most. I don't know what he thought about while we were keeping each other company, two chaste little boys. I never asked him. I knew he wouldn't tell me.

Wednesday 16th April 1997

By now, I imagine, you want to know what exactly went on that Wednesday in April, the end of it all, the end of my world at quarter past three in the afternoon. You've probably guessed what happened. I suppose I should have foreseen it too, really.

Si and I got back to the school and headed straight for the showers. I can't speak for him but I was feeling pretty electric with the anticipation. We left the showers running, rather optimistically hoping they would achieve a temperature you could call 'warm' rather than just 'tepid'. I have the image of Si Jones's long thin body, streaked with greying mud, imprinted on my mind, and, like a series of snapshots, the sequence of images as he pulled down those same jockey shorts and great clods of mud came tumbling out. The grin on his face lit up the whole changing room. 'To the showers!' he ordered. I slipped out of the rest of my grimy clothes and danced madly across the cold tiles through the door into the showers.

He was just standing there, dripping mud at the centre of the room, with the hissing jets of the shower-heads turned attentively towards him. He'd dunked his head under one of the showers and his glossy black hair was turning to ringlets, smearing across his square face. By this time, we'd been sort-of lovers for more than a month. I could say pretty much anything I liked to him. Si had a nice sense of irony. 'Hello, big boy,' I said to him, hooking a finger into my mouth. There it was, the hard-on that had haunted me all that month. It looked, frankly, rather threatening, just standing there insolently. 'You've been a bad boy today, haven't you?' Warm water splashed against my neck and down my back as I sank to my knees and kind of shuffled towards him. It was a lot sexier at the time, incidentally, than I'm perhaps making it sound. 'Shuffle' isn't really a very sexy word, is it? 'You deserve a good lashing,' I breathed, just loud enough so he could hear me over the shower noises. I thought I heard him snuffle with laughter.

I swear, I swear I nearly had him in my mouth when the showers suddenly cut out. Their sputtering had masked the sound of the shower door as it scraped open. Si's erection started to subside before my eyes. If I'd been so inclined, I'd have had time for a quick prayer before I turned my head and lifted my eyes.

Framed in the changing room door was a chunky, moustached silhouette.

I stood up as quickly as I could. I just looked at the floor, away from Simon's muddy, dripping body, away from the furnace of anger rushing out from that shape in the doorway. I later learned that Mr McKay's bad mood that day came after an argument with Madame, and he had abandoned his class at the field in favour of returning to the school to try and patch things up with the ice-queen. On his way to her photocopying cupboard, where she was usually to be found, he had decided to check up on Si and me and see there was no more carrying on. I doubt even he expected to see what he did.

Mr McKay spat only one word at us before storming out of the changing rooms. 'Perverts!' It's a word that seems to have followed me around all these years.

James McGonigal and Hamish Whyte

from virtual memories

The first time I saw a circumcised
penis, knowing neither of those words:
Dobie Dobson whose father owned a sweetshop
and was maybe keen on hygiene.
His son pissed happily enough
against the chestnut tree.
I pissed more puzzledly.

*

My father brought back the bread
and my mother cooked bacon.
This was after his nightschool supervision
and these were the loaves
of apprentice bakers. Not bad, boys.
Not bad boys. You could slice
through them to the slight warmth
equidistant from the crusts.

*

By the time I joined the Boys' Brigade
the band had disbanded
and all that was left,
in the cupboard among the Indian clubs
and bits of drill rifle,
was the bass drum beater –
which I liberated.

*

Where the station was at Aberlady
British Railways had turned old carriages
into post-Beeching holiday homes:
sleep sideways and go to the toilet
along the abandoned platform
to the waiting room, also refurbished
except for the familiar draught and the smell
of ingrained smoke. Make your own steam.

Matthew Sweeney

THE ATTIC

I've finished my mural of you naked,
and only I will see it.
The sun streams through the skylight,
lighting your face, your breasts.
I lie in the hammock remembering
the afternoon hours I spent with you
up here, where no one goes.
We'd have Van Morrison singing
low down, and sometimes wine.
Always there'd be a vase of flowers
in the corner, on the trunk –
you'd smuggle them up the stairs
until you closed that black door
and the rest of the house wasn't there.
I remember the day we fell asleep
until they came looking for us –
my mother calling my name,
but not coming up. We waited
till all was quiet, then reappeared
in the living room, and sat apart,
like we had to, for half an hour –
the longest you spent down there –
then I went with you to the door.
I wouldn't accompany you to the bus-stop,
instead went back upstairs
to lie there in the growing dark,
listening to Van over and over again.
I must have known you'd never return.
It was weeks before I started the mural,
and I took my time, I wanted *you* there,
on my wall, right in every detail,

looking as if I could lift you down.
I wanted you, and now I've got you
and you'll never go downstairs.
Tomorrow I'll paint a vase of flowers,
irises, to match your eyes,
but tonight I'm sleeping here,
the first night I'll have spent with you.

A DAY IN CALCUTTA

The flesh of the Indian mango is red
    like a pawpaw
but the taste is all mango.
I had it for breakfast one morning
    with watermelon juice
in that sumptuous hotel in Calcutta
    before heading off
in one of those 50s Rovers
through the crazy beeping streets
    to visit the temple
of Kalighat. It was early
    but already
there were plenty of would-be guides,
the least insistent of which we chose
    to lead us
barefoot, into Kali's sanctum
    where hands pushed us
up to her idol (black goddess
with fierce red eyes, looking as if,
    despite being stone,
she could tear us into pieces),
    as ochre marks
were thumbed on our foreheads
and offerings were requested,
    More, more
you rich Westerner! ... Eventually
    we were outside

and heading back to our shoes
when I saw, in a crowd of men,
    two tethered goats,
one young, one a baby, both
    big-eyed and curious,
especially the eldest, until grabbed
at both ends, his neck stretched,
    then a flash
of a knife and his head was in the dust.
    The younger's bleats
were cut short in the same way,
and both bodies were dragged
    over the ground
(getting blood on my feet) and away.
    I shrugged off
the demands for money, caught up with
the others, and climbed back in
    the 50s Rover
to join the maelstrom of traffic again,
    the constant beeping
and weaving across lanes,
the certain collisions avoided,
    jaywalkers dodged
with that special skill that's the mark
    of Calcutta,
till I ended up in the leafy calm
of the British cemetery, where the Raj
    has never ended,
or so I thought, until I strolled –
    reading the names
and epitaphs – to the far end
where Indian boys were playing cricket
    among the tombs.

Marc Weinberg

HATE SONGS FOR EMILY

'RICK CAESAR IN the morning,' a chorus of girls chirruped, placing a great deal of emphasis on the last syllable of morning. Edward felt pity for those poor souls whose alarm was set to WMKP 98.5, so that this jingle would slither into their ears and tear them from slumber. He was already manoeuvring his Honda Civic onto the crowded beltway, shouting out expletives as driver after driver refused to allow him to merge. Leaving before eight was meant to solve this problem, but a ridiculous number of cars continued to fly past his sideview mirror. Other motorists did not grasp the simple point that a single mistake, bending down to scoop up doughnut crumbs from one's crotch, swerving into another lane without signalling, suddenly braking because of an acute itch above the right heel, a sneeze at high speed, could all lead to multiple deaths. He made sure that his doors were unlocked in case paramedics had to pry him from the mangled teal remains of his little car. Sometimes he felt so drained by the prospect of driving in to university in the morning that he entertained the thought of calling Ms Stanowski to inform her that his classes were cancelled for the day. Then he would dismiss his fear as ridiculous and hurry the thought out of his mind as if it were a cocktail guest who had lingered in his lounge far too long. All of his irrational fears wandered around his brain in this way: impeccably well put together and devoid of substance. He could not bring himself to eject them from his home. They were thoughts after all, and as he repeatedly informed his gum-chewing, frozen menagerie of freshmen, all thought is precious.

'Hey, hey, hey it's 98.5 modern rock, and you're travelling on the morning drive with Rick Caesar, the emperor of ice cream. Our intern who is earning seven dollars an hour told me yesterday that that's a poem by Wallace Stevens. I said who? and he replied that Wallace Stevens was a famous poet. That must have been in the past when people cared about poets. Apparently there was a time when being a poet was considered cool, and they were viewed in the way that rock stars are today, as society's bad boys. Radio and television have blessed our lives in ways that we can't even begin to appreciate. So, our new crop of interns have turned out to be very smart, in the sense of placing your hand on a branding iron rather than solving Fermat's last theorem smart. We're calling this poetic intern The Professor, and I'm thinking of changing my nickname to the emperor of cheese. Hey, I don't care, as long as all the faithful listeners out there get a mental picture of how fat I really am. Gary, what's up with traffic?'

Gary was Rick's traffic boy, weather barometer, and tireless straight man. The realization that one is a disc jockey's flunky must lead to night sweats. Gary probably woke up screaming: ha, ha, Rick you are so funny, I cannot believe that you thought of that, that you would dare to say that. Wasn't Gary meant to be the fat one? That quivering mass of flesh smiling so politely in the seat next to Conan or Johnny or some other condescending sneer behind his chat show desk. Edward reduced Gary's body to Lilliputian scale because any jockey's assistant demanded to be that small. Edward's commute was around half an hour and he could usually rely on hearing two songs in that time. It was the music that he loved and the other stations in Baltimore were so disappointing he decided that listening to Rick Caesar was a sacrifice he was willing to make.

'Gary, I know that you're single and kind of lonely so this probably won't mean anything to you, but last night the girlfriend forced me to sit through *The First Wives' Club*. And it was cute, but that's the sad thing with girl power, it isn't exactly the most intimidating thing in the world. Three chicks get together and decide to teach the world a lesson, and so they all dress up in white and they sing and dance. Now, three guys in a Scorsese film decide they've had enough and decide to teach the world a lesson, and I close my eyes and can't look at the screen. I mean they're pureeing brains with bats while Bette Midler, Diane Keaton and Goldie Hawn are getting really fabulous new hairdos.'

'*Goodfellas* was a superb film,' Gary chimed in briefly.

'You lookin' at me, Gary? Or how about any scene with DeNiro. A heifer with that baseball bat in *The Untouchables*. That's like my role model. I want to invite all the execs, all those suits to my house for dinner and I'll greet them tapping my bat against my palm.'

'That was a DePalma film, wasn't it?'

'That's real menace,' Rick continued, 'when I see chicks slappin' and clawin' each other I feel embarrassed. It's a turn-on for some guys, but me, I just think of little kids. There's no tension, you know what I mean? Nothing can happen. Someone might chip a nail. And when they give them guns or make them action heroes, it's so, so . . .'

'Incongruous?' Gary offered.

'Yeah. I was heading more towards pathetic and sad, but incongruous is a good word.'

'The Professor taught it to me yesterday.'

'Hey, that's funny Gary. Keep it up and maybe one day you could be the DJ.'

Edward wondered what this girl who dated Caesar looked like, this hapless Calpurnia. She was probably young, dazzled by the shabby allure of his celebrity status. He was popular, though, and perhaps she found his sophomoric misogyny strangely erotic. Edward spent his life researching and lecturing on despicable men who always managed to find women who were attracted to them. Rick Caesar wasn't despicable, he wasn't worth a word like that, and he certainly wasn't as powerful as a historical figure, but this kind of situation was indicative of life. Calpurnia was surely beautiful

and interesting, convinced that she could change this swag-
gering oaf, or under the illusion that his crass observations
stopped short of her. Edward moved to Baltimore two
months ago and still stayed in the right lane all the way down
the 695 until he exited onto 83 South. He had managed
without a car while he was at Princeton, and he was in the
process of adjusting to Baltimore where a car was essential.

'I have Pearl Jam tickets to give away.' Rick crowed after the
commercial break.

'I thought they were sold out, like months ago?' Gary
responded.

'Indeed they were. Hot cakes, Gary, priceless and beyond
the grasp of mere mortals. But I have managed to squirrel
away a pair of these babies for the concert on Saturday night.
Included in the prize are backstage passes so that you can
meet Eddie and the boys, and perhaps if you behave yourself
you can meet me as well.'

'You're going?' Gary asked in his dazed sycophant voice
that Edward was convinced required no effort at all.

'Of course, Gary. I have stood by the band for years, even
through their unfortunate Ticketmaster phase. They worship
me. The sixty-ninth caller wins it all.'

'Sixty-nine,' Gary repeated salaciously for those who might
have missed Rick's risqué cleverness.

Edward adored alternative music and he had a soft spot for
the Seattle bands who had been the vanguard of the
renaissance that rescued music from the darkest age. His
passion was for Soundgarden, Screaming Trees and Alice In
Chains, but he owned all of Nirvana, Pearl Jam and
Mudhoney as well. Each band was the equivalent of a
Frankish king. Those Northwest bars had bristled with
Charlemagnes. They stayed with him during those endless
four years when he had struggled to write up his doctorate,
and although alternative music was rapidly becoming indistinguishable from toothless pop it remained preferable to the
other aural dross that plagued the radio.

Rick Caesar finally deigned to play a song after twenty minutes of blather and several commercials for cars. Edward enjoyed the audible equivalent of small print, that nanosecond at the very end when the announcer sped through the hidden costs and pitfalls in a breathless mumble. Everclear came on with a song from their second album. Edward liked them a lot, their fluffy melodies mitigated by honest lyrics. From Portland. Close to Seattle. He turned into the faculty parking lot singing along to *Father of Mine* when a red Saturn drifted into his passenger door as slowly as honey falling off a spoon. The Saturn was reversing, and had not seen him at all. He could see the lights flaring red and had plenty of time to realize that he was about to be involved in an accident.

The passenger door crumpled as gently as a finger tearing open a letter and as he censured himself for that simile his head hit the side window. He was wearing his seat belt and for some reason he reached for it with his mouth and began to bite down on the material which tasted black. His head did not hurt but his heart was racing as Death passed by. For his sixteenth birthday his crazy aunt, the one who once married a man based solely on a description given to her by a Gypsy palm reader, gave him a pack of Tarot cards. The Major Arcana cards used to terrify him, especially the drawing of Death, balancing on a field of skulls while holding a scythe. At least that was how he remembered the card. There was also the Tower with a lightning bolt cutting across a castle's turret and all these people falling to the ground, arms flailing in the big sky, and the Wheel of Fortune where screaming souls were trapped within the spokes. She told him to wrap the cards in a silk scarf and keep them under his pillow for a month so that they became his own. Instead he hid them in his sock drawer and at night he imagined them shuffling themselves to determine what would happen to him in the morning. There was a tapping at the window, and at first Edward thought that it was the glass spreading like a spider's web before it fell to the ground in shards. He spat out the belt and turned his head slowly, in case his neck was broken. A concerned woman stared back at him. He opened his car door and carefully extricated himself from the Honda.

'Are you all right? Oh God, I am so, so sorry. I wasn't paying attention at all.'

The woman was emotional and Edward raised his hand to indicate that he was fine. The Everclear song ended and he could hear some dreadful noise coming from her car stereo. Instinctively he recognized that it was Devo and he hoped that she had no insurance so that he might sue her.

'I hit my head. Are you okay?'

She nodded. She was wearing a canary-yellow blouse and a long skirt that seemed to be made out of crepe. Her hair was straight brown and fell to her shoulders which were broad enough to give her torso a tapered look. She was standing with her left foot slightly in front and at right angles to her right foot. Her arms were folded across her chest.

'How long did you do ballet for?' Edward felt that he might be concussed, or at least out of his usual dull mind that struggled to articulate a decent opening line.

'How did you know that I did ballet?'

'Your feet. Every little girl who did ballet ends up standing like that when she grows up.'

'Six years, but I had this growth spurt when I turned twelve,' and took up swimming, Edward was about to add confidently, wondering if the accident combined with the dredged up memory of his Tarot cards had somehow conspired to bless him with psychic powers, when a second Devo song began. It had not been a momentary lack of taste on the part of an eighties radio station, but far, far worse, an entire Devo album that this woman owned.

'It's the best of Devo.'

He must have been craning his head toward the Saturn.

'A gift?' He inquired hopefully.

'I love eighties music. Those Retro lunch hour specials aren't enough for me. By the way my name is Emily.' She extended her hand which was so soft and beautiful that it demanded to be placed on top of a crimson pillow. Her long fingernails were painted charcoal grey. Her fingers were sexy. So were her shoulders. He hadn't even glanced at her chest and he was already aroused. He felt giddy.

'Edward,' he introduced himself. 'Do you teach here?' He gestured at the parking lot.

'English department. How about you?'

'History. Medieval Europe.'

'You know, Edward, I don't have to be in class for an hour. Could I buy you breakfast and we can trade insurance stuff?'

They drank coffee and ate muffins at an espresso bar across the street from campus. Her hair was parted in the middle and fell down so as to accentuate the oval shape of her pale face. Haircut100. Her eyes were as brown and rich as her hair. Naked Eyes. She wrote her doctorate on Eliot at Yale. Modern English. She loved portraits by Hals and Van Dyck, cats and Jane Fonda films, particularly *Barbarella*. Bauhaus, Stray Cats, Duran Duran. He could have listened to her for hours, delighting in her interests, if it were not for this invidious game that he was playing to torture himself. Talk Talk. Talking Heads. When she mentioned *Barbarella* she paused.

'Did you know . . .'

He had to stop this immediately. 'Yes, I know, Duran Duran got their name from the film.' And his infuriating mind chuckled to itself as he prayed that she was not appalled by this moment of rudeness. He told her that he liked Modernist poetry, the Dutch masters, *On Golden Pond* and *The China Syndrome*. He admitted that he had never owned a cat but for some reason had disliked all four people that he had met who were allergic to cats.

'You're just saying that to get on my good side,' she chided.

'Is it working?' he asked.

Long ago Edward had decided that his strategy with girls would consist of being as corny as possible. He brought flowers on first dates, red roses for special days, copied out poems by Donne, seized every opportunity to play on words, and complimented any special effort that they might have made with their outfit, hair or accessories. He lived for the moment when they invariably brushed his cheek and told him that he was cute/adorable/the sweetest man that they had ever met. He had no success in bars or loud venues where first impressions and visual impacts counted. He needed time, long conversations over coffee where women were exposed to his brand of sarcastic arrogance that was part serious, part mockery. And while he deprecated his own heroic posturing, he visualized Cary Grant as directed by Frank Capra, debonair in a Christmas snow storm.

They exchanged phone numbers and four days later she called him. He had no intention of phoning her first, and over the years he had taught himself the necessary patience for these matters. There had been a time in his life, in his early twenties, when the artifice of courtship was genuinely upsetting. Why must we play games? Why can't we mean what we say and say what we mean? He posed these questions to a girlfriend, who was now married and breeding in Chicago. Her response was to kiss him tenderly with a great deal of pity in her eyes. She loved him for his desire to be noble. He found her to be quite possibly the most patronizing individual that he had ever met. In his memorable speech that had ended their relationship he compared himself to Sisyphus and depicted her as standing on the top of the mound, applauding his struggle with the rock. But there had been something pitiable and admirable about him then.

'Should we go see a movie tomorrow? There's a new DePalma film,' Emily suggested.

'We might as well stay at home and watch an old Hitchcock film. I have a better idea. Come to my apartment and I'll make us dinner. Then we can see how we feel, and either go to the late show or get a drink somewhere.'

'That sounds wonderful.' He could hear the surprise in her voice.

'Come over at seven-thirty.'

'Do you need me to bring anything? I could make a salad.'

'Don't worry about it. What do you like to eat?'

'Everything. It doesn't matter to me. I don't like peppers or olives,' she added hastily.

'Damn. Scrap my original plan to bake the perfect pizza.'

She laughed. There were moments when people first met, when they fumbled for each other's company, and reached out beyond their past experience, vulnerability, and a future that could not bear the weight of mutual expectation, that Edward found exhilarating.

His apartment was small, conducive to cooking an aromatic meal that would fill all the rooms with warmth and flavour. He butterflied two baby chickens and grilled them with tarragon and orange juice. It was a simple recipe and a smell of summer nights in the countryside drifted out of the kitchen. He greeted Emily wearing a white apron over his tan slacks and his blue striped shirtsleeves rolled up to his elbows. She handed over a good bottle of merlot that he decanted while they stood talking in the living room. Her eyes moved across his bookshelves which were brimming with paperback novels and biographies, the few pieces of art on the walls, and the three tower cases of compact discs next to his stereo.

'That smells so good,' she declared.

'I'd better see to it before it burns to a crisp.'

He sliced an avocado pear in half and stuffed each one with shrimp and a simple sauce that he made up of mayonnaise, Tabasco, and tomato sauce. He placed the halves on top of lettuce leaves that were unfortunately limp. His heart was racing and he was perspiring a little. He was frying shallots over a low heat, and the pot filled with baby potatoes bubbled merrily. He opened the oven to check on the chicken that crackled and spat flecks of burning orange. When he stood up Emily was standing in the doorway, leaning with her arms folded, watching him.

'God, you kind of startled me,' he said, holding up his oven mitts in a gesture of surrender.

'I was watching you,' she was moving into the kitchen as

she spoke. 'It's warm,' she mumbled, kissing him with her tongue rolling into his. Her hand cradled the back of his head and her fingers played with the short hair on his neck. Her body felt soft and forgiving as he clasped his hands around the small of her back.

He kissed her ear, flicking the lobe and biting down on it softly. Then he pulled away and smiled: 'We're on a tight schedule. The main course will be ready in twenty minutes.'

'I'm already impressed. Turn off the oven, put the avocado Ritz in the fridge, take me to bed, and we'll order in if it comes to that.'

They lay in bed watching a black and white comedy with Alec Guinness. Two plates with the blackened skins of the avocados and two empty wine glasses were on a breakfast tray on one side of the bed. Edward was hastily revising his plans, although the purpose of his strategies had suddenly been achieved. For a moment he was disappointed that so much of the delicious agony of waiting and worrying, so many gestures that could be analysed and debated over, had been summarily passed over. His intention was to make her a tape of his favourite music, and if nothing else were to come of this relationship at least he could make the effort to save her from heresy. The only thing in the world that upset him more than *Karma Kameleon* was the thought that someone actually enjoyed listening to Culture Club. In the eighties he survived with classic bands like Led Zeppelin and Pink Floyd, and the occasional surprise like U2, Stone Roses and the Violent Femmes. He was too young to have been damaged by disco but he was truly miserable between the twin evils of New Wave and Michael Jackson albums. Emily had flung herself at him with distressing abandon and she was not the sort of person one considered taking home for the holidays, but that was no excuse to decline the opportunity to educate her.

Emily burst into tears at the very moment that Edward was

about to suggest that they move to the living room and listen to music.

'I can't believe what I've done,' she began. 'I'm not like this. I'm never . . . I owe you an explanation, Edward. You must think I'm such a tramp.'

'No, not at all. It was great.'

'I'm seeing someone else. We've been going out for two years. It was two years yesterday. We're having problems, and I so enjoyed talking to you the other day. I wanted something more, something different.'

'He forgot your anniversary didn't he?' Edward was smiling and the question sounded more derisive than he had intended. He had meant it as a joke that might be true, which was also an excellent definition of life in general.

She stopped crying. 'It wasn't funny, okay? I came home early to make an elaborate meal, even more elaborate than your fucking little chickens, and he blew me off. He called to say that he was working late, if you can call it work, and you're quite right, Edward, he did not remember. But it wasn't that, so much as the fact that I cared so much. Does that make sense? I shouldn't need those days, they would not be that significant if every other day meant something. I don't require a birthday to buy a person a gift or tell them that I love them, but with him I now need those days.'

'So was this your great revenge?' Edward was angry. He knew that the question was stupid but he asked it anyway.

'You don't understand anything. This isn't the answer,' she indicated the bed and swept her hand over his chest, histrionically. He wanted to pull the sheets up to his chin. Instead he said: 'Just something you felt like.'

'You're an asshole. I don't even know you but I know that.' She got up and walked toward her underwear on the floor. She reached down while keeping her legs perfectly straight and he could see her hamstrings tense and tighten. He was going to say that she shouldn't have screwed him if she knew so much, but that motion was so elegant that he stopped himself.

'I'm sorry, Emily,' and she turned on these words holding

her underwear close to her. She was breathing as though restraining herself from tears. 'You look so beautiful right now. Please, don't think this was a mistake. I've never seen someone pick up their panties with grace before. And I cannot believe that I just said that out loud. But it's true. You're not like anyone else that I've met. I guess I felt used, and overwhelmed, definitely overwhelmed by you. Come back here, and talk to me.'

She came back and told him that her boyfriend was Rick Caesar and that he spent Saturday evening at the Pearl Jam concert. Two years ago she had been unable to contain her excitement when they went to concerts and parties and met all of the big names in music. He was even able to introduce her to Deborah Harry and Jim Kerr. Edward associated the former with several episodes of *Wiseguy* which caused him to sever his relationship with television permanently, and the latter with *The Breakfast Club*, during which he was removed from the theatre because he could not help laughing loudly whenever Emilio Estevez delivered a dramatic line.

'What's Rick really like?'

'He is a wonderful guy, but when we're together it's all at the same level. My life is so comfortable, always the same pleasant temperature. I need seasons, heat and cold. I'm too young for climate control.'

'He seems so crazy and lively on the radio.'

'You listen?'

'On the way in. I'm still hanging on to grunge.'

'The two of you should get together. He adores that stuff. He's always criticizing my taste in music. Thank God we both like U2 and The Cure. He thinks that just because he's a DJ his opinion is somehow more than an opinion. That annoys me as well. It's funny because when we first started seeing each other he was so judgmental, and I thought that was strong and attractive. But it's just fucking negative and arrogant.'

'You like U2?'

'Sure. *Under A Blood Red Sky*, *Joshua Tree*. Only the early ones.'

'Me too. They're the band of that decade.'

She stared at him, waiting for something more, and he sensed that she might get angry very quickly if he left it at that.

'People grow apart, but I mean more than that. It's as though people agree to ignore the things about each other that they don't like because there is so much that they do like. But that stuff doesn't disappear, and when one person is looking for an excuse to end the relationship they start to focus on those characteristics as though they are newly discovered. It's a choice, Emily. You can remember the good or the bad about Rick, because they're both still there.'

Before she left early in the morning, they talked for another two hours about love and sex. Emily stayed in her underwear, sitting cross-legged next to him. They ate bowls of chocolate chip ice cream and Edward listened while she told him about her love of Blake and the book she hoped to publish on the songs of innocence and experience. Edward let her speak for a long time before he interrupted:

'I read those poems when I was a freshman in college. I was in love at the time with this girl who was a few years older than me. When we were alone she would speak to me in this five-year-old voice. She gave me pet names and squeezed my cheeks like I was a baby, and it felt right because it was intimate. But then we'd make love and she'd scream out for me and beg for me to do things to her. And she knew a lot about life, a lot more than I did. When she pretended to be five she didn't magically forget about all of that. Both of those sides were there, and I could never deal with that. Basically, I blame Blake. I think he fucked me up for life. Thanks to Blake, as far as I'm concerned, women are either ignorant virgins frolicking with lambs, or bitter and fallen urbanites. I never stopped to think that women could be both at the same time.'

'Don't blame Blake alone,' she said, stroking Edward's face with her palm.

The next week they had dinner at her apartment. It was a rowhouse in Mount Vernon with hardwood floors and real fireplaces. She liked wrought iron decorations and the cream couches were covered with burgundy pillows made out of velvet. They were talking about films when the doorbell rang. Edward considered climbing on to the fire escape, or hiding underneath the bed. He knew who was waiting on the other side of the door, waiting to crush him by compressing his mammoth frame around Edward's terrified body. Without hesitation Emily stood up, went to the door and leaned down to greet Rick Caesar with a peck on the lips.

'Honey. What a nice surprise. This is Edward, remember I was talking about him the other day?'

'Sure,' the man whom they both claimed was Rick Caesar said. 'The history guy, right?'

Edward was also standing, although he was clutching his napkin in his left hand for support. They shook hands.

'I'm sorry to drop in like this. Emily mentioned that she was having dinner with you this evening. I left my brown jacket here the other day and it has the tickets that I promised to give Sammy tonight at the club. Please don't mind me, I'll be out of your hair in a second.'

Edward could not stop looking down at the man who was talking. He was bald, thin, and wore a black turtleneck sweater. He had a goatee that was neatly trimmed and looked like the kind of man who always works in an art gallery in Hollywood movies. It was the right voice, but slower and softer. As Rick Caesar walked into the bedroom, Edward blurted out:

'One question, I have one question. Gary is fat as a house, isn't he?'

Rick came back with the jacket draped across his arm. 'He sure is. How did you know that?'

'Edward has these flashes of insight,' Emily said with a hint of mischief that only Edward seemed to notice.

'He's portly and married with three kids,' Rick said. Then he waved his hand as though it held a wand. 'The power of radio.'

When he walked out the door, Edward felt sad and wished that he had stayed longer.

'Oh God,' Emily reached up to hug him, 'I am so sorry. I had no idea.'

'It's okay. He's really nice.'

They continued to meet, mostly during the day, always at remote locations where no one would identify Emily. She did not want Rick to find out because he would be devastated. Edward was tempted to point out that her actions were hurtful, not the discovery of those actions. He did not know anyone in the city and enjoyed being taken to new neighbourhoods that he otherwise would not have visited. He did not go to her apartment again. That night she had pleaded with him to stay but staring at the armoire where Rick kept his clothes had convinced him to climb out of bed and drive home. When Emily came to Edward's apartment, though, she would invariably stay, but this happened no more than once a week. One morning she said to him:

'I'm thinking of leaving Rick, but then I can't stop thinking of Alsemero's paradox as well.'

Edward knew what was expected of him, and although he resented the way she introduced her observations as though they were unsolved mysteries, and these observations were consistently derived from a piece of literature that she read at graduate school, he played along. 'What's the paradox?'

'There's this play called *The Changeling*. I don't remember it that well, but I wrote this essay on it called Alsemero's Paradox, and that stuck in my mind. Alsemero meets a woman in the first scene and falls in love with her. But she's already engaged to another man, partly due to the wishes of her father, but also because she cared for the other guy. She apparently feels far more for Alsemero, and the two of them plot to find a way to eliminate the fiancé. After she marries Alsemero she cheats on him as well with her hideous servant.

It's a tragedy and in the end most of them die.' She stopped for a moment, hopefully aware that it all sounded like a lecture on the first day of a course.

'It was more complicated than that. The point was Alsemero initially reasoned that because this woman was risking everything to be with him that this was an indication of what he meant to her. It had to be true love. Later, though, he comes to believe that her adulterous actions are only a part of her nature.'

She had this look in her eyes that seemed to be saying: do you see what I mean?

'I read an article in a women's magazine,' Edward responded, 'can't remember which one, but it was about how the way in which a person ended their last relationship was likely to be the same way that their current relationship would end. Is that what you're getting at?'

'Edward, I care about you. I know that a lot must be wrong with my relationship with Rick, otherwise I wouldn't be here. I just don't know if that's the only reason that I'm here. I want to be honest with you.'

Edward thought about saying that the way things were was fine with him. He didn't want a high-maintenance relationship. He liked being the other man. His role was clearly defined, expectations were few, responsibilities as minimal. He now looked forward to his morning drive. Rick Caesar's juvenile voice reminded Edward that he kept secrets that could alter if not ruin the life of a minor celebrity. That alone was almost as gratifying as the prospect of arranging furtive liaisons with Emily. He wasn't idealistic like Alsemero sounded, and Emily didn't suffer from some fatal flaw of nymphomania, she was searching for something, that was all.

'I think you're great, Emily, and I love spending time with you. But I think you realize that if you leave Rick that's something between the two of you alone. You can't leave him for me because it will inevitably end up as some circular process. You know, I absolutely despise eighties music.'

He stared at her, willing her to see his point. She was

perplexed. It had come out of nowhere, although it made perfect sense to Edward.

'When you talk about XTC or the Psychedelic Furs it actually upsets me that a person who is otherwise so intelligent could have suffered such a critical lapse. The eighties produced the most fucking awful music of all time.'

She looked at him for a long time, saying nothing, and the silence between them did not feel comfortable. Then she smiled.

'Edward, I think I'm falling in love with you. Music doesn't matter.'

Edward had a startlingly vivid vision of Rick and Emily, in bed two years earlier, having the same conversation about minor disparities that their love would leap over. She had turned to Rick and said the same words. Edward held her close to him, kissing her face while she mumbled that she loved him, and he saw their future beginning to stretch out from this night. There would be time for her to figure out that cats were remorseless, that Jane was even less talented than Peter, and that portraits of unattractive medieval Dutch people all looked identical. He did like some of Blake's poems, though, he definitely meant that.

Richard Holmes

BIOGRAPHY AND DEATH

The text of the 1997 Huizinga Lecture

I

THE WORD FOR 'biography' has been universal in all European languages for the last two hundred years. Since it is derived from the Greek root 'bios' meaning life, there appears to be some serious error in my title. Surely I mean, 'Biography and Life'?

Well, perhaps the first lesson of Biography is that appearances are deceptive.

It was the 18th-century wit and scholar Dr John Arbuthnott who originally observed that 'Biography has added a new terror to death', and the great modernist James Joyce who coined the baleful term 'Biografiend', a pursuing angel of death like the ancient Eumenides. Oscar Wilde gave this *timor biographicus* a more Biblical turn: 'Today every great man has his disciples, and it is always Judas who writes the biography.'

We know what they meant. It is true that we live in a busy age of biographical writing, and the form has never been so popular. In Britain something like 3,500 new biographies are published every year. James Boswell's *Life of Samuel Johnson* has never been out of print this century. Andrew Morton's *Diana: Her True Story* has currently sold five and a half million copies. The British in particular seem almost religiously dedicated to the form in every manifestation. A *New Dictionary of National Biography* is under way at Oxford. The National Portrait Gallery, not to mention Madame Tussaud's, are visted by tens of thousands every year. There are degree courses in Life Writing, and one of the national Millennium projects is to be a multi-media Biographical Museum to be called the Biorama, where long-departed celebrities will rise up again on video screens and converse on interactive CD-Rom.

And yet there is something deadly about the form, some whiff of brimstone in its nature. It seems inherently lethal. From its birth it has been associated with cheap gossip, scandalous revelations, commercial exploitation, invasion of privacy. In recent lives of Picasso, Sigmund Freud, John Lennon, Nancy Reagan, Sylvia Plath, even the great American sexologist Alfred Kinsey (what more could there possibly have been to reveal?), we are aware of its power to destroy celebrity and reputation. The feminist Germaine Greer has recently remarked that famous people will have to copyright their lives. The last Archbishop of Canterbury, on hearing that his biography was imminent, said he had tried to co-operate fully and done his best to decease before publication. The poet Sir Stephen Spender, on the other hand, said his main reason for staying alive was simply to forestall his biographer.

In the literary world, the fear of biography has been marked by a long series of bonfires of private papers – Byron's autobiography, Henry James's letters, Philip Larkin's diaries. Kipling, in his autobiography *Something of Myself*, referred to it as 'the Higher Cannibalism'.

> *If I have given you delight*
> *By aught that I have done,*
> *Let me lie quiet in that night –*
> *Which shall be yours anon:*
>
> *And for the little, little span*
> *The Dead are borne in mind,*
> *Seek not to question other than*
> *The books I leave behind.*

Biography is regularly assaulted in the newspapers and

journals. In 1993 a famous attack appeared in *The New Yorker* by Janet Malcolm, corruscating the invasive biographers of Sylvia Plath.

But the criticisms go back much further. Listen to this:

> There is a race of men lately sprung up whom one cannot reflect upon without indignation as well as contempt. These are Grub-Street biographers, who watch for the death of a great man, like so many undertakers, on purpose to make a penny of him ... Their manner of exposing the private concerns of families, and sacrificing the secrets of the dead to the curiosity of the living, is one of those licentious practices which might well deserve the animadversion of our Government.

That was Joseph Addison, the great essayist and arbiter of urbane literary manners, writing in the *Spectator* in 1716.

But these are relatively superficial matters. It was Freud who first questioned the whole psychology of modern biography. He suggested that it was founded on a form of Oedipal rivalry between biographer and subject, and the unconscious aim of all biography was to destroy the father-figure. Biography would always undermine our notion of the heroic, and because of the transference relationship implied, no objective knowledge was possible. When in 1936 the German novelist Arnold Zweig proposed himself as Freud's own biographer, Freud turned him down in a classic letter.

'To be a biographer,' Freud told him, 'you must tie yourself up in lies, concealments, hypocrisy, hero-worship; and even in hiding your own lack of understanding. For biographical truth is not to be had, and even if it *were*, we could not use it.' Then Freud added, with what we may take to be a smile and a puff of that cigar: 'That kind of truth is unobtainable. Humanity doesn't deserve it. And anyway, isn't our Prince Hamlet right, when he says – if we all had our just deserts, who would 'scape whipping?'

There are also epistemological objections to biography. By

basing itself on the shifting sands of letters, diaries, memoirs, interviews – all fatally subjective forms – it has no solid foundation in historical fact. It can claim to produce the bare skeleton chronology of a life, a sort of extended obituary of dates and events and encounters – a sort of Filofax record. But beyond that, it is essentially fraudulent. As the novelist John Steinbeck observed during his acceptance speech for the Nobel Prize, literary biography was particularly unnecessary in this respect. All literary biographies should consist of just ten words. 'He was born (date), he wrote the books (titles), and he died (silence).'

Many new American critics have gone on to suggest (see Ina Bruce Nadel, 1994) that its epistemological grounds are essentially those of fiction. But it is fiction doubly falsified, because it claims to be fact. The French too have a long and honourable tradition of dismissing the form as an intellectual vulgarity, a reduction of great ideas and causes to historical costume drama. The continuing low estimation of the work of André Maurois (a great Anglophile) or of Henri Troyat reflects this position. Gustave Flaubert, who claimed that his only true biography took the form of *Madame Bovary*, has a haunting aside in that novel to the effect that 'all lawyers carry deep within them the tragic wreckage of a poet.' By extension one could say that many French critics believe that 'tout biographe porte en soi les débris d'un romancier.' But we shall return to this delicate matter of Anglo-French diplomacy.

To me, as the biographer of English Romantic poets such as Shelley and Coleridge, the most provoking line of scepticism comes from closer to home. The essayist Maurice Baring, a man incidentally of the best European credentials, part French and part Russian by birth and a diplomat by profession, suggested that the fundamental problem with biography was its ontological dullness, its deathly certainty of ends. We know where a biography is going, and sure enough it plods there.

Yet the essential nature of a human life, as we actually experience it through the years, is the ignorance of our destiny. We do not know what life holds from year to year, from day to day, from hour to hour. We do not know what will become of us; or what we will become; or how we will stop becoming. Anything may happen, and probably will. So Baring suggested that the only true function of the biographer was to write what he called Alternative Lives, the lives that might have happened. Only then will biography be truly life-like, and not death-like.

The kind of thing he suggested can be presented as snapshots.

Lord Byron was given penicillin at Missolonghi, won the Greek War of Independence, was elected King of the Pelopponese, gave up poetry and retired to the House of Lords to defend Fox-Hunting.

Napoleon Bonaparte ran away to sea. Disembarking in the Kingdom of the Two Sicilies, he was press-ganged into the British Royal Navy, rose rapidly through the ranks to become one of Nelson's most daring Admirals, and died heroically while leading a squadron at the Battle of Trafalgar.

Coleridge completed the ballad of 'Kubla Khan' in 25 cantos and became Poet Laureate . . .

Shelley learned to swim . . .

And so on.

Of course these are rich impertinences on my part. But as Lytton Strachey once said, 'discretion is not the better part of biography.' So the question stands, does biography bring life in any true sense? Or is it as hollow as the grave, that 'fine and private place, where none I think do there embrace'?

II

Let us consider that simple notion of the human embrace. I believe this most naive and profound of human gestures is the true impulse behind all great biography. And it is an impulse as old as humanity. Sylvia Plath once said that if the novel was like an open hand, then poetry was like a closed fist. On that wonderful analogy, I would suggest that biography is like a hand-shake: a hand-shake across time, across the solitude of the human condition, across death itself. It is an act of touch, of 'con-tact', of confidentiality between two human beings.

The history of that embrace, in its earliest literary forms, obviously goes back like most good things to the Greeks. There is a complex tradition of life writing that runs from Herodotus and Thucydides, through the Roman Plutarch, to the great Renaissance collections of Vasari and the splendid boastings of Cellini. There are specialist backwaters in the growing flood of European biography, none more curious and instructive perhaps than the Vatican Library of Canonization, with its great archives of possible beatitude, and its salutary tradition of the *Advocatus Diaboli* who eternally patrols them. The Devil's Advocate continues to greet the modern biographer with a professional gesture.

But the essential paradigms here, those of exemplary greatness – great emperors and great ogres, great kings and great tyrants, great saints and great sinners – are not yet modern. If anything they belong to the early history of public relations and national propaganda, and their terms are inspirational rather than empirical, easily lifting off into hagiography or mythology or tales to frighten children by the fireside. Yet the spirit of biography is already recognizably there. Plutarch's great Elizabethan translator Roger North remarked in his Preface: 'What signifies it to us how many battles Alexander fought; it were more to the purpose to say how often he were drunk.'

It is central to my argument that biography comes of age with the 18th-century Enlightenment. One of its first declarations is exactly the idea of touching upon intimate human truth, in confidence. In England it announces itself, with typical eccentricity, in the *Brief Lives* of John Aubrey, completed in 1693 but not published until 1813. Aubrey is a strange mixture of scurrility, candour and true biographical perception. He wrote in his preface:

> *I here lay down to you (out of the conjunct friendship between us) the truth, the naked and plain truth: which is here exposed so bare, that the very pudenda are not covered, and afford many passages that would raise a blush in a young virgin's cheek . . . Yet what uncertainty do we find in printed histories . . . They dare not speak plain; or else for want of intelligence become too obscure and dark!*

It is significant that Aubrey, and several other early English biographers, were members of the Royal Society in London, one of whose first presidents was Sir Isaac Newton. They worked within the new culture of rationalism, and scientific humanism, which in Kant's phrase was to produce 'a Copernican revolution in philosophy'. In the same way, many of the first great essays in French biography appeared as articles in great *Encyclopédie* (1765), written by Denis Diderot and Voltaire. It was, incidentally, Diderot who wrote one of the earliest biographies of Erasmus, a connection which will eventually take us to the great Huizinga himself.

What were the principles that animated these great figures of the Enlightenment, as far as biography was concerned? First, quite simply, that it was a legitimate subject. In Alexander Pope's momentous line, that so influenced the young Voltaire during his exile in England, 'the proper study of Mankind is Man'. Second, that scientific objectivity, the critical spirit, could be brought to bear on the historical evidence for a past life. Rational understanding, not merely of human actions but also human motivations and passions, was possible and indeed highly desirable. There was a universal human nature, common to all mankind, and biography could bring it within a single embrace uniting both the great and the humble.

When Voltaire was composing his mighty study of Louis XIV, he wrote in a letter to the Abbé Dubois in 1738: 'It is not simply the life of a great Prince that I am writing, nor merely the chronicles of his reign; it is far more the history of the human spirit itself.' When, four years later, Samuel Johnson began the first of his great *Lives of the Poets*, he chose for his subject not one of the great bards – a Milton or a Dryden – but one of the spectacular failures of English literature, the penniless poet and convicted murderer, Richard Savage – who had also been his friend. From this unpromising material he created a masterpiece, combining the moral vision of a small man battling against his destiny with a universal appeal to sympathy and understanding:

Those are no proper Judges of his Conduct who have slumbered away their Time on the Down of Plenty, nor will a wise Man easily presume to say, 'Had I been in Savage's Condition, I should have lived, or written, better than Savage'.

Out of this new humanism grew the third great principle, that biography generates notions of justice and toleration. By understanding our fellow human beings, most especially those who are separated from us by social standing, creed, condition and culture, or most of all by death itself, we learn a concept of univeral human rights and its continuity through history. We recognize the right of the other to exist, in all the astonishing diversity of human experience. This concept is essentially secular and pluralistic; it is opposed to the notion of totalitarian ideology, whether political or religious.

It is often forgotten that Voltaire's great *Treatise on Toleration* of 1762, which put forward the actual phrase 'human rights', began with a miniature biography. It recounts, in superb forensic detail, the story of Jean Callas, the humble clothes-merchant from Toulouse, who was unjustly executed for a murder he did not commit, during a period of anti-Protestant persecutions in the city. Out of that single life-story Voltaire built a philosophy that would shake thrones and assault the great institutionalized prejudices and cruelties of his age. It was what he called the small, relentless foot-soldiers of fact attacking the great armoured battalions of power and ideology. Biography drew this extraordinary strength from its dauntless commitment to human truth at all costs, and most especially the truth locked away in past lives and awaiting our recall. 'We owe respect to the living, but to the dead we owe nothing but the truth.'

These three principles represent what one may call the classical aspects of the rational Enlightenment. For modern biographers they still represent our essential birthright, our claim to any kind of serious hearing. If we betray them by triviality, or falsehood, or prejudice, then Voltaire grins down at us showing his teeth; and Johnson advances upon us with a growl.

III

But there was also a counter-movement in later 18th-century Europe, which gave biography a wholly different kind of strength and fascination. It was of course that extraordinary explosion of sensibility which we now know as Romanticism. With the *Confessions* of Rousseau, the *Sentimental Journey* of Sterne, and the *Young Werther* of Goethe, the individual human heart proclaimed its intensity, its eccentricity, its solitude, its endless depth. It also admitted, with a new candour, the central radiation of sexual longing in the formation of personality. Biography was thus inspired by the recognition of a new kind of inwardness, what Keats in a wonderful phrase was to call 'the egotistical Sublime'. What was important about a life might be its most intimate circumstances, the private life behind the public action, the man behind the mask. In a word, 18th-century biography had discovered the notion of 'interiority'.

It was, paradoxically, the great classicist Samuel Johnson who first proclaimed this romantic doctrine in a famous essay on biography, published as the 60th number of his *Rambler* as early as 1750.

No other form, he claimed, not even the novel, 'can more certainly enchain the heart by irresistible interest'. There was probably no life, however outwardly mundane, that would fail to engage the reader if it was 'faithfully and judiciously narrated' in its innermost emotional truth. 'We are all prompted by the same Motives, all deceived by the same Fallacies, all animated by hope, obstructed by Danger, entangled by Desire, and seduced by Pleasure.'

Johnson's dismissal of the biographers who wrote in the old tradition of public hagiography and virtuous memorials, still carries a wonderful, ironic flourish.

> They rarely afford any other Account than might be collected from publick Papers, but imagine themselves writing a Life when they exhibit a chronological Series of Actions or Preferments; and so little regard the Manners or Behaviour of their Heroes, that more Knowledge may be gained of a Man's real Character, by a short Conversation with one of his Servants, than from a formal and studied Narrative, begun with his Pedigree and ended with his Funeral.

Johnson's crucial recognition of the intimate and inner life as the central feature, and indeed central challenge, of modern biography did not of course emerge in isolation. But one may say that it became a peculiarly powerful aspect of the English tradition, with its singular emphasis on the animation – literally the 'spirit moving' – element in biographical writing. A biographical narrative should bring the inner life of its subject back into existence, with an intensity that rivalled the novel. A biography should 'resurrect' a man or woman, so that they live and think and feel again in our company. We must be able to embrace them in all their complexity, in all their flickerings of light and shade.

It is no coincidence that Johnson's colleague, the great English portrait painter Sir Joshua Reynolds, after a lifetime of fixing portraits statically on a flat canvas, should have made the wonderful remark that true biography began 'with the discovery of inner contradiction within a character'. (I am reminded that the great scientist Stephen Hawking, a present member of the Royal Society, recently observed that all advances in astronomy were made 'by concentrating on the paradoxes within existing theory'.)

The English, or rather the Scottish philosopher, David Hume also supplied a theoretical justification for this biographical concept of inwardness in his *Treatise of Human Nature* (1740). Not merely did he champion the notion of fearless, sceptical enquiry, which belongs in my account to the classical aspect of biography. But he wrote a brilliant chapter with the title 'Of Personal Identity', which underwrites the romantic one. 'Could we see clearly into the breast of another,' he argued, 'and observe that succession of perceptions which constitutes his mind or thinking principle, and suppose that he always preserves the memory of a considerable part of past perceptions, it is evident that nothing could more contribute to the bestowing of a relation . . . which constitutes identity.'

In that extraordinarily acute analysis, Hume actually set out a philosophic programme for the kind of biographical narrative that can capture an inner life and unique identity. It must move forward in time along a path of *perceptions*. But it must also move backwards in time along a path of accumulated *memory*. Biographical subjects live their lives facing forward into the unknown future, but become themselves by facing backwards into the known past. A true biographical narrative must recreate both movements. And this might be a first answer to Baring's ontological problem.

But I have run too far ahead myself. For one figure is now demanding, and indeed clamouring, for recognition, and the word Scottish announces him to the whole of Europe. James Boswell once wrote that he considered applying for a royal patent, 'By Appointment to His Majesty King George the Third, Biographer of Samuel Johnson LLD' – like a peculiarly fine pot of marmalade. But he also added, so proud was he of his profession, that he would rather be known as 'plain Mr B the biographer, than as Sir James B. Bart, the distinguished High Court Judge.' Which in the circumstances of Boswell's own life, with its lower-case 'I' and its low-life lovelife, is probably just as well.

Boswell produced the first great full-length biographical masterpiece, not only of English but I think of European literature. He brought together both the classical and the romantic principles I have been discussing. He wrote a fearless, meticulously-researched chronological epic – it runs to 1,500 pages in modern editions – which is justly famous for its great social setpieces, its witty conversations in London taverns and its thunderous repartees on the Scottish moors. 'Sir, the noblest prospect which a Scotchman ever sees, is the high road that leads him to England!'

But Boswell also produced the inner portrait of a driven, melancholy genius, tragically frustrated in his married life, and tortured by religious doubts, fears of damnation and a sense of metaphysical futility. He showed Johnson in every aspect, talking to half-naked actresses, talking to God, talking to his cat. He called it 'a true Dutch portrait'. There is an argument that nothing Johnson himself wrote is so intellectually rich, so emotionally moving, as the life which he bequeathed to his greatest friend. It might seem a demonstration of Goethe's penetrating dictum that 'the proof of genius is posthumous productivity'.

All this is sufficiently well known, and indeed to the English so belovedly familiar that Boswell's Johnson has achieved that status granted to few outside some of Shakespeare's greatest characters. He is known to people who have never actually read the biography at all; he has become part of a national consciousness, like Hamlet. When an Englishman argues, you will still hear Johnson; when an Englishman grows silent and introspective you will still see Hamlet. And I will return to the significance of this shortly.

The point I wish to make rapidly now is that Boswell learned his art essentially in Europe. It is often forgotten that as a young man in 1762, he embarked on a two-year tour which took him not to monuments but to men, to exactly the great figures of the Enlightenment who were shaping the biographical idea. He had already studied under David Hume in Edinburgh. He went to Holland to learn Dutch law and French literature, and fell in love at Utrecht with one of the great belles esprits of her time, the enchanting and cantankerous Zélide. Here he took his first steps in biography, not only keeping his famous and lubricious Journal, but writing romantic sketches of Zélide's circle. Then he went on to interview Voltaire at Ferney, Rousseau at Lake Geneva, and very nearly the young Bonaparte in Corsica. Boswell had to make do with the great General Paoli, since Bonaparte had not yet been born – a circumstance that would not necessarily have deterred young Boswell in his intimate investigations. All this time he was experimenting with sketches, Journal notes, interviews and character-studies. He came home and wrote a life of Paoli and a marriage proposal to Zélide, the former rather more rapidly than the latter. Then, at last, he was ready to settle down to Johnson, his European education as an English biographer complete. In fact Boswell only completed his great work four years before his death in 1795. It had been a lifetime's effort, and it had almost driven him, he said, to alcoholism – and even worse, to teetotalism. But he had created a new form, and a new tradition, and with writers like Carlyle and Froude in England, and Sainte-Beuve in France, it flourished mightily. It was said, in a Voltarian spirit, that if Plutarch was the Old Testament for biographers, then Boswell was the New Testament.

Or at the very least, the Act of the Apostle.

IV

You will be disappointed to hear that I do not propose to deal with the growing iniquities of Victorian biography. The problems of monstrous size, of sleep-walking style, of slumbering propriety and politeness, are well-known. It is sufficient to quote Lytton Strachey writing in his most dulcet tones in 1918:

> *With us the most delicate and humane of all the branches of the art of writing has been relegated to the journeyman of letters; we do not reflect that it is perhaps as difficult to write a good life as to live one. Those two fat volumes, with which it is our custom to commemorate the dead – who does not know them, with their ill-digested masses of material, their slipshod style, their tone of tedious panegyric, their lamentable lack of selection, of detachment, of design? They are as familiar as the cortege of the undertaker, and wear the same air of slow, funereal barbarism.*

As the form degenerated it again became vulnerable to attack. Nowhere was this assault more brilliantly mounted than in France. In this perhaps we find a reflection of an old Anglo-French cultural rivalry; and even a continuing shadowy opposition between a Protestant tradition dedicated to the value of the individual conscience in all its eccentricity; and a Catholic tradition dedicated to the authority of the central idea. Perhaps the Dutch, with their long tradition of gentle and inclusive humanism – and again our thoughts move to Huizinga's great biography of Erasmus – are in a position to mediate again, as so often before.

The French, with their fine tradition of public 'éloge' and great political historiography by writers such as Michelet, concentrated their criticism on the biography of those most private of men and women, artists and especially writers. Here, where the 'Life' has already fully reproduced itself in an aesthetic dimension as the 'Work', they argued that the intrusions of biography were both fraudulent and impertinent. Many English novelists and poets, whose line of bonfires – those beacons of alarm – we have already scanned, were now in agreement.

Marcel Proust, in a wonderfully delicate and feline essay *Contre Sainte-Beuve*, gently suggested that the social nature of biography could never reach the 'moi' or deep private inner self where works of art were created. He looked quizzically at the kinds of question that Sainte-Beuve posed using his celebrated biographical 'method'. What did the artist think of religion? How was he affected by 'the spectacle of Nature'? How did he behave with regard to the 'question of women, or the question of money'? What was his daily timetable, what was his characteristic vice, what was his particular weakness?

Proust poured scorn on this whole line of biographical inquisition.

> *This famous method totally ignores what the least familiarity with our own inner nature so abundantly teaches us. That a book is the product of another self* (un autre moi) *from the one that we habitually expose in our daily lives, in social situations, or indeed in our vices. If we wish to understand that other self of the artist* (ce moi-là), *we will only reach it by trying to recreate it in ourselves, in the depth of our own being.* (Chapter 8)

The power of this argument had been seen long ago by Shelley, who once wrote in a letter from Italy: 'perhaps in my daily life here I am never properly aware of the poet's existence, which takes place altogether elsewhere and belongs to someone else'. However, it is also true that one of the great triumphs of recent English biography has been George Painter's *Marcel Proust*; and that having widely denounced it, French biographers have produced no fewer than three lives of Proust in the last decade, the last by Professeur Tadié.

Some thirty years later, the underlying epistemology of biography was brought even more fiercely under fire by an equally influential French philosopher. In his novel of 1938, *La Nausée*, Jean-Paul Sartre depicted a young provincial researcher attempting to write an historical biography. Working in the bleakness of a municipal library, with its pompous and absurd portraits of long-forgotten worthies,

RICHARD HOLMES

Antoine Roquentin is gradually overcome by the meaning-lessness of his task. He is assailed by the ambiguity of all human evidence, and above all by the falsifications imposed by producing a rational and chronological story-line. Sartre argued from this chill scenario, that the narrative form of all biography imposed a metaphysical falsification on life as it actually occurs, an entirely fictive logic of events and causation. It denied the existential chaos of life:

> When you are actually living, nothing happens. Settings change, people come in and go out of the room, but that's all. There are never any beginnings. Days are tacked on to each other without rhyme or reason, in an endless monotonous meaningless addition ... That's real living.
> But when you start to recount a life, everything changes; only it's a change that nobody notices. The proof is that people talk about true stories. As if there could possibly be such a thing as true stories. Events take place in one way, and we recount them in another.
> The moment you have a beginning – 'It was a fine autumn evening in 1922' – then the end is already there transforming everything, and the fellow who walks in is already the hero of the story of his life. (La Nausée, Diary, 'Saturday Noon')

The English in fact have long had a phrase for this view: 'life's just one damn thing after another'. But it is usually uttered in the pub before the first drink. Nevertheless, one can see that Maurice Baring would have recognized the argument, though he might not have been impressed by Sartre's eventual solution. Unable to resist the lure of biography, Sartre returned to it after the war and wrote two gigantic studies, both far longer than Boswell's. He replaced chronology by a discursive form of psycho-analytic enquiry, which invented primal scenes if he could not actually find them. The subject of the first study, *Saint Genet: Comédien et Martyr* (1952), was still alive when he wrote, and announced succinctly that

402

he did not recognize himself; later adding that Sartre had 'stolen' his identity and he would consider suing for its return. The subject of his second was none other than *Flaubert: The Idiot of the Family*, and it appears to have been a relief to both parties when the book was finally abandoned (1971).

Finally, Roland Barthes, in his classic essay of 1968 argued that 'the author was dead', and did not exist as an objective presence in works of art. His colleague Phillipe Sollers added that as an author's life, if he still had any, existed subjectively in his works alone, then the proper term for what was left over could not be 'biography' but 'thanatography' – death writing.

It has to be said that after this, French biography immediately burst into a rich new lease of life. Apart from major studies of La Fontaine, Voltaire, Racine, and Proust – and tender evocations of Suzanne Vallodon and Jacques Prévert – there was a particularly racy and incisive life of Sartre by Annie Cohen-Solal. She has since been appointed a French cultural ambassador.

V

I have been of course a little sweeping in this account. The anxieties and self-questioning of the modern biographical form are an essential feature of its energy.

Much has been absorbed in England, and every English biographer is now familiar with W. H. Auden's wonderful sonnet 'Who's Who', which so eloquently dramatizes many of these most necessary doubts:

A shilling life will give you all the facts:
How Father beat him, how he ran away,
What were the struggles of his youth, what acts
Made him the greatest figure of his day:
Of how he fought, fished, hunted, worked all night,
Though giddy, climbed new mountains, named a sea;

> *Some of the last researchers even write*
> *Love made him weep his pints like you and me.*
>
> *With all his honours on, he sighed for one*
> *Who, say astonished critics, lived at home;*
> *Did little jobs about the house with skill*
> *And nothing else; could whistle; would sit still*
> *Or potter round the garden; answered some*
> *Of his long marvellous letters but kept none.*

One of the suggestive things about this elegy is that it itself takes the form of a miniature biography. This is representative. English biographers have characteristically produced very little defence of the form in terms of theory. What they have done, instead, is to write a series of 'maverick' or poetical or experimental biographies to test the limits of what can be said or discovered. This experimental tradition, with strong elements of satire and parody, has become one of the most distinctive parts of 20th-century biography. The English have responded to French theory by going out undaunted and breaking the rules in practice. There are many examples.

Lytton Strachey's four brilliant, sardonic portraits in *Eminent Victorians* (1918) are not merely an attack on the hypocrisy of Victorian values, they are an attack on the restrictions of Victorian biography. They champion wit, scepticism of convention and declared motive, and an incisive psychologically penetrating narrative which moves with great speed and artistic elegance. But this attack had already begun with Edmund Gosse's *Father and Son* (1908). Gosse first wrote a conventional respectful biography of his father, P. H. Gosse, a marine biologist and religious fundamentalist. But twenty years later he rewrote it, with devastating effect, as narrated by himself as a child and adolescent. By shifting the narrative point of view, he revealed a tragic tyrant living in an emotional wasteland.

Virginia Woolf's *Orlando* (1928) investigated the whole notion of personality and chronology. Its subject, her friend Vita Sackville-West – aristocrat, poet and lesbian – is made to live for no less than four centuries and to change sex from man to woman half way through. Throughout this delightful jeu d'esprit, Virginia Woolf reflects on the nature of the biographical form. 'The true length of a person's life – whatever the *Dictionary of National Biography* may say – is always a matter of dispute. A biography is considered complete if it merely accounts for six or seven lives; whereas a person may contain a thousand.' She then went on to write a life of the Brownings, but narrated it through the eyes of their family dog, Flush. This wonderfully inventive line of experiment – via A. J. A Symons's *Quest For Corvo* and Brian Matthew's *Louisa* (a brilliant Australian contribution) – continues right up to the present. Ian Hamilton's *In Search of J. D. Salinger* (1988), for example, uses the circumstance of Salinger's refusal to co-operate in the writing of his own life, even to the extent of threatening legal proceedings against his biographer, to develop a mordant and searching examination of the ethics of biography.

Most brilliantly of all perhaps, Julian Barnes's *Flaubert's Parrot* (1984), turns the procedures of academic biography inside out, by calling all evidence – even the colour of Emma Bovary's eyes – into question. One of Barnes's many revealing devices is to produce a chapter of chronologies – not one, but two – which are both historically correct but which produce absolutely contradictory impressions of Flaubert's life, and whether it was a success or a failure in human terms. Here are his entries for the formative year 1836, when Flaubert met the woman who would inspire *A Sentimental Education*:

Version one.
Meets Elisa Schlesinger, wife of a German music publisher, in Trouville and conceives an 'enormous' passion for her. This passion illuminates the rest of his adolescence. She treats him with great kindness and affection; they remain in touch for the next forty years. Looking back, he is relieved she didn't return his passion: 'Happiness is like the pox. Catch it too soon, and it wrecks your constitution.'

Version two.
Start of a hopeless, obsessive passion for Elisa Schle-
singer which cauterises his heart and renders him
incapable of ever fully loving another woman. Looking
back, he records: 'Each of us possesses in his heart a
royal chamber. I have bricked mine up.' (Chapter 2)

What all these books do is to ask questions about the
relationship between the biographer and the subject. They
demonstrate that it is always provisional and never absolute.
There is no such thing as a 'definitive' biography. But this is
precisely the reason that the form has remained alive. Every
good biographer forms a new and particular relationship
with the subject, seeing new aspects, making new interpreta-
tions, suggesting new answers. So in theory a biography can
be written many times over. And in practice that is exactly
what happens. It is one of the distinguishing characteristics of
biography that it is never finished. It is not a classically closed
form like the novel; it always remains open-ended. When
Flaubert put his life into *Madame Bovary*, or Charles Dickens
into *David Copperfield*, there was nothing more to be said,
not a word to be added. The work of art was complete,
splendid, perfectly contained in its moment. But that is not
true of Flaubert's life, or Dickens's life, in biography. There
are half-a-dozen major biographies of Flaubert, a dozen of
Dickens, and there will certainly be more.

Some figures indeed attract an extraordinary outpouring of
biography. There are over 200 lives of Byron, and over 200
lives of Napoleon. Boswell would no doubt be surprised to
learn that there are now over 20 lives of Johnson. At the
latest count there are, according to Norman Mailer, over 40
lives of Marilyn Monroe. Like the myths of classical Greek
drama, certain lives seem to need telling over and over again,
at least once every generation. This tells us something
essential about the nature of the form, and one of the simplest
is that it seems to respond to an almost inexhaustible human
need. I believe this is something far more profound than mere
curiosity. It is something to do with historical continuity,

with finding our bearings and our human values living – and I stress that word *living* – in the past. It is in this sense a humanist pursuit of the greatest possible significance. I will return to this final claim in one moment.

VI

We are, I believe, living in a golden age of biography in England. The mood of self-doubt, of self-questioning, of searching for a new identity – the very mood that has perhaps held us back from Europe since the War, and made us such difficult, sceptical partners – has also led us to an immensely fruitful re-examination of our past through biography. Our best biographers have been working on a large scale, and one of the shapes I have noticed emerging is that of a certain patterning or historical grouping of subjects. If I were a French critic I would observe the recurrence of a particular formal shape: the three-sided structure, or trilogy of linked biographies which form a larger imaginative concept. Let me rapidly survey some of these triangulations.

Richard Ellmann's great trilogy of Irish literary lives – the visionary poet Yeats, the modernist Joyce, the wit and homosexual rebel Oscar Wilde – has brought the question of Anglo-Irish relations into a new historical focus. They suggest that the Irish have in some ways been the radical conscience of post-Imperial England. Similarly Michael Holroyd's splendid, flamboyant trilogy of bearded, bohemian spirits – Lytton Strachey himself, the painter Augustus John, and the dramatist Bernard Shaw – has posed the most searching questions about the survival of English liberalism into a new age. Claire Tomalin (herself half-French) has written lives of three embattled women – the feminist Mary Wollstonecraft, the great comic actress Dorothea Jordan, and the spirited Ellen Ternan (the 'invisible' mistress of Charles Dickens) – which bring wonderfully and tragically alive the contradictions which we have inherited in the role of modern women as equal partners in society.

Other great trilogies are currently appearing or under way. Roland Huntford's study of explorers and the British spirit of suicidal adventure. Ray Monk's limpid study of philosophers – so far Wittgenstein and Bertrand Russell – and the peculiarly difficult role of the professional thinker in British society. Peter Ackroyd's conjurations of metropolitan genius in his 'London Visionaries' – William Blake, Charles Dickens and T. S. Eliot. There are many others which I do not have time to mention.

But you will see, I think, that we now have an extraordinarily rich and multifarious flow of biographical work – the experimental and the mainstream – bubbling up in England. It is a marvellously exciting time to be working in the genre. And I can predict something of the future. More pressing perhaps than anything else is the need for lives of scientists, lives which go back indeed to the earliest days of the Royal Society. What is the difference between the artistic and the scientific imagination, and how similarly has the creative spirit worked in both? Is scientific discovery really a matter of teamwork? Is science, any more than art, value-free when we examine it through the lens of biography? These seem to me most urgent questions.

Again, how far can biography contribute to the most universal and influential of all modern art forms, the cinema? In many ways it is film – with its primary reliance on visual narrative and symbolic surface – which now finds it most problematic to render what Proust called the deep inner 'moi' of the literary biography. But equally cinema can reveal the lives of musicians, with wonderful combinations of images and sound track. Surely that most ludicrous and unsatisfactory of film genres, the historical 'biopic', should have a serious future?

And what of the discipline of biography itself? Should it become a subject for formal study and academic theory? Or should it run free, remaining close to its natural readership, extravagant and extracurricular, always asking the forbidden question but always questioning its own right to exist? Should we have University chairs in comparative biography?

Or should we, like Plato with the poets, only allow biographers to roam society and history on sufferance?

I must proclaim here a particular dream. It does seem to me that comparative biography in a European sense might have a vital role to play in the next millennium. Nation might speak more freely to nation through the communal language of biography. I do not merely speak of dictionaries of European biography, or international conferences of scholars. I mean that after two hundred years, biography already holds out an astonishingly rich literary resource for international human understanding. I am speaking, once more, of that simple primary human embrace – across time, across language, across frontiers.

Johann Huizinga's great *Erasmus* (1924), so elegantly compact and yet so profoundly and even melancholically thoughtful, is one of the finest expressions of humanism in Dutch literature. It has been translated into virtually all European languages.

Yet it is also true that there are a dozen other lives of Erasmus from every epoch and every country – Denis Diderot's in France (1765), J. A. Froude's in England (1893), Stefan Zweig's in Germany (1920), Preserved Smith's in America (1923) and quite recently the poet George Faludy's in Hungary (1970). Biography, as I say, is always an open, unfolding form. But isn't this the very grounds for seeing it as an international endeavour? Wouldn't it now be possible to study these lives comparatively, as an extension of the Erasmic spirit through time and across Europe? And couldn't the same comparative approach be applied to innumerable other biographies?

Thus biography might find its fullest flowering, its true humanist destiny, in the coming century. Here is a form, miraculously adapted to our contemporary needs, critical and yet imaginative, popular and yet ethically challenging, which offers the possibility of a new cultural dialogue. Here is the ground for what Huizinga himself called, in his last visionary work *In the Shadow of Tomorrow* (1936), the necessary change in 'the spiritual *habitus* of man'.

409

I offer this as a modest English proposal for a new European currency. I offer the golden form of biography as a true rate of historical value and exchange. Here is biography, that can already bring its subjects a *second life*, a life that may continue fruitfully for many generations. Here therefore is the chance to create something larger still, a second biographical life of nations; especially now, and in Europe.

So it is true, my title was not quite accurate. It should have been, 'Biography versus Death'.

Niall Griffiths
THE BEST DEATH EVER

WE WERE ABOUT six years old, seven, playing Best Deaths in the back yard of my house in Netherley, Liverpool, using my dad's bags of cement, some gone hard in the rain, as a barricade to hide and shoot behind. There were four of us but we only had three guns, so Stevie was using a stick, and I felt sorry for him because we had played Touchbums in the woods the day before so I pointed out that we really only needed three guns because the person who was doing the dying didn't have to be shooting, all he had to do was get shot at and die. My gun was brilliant, a present from my grandad, made out of wood and steel with an authentic bolt-action mechanism which I loved to use, the clanking sound and the brisk hand movement. A Lee Enfield imitation, my grandad said it was, and he'd been in the war. It had come with dummy bullets, bronze and conical, which would leap realistically out of the breech when the bolt was yanked back, but I'd lost them all and was using cigarettes instead, stolen from my parents. They didn't make a satisfying, important clink when they shot out and landed on the flagstones like the bullets did but they were roughly the right size and shape and they'd do.

– Who's first?

– Me, said Mick, and went and hid at the other end of the yard behind the coal bunker. Stevie and Gavin took aim with their placcy machine-guns; I slammed the bolt back and loaded up with a Number 6.

– Ready? GO!

Mick came running out from behind the coal bunker, face screwed up and streaked with dust, shouting. Stevie and Gavin let fly: UHUHUHUHUHUH! I took careful aim at his chest and squeezed the trigger, squeezed, not pulled, and his run gradually became a slow-motion jog, winding down like a toy running out of battery power until he collapsed unconvincingly on the floor.

– That was rubbish! Yer meant ter *die*, not just fall over like a fart. Since when did you see anyone die like that?

– Yeh, after being shot?

Mick came back behind the barricade, looking embarrassed. – Well I didn't want to fall over on the floor an hurt meself, did I? It'd be better on the grass.

– Soft lad. How can you hurt yerself if yer dead?

I wanted to go next but Stevie had beaten me to it, he was already crouched down behind the coal bunker. You could see a tuft of reddish hair sticking up over the top like the end of a carrot, only not green. I loaded up with a new fag; the first one had been broken in two by the ejector spring.

– On yer marks, get set . . . GO!

Stevie came running towards us, bellowing. Gavin and Mick let him have it; I didn't really want to shoot him because, well, we'd touched each other's bums only the day before, but he was the attacking German and I was the defending Brit so I took aim at his head (brain shot, clinical and quick, painless, won't know what hit him) and fired. It was a good one; he leapt backwards in mid-run, as if suddenly jerked on elastic, flew through the air and landed on his back. I heard him yelp as the air was whacked out of his lungs and the THOK as his skull hit the concrete flags. It was very impressive. Even more so when he stood up grinning and rubbing the back of his head, not a bother on him.

– See?, said Mick.

We were a bit overawed by Stevie's death and no one said a word as I handed my gun over to Stevie and went and crouched down behind the coal bunker. It was dirty and smelly. I wished they would hurry up because I could see

412

harvestman spiders crawling towards me with their nightmar-
ishly long legs waving and twitching in the air. It was an odd,
suffocating feeling, being a German.

– GO!

I sprang up and ran down the yard towards them, roaring.
All I could see was the three guns pointing at me over the tops
of the cement bags; the three little round black holes out of
which would shoot at twice the speed of sound hot leaden
death.

– UHUHUHUHUH!

– BRAKKABRAKKABRAKKA!

– BANG!

That last one was my gun, the killer blow; the single
decisive fatal round right between my eyes, no messing
around. I jerked my head back and spun on my heels, my
arms outstretched, my face contorted in agony. I imagined
my chest torn open by the bullets to expose my still-beating
heart like in the painting of the Sacred Heart of Jesus above
the piano in the assembly hall at school. I felt majestic,
sacrificial. I toppled as I imagined a tyrannosaur would
topple; straight and statuesque, dignified, slamming into the
ground with an earth-shaking boom. My elbow thudded into
the flagstones and hurt.

Resurrected, I stepped back behind the barricade and took
my rifle back off Stevie.

– Not bad, that, he said. – Looked dead real. I shot you in
the shoulder, that was what spun you round.

Gavin shook his head dismissively. – Made a meal of it.
Melodramatic, it was, he said, using a word probably picked
up from his mother whilst watching *Play for Today*.

– I hurt my elbow, I said, rubbing it and looking around
for an intact cigarette with which to re-load.

Mick said: – See?, and lit up one of the broken ones,
taking tiny rapid puffs and whoofing the smoke up into the
air. He blew some smoke down the barrel of his gun and we
watched impressed as it trickled out.

– My turn now, Gavin said. – And this'll be the Best Death
Ever.

He strode determinedly over to the coal bunker but climbed up on top of it instead of hiding behind it.

– What are you doing? Yer doing it wrong. Yer meant to –

– Just watch, he said. – This'll be the Best Death Ever.

There was a length of frayed blue nylon washing-line attached by a rusty nail to the fence above the coal bunker; I'd snapped it last week playing Cross the Crocodile River and been told off. Gavin tied it around his neck as we watched. He turned to face us, crouched down, tethered to the fence by his neck.

– Are yis ready?

– What're you going to do?

– Are yis ready?

We shrugged and took aim.

– FIRE!

We opened up and Gavin leapt off the bunker, jerking to a stop about an inch above the floor. He went ACK! and his eyes bulged and his legs started to kick. His hands were clawing at his throat.

– UHUHUHUHUH!

– BRAKKABRAKKABRAKKA!

His face was turning blue. I sighted on his kicking feet because of the challenge of a moving target; I saw the ends of his red socks through the ragged holes in the toes of his black pumps. They were writhing and pointing, trying to reach the floor. I remembered what I'd learned in the schoolyard games of IRA v. UDA and aimed for his knees instead.

– God, look at him. He's really dying, inny?

– Look at him go. He's like a fly.

I decided to put him out of his misery and aimed for his head. His face was purple now, deep purple, and his eyes were red and bulging right out of his head and his black tongue was squirming around on his chin. I sighted on the skull, an angry maroon colour beneath the cropped fair hair, and pulled the trigger.

– BLAM!

SLAM! The house door flew open and whacked against the wall. My mam ran across the yard in her mules screaming.

– He's strangling himself bichrist! What're yer doing just sitting there watching him! He's choking to death!

She put her arms around him and hoisted Gavin up onto the top of the coal bunker and began to free his neck. I could hear him wheezing and choking and gasping for breath. Me, Mick and Stevie looked at each other and then fitted silencers to our guns and shot my mam in the back; I caught her a cracker in the arse, but she didn't die.

– What are yer trying to do, yer daft little sod? Hang yourself! What the bloody hell were yer playing at?

She untied Gavin and he ran off home, crying and wheezing. She sent Mick and Stevie away as well and I was dragged into the house and shouted at and smacked. I didn't cry, though, at least not until she confiscated my special gun and hid it somewhere, and I was made to anticipate with primal terror my dad coming home from work later on that day.

Gavin was off school for a few days, and when he came back he had a scarf tied loosely around his neck and at playtime he showed us what it was concealing; a bright red ragged abrasion across his throat, the skin scraped off and dangling in little white worm-like threads over the bared flesh. It looked like a priest's dog collar, or as if a little motorbike with chunky wheels had done a wheel-spin all the way round his neck, or as if he'd been choked by a man with hands of flame. Out of respect, we awarded him the title of Best Death, but I secretly felt that the honour was unwarranted; I mean, Stevie and me, we'd done the best dying, Gavin had just had a stupid accident. Daft thing to do, tie a rope around your neck and jump off the coal bunker. What was he playing at? I vowed to myself to take the crown from Gavin the next time we played Best Deaths; I would shock and shake them all with the violence of my going. But we never played the game again.

Vicki Feaver

THE KINGDOM OF MUD

In the distance, lit by sun,
it's tin, gold, violet snow;
under unlit cloud, lead, ash.
Close up, it's a palimpsest
of claws and feet, pegged
with rotting posts. Dig into it,
you uncover a gassy blackness.
Its laws are simple, inviolable.
Twice a day, it disappears.
It can swallow you. I lost a boot,
sucked into a hole that closed
over it; a boy, stuck as the tide
poured in, had to be pulled out
with a hook on a long pole.
There are two ways to enter.
The clam and cockle collectors
strap rafts of wood to their feet
to spread their weight, and follow
tracks their fathers showed them.
Seen far out, when the mud shines,
they appear to be walking on water.
Or there's the stream that gushes
from the sluice wall, coiling
like an eel through the flats,
washing mud from its flint bed
into high banks. You have to feel
each step by the degree of hardness
under your feet, disturbing flounders
that flee in cloudy flurries, wading
until you've lost all sight of land,
of everything solid and familiar,

and are surrounded by nothing
but mud – sinking, slippery,
full of holes that you think
must be homes of animals,
then realise are the nature
of mud, unstable, shifting,
and when water flows
under it, opening up.

SARKAZO

The Greek word meaning 'to tear flesh'
from which 'sarcasm' derives, a tearing
of the spirit he achieved with the lash
of a tongue wielded like a whip, fearing
to lose control. He didn't waste words
if he didn't have to. There was mention
in a radio programme of 'a very foolish bird,
eyes set close together'. He glanced in her direction.
The children, bored in the back of the car, howled.
Taught by his father, he passed the skill to them.
Learning to taste their mother's blood was called
'a bit of fun'. When she tried to talk to him
he'd cup his hand in a trumpet to his ear,
pretending he couldn't hear.

David Morley

MOONLIGHTER

He might be my brother for all he is gyp.
His is not the time for pullovers and combs;
his plum shirt is Blackpool, very Blackpool.
I have watched his van for hours, from Marton Estate
to this traveller site, a mole in mole's clothing.
He will scrabble through the mud of everything:
the nuts and nuggets of marriage, a bolt of a ring,
weights of children, slack pullies of police.
Burglar by night, a rain-soaked genius
of the jerry-built, coastal pre-fab,
he stacks his van with valuables:
a deadman, a handspike, a parbuckle.
Lightning moves its show across the camp.

CLEARING A NAME

Spindrift across Stalmine, a place you won't know.
Reedbeds, gyp sites; flat Lancashire's Orinoco.

I watch a mistle-thrush on a blown telegraph wire,
leave my car by the dead elm above the river.

The camp is two caravans. The police have just left.
Two blue-tacked Court Orders this wind can't shift

or the rain read. A girl squatting with a carburettor
on her bare knees. Another, older, in a deck-chair

spoons Pot Noodle. Their dad with his pride, no joy,
wrestles over the yawning bonnet of a lorry.

Mum is out, knocking Blackpool's door
with her basket of tack, toddler dressed-down with care

for the rending detail: no shoes. I watch
the father unbend, fumble at the fire, splice a match

from a stray half-wicker, then I come down.
He lets a welcome wait in another time;

twists a roll-up, nods OK to his staring daughters.
Eyes me like fresh scrap fenced from a dealer,

half-sorted, half-known. Yes, he knew our family
'more for what they were' – Hop-girls, metal-boys –

'but they married out, and there's the end of it.
Your muck's paid no muck of our's a visit'.

A thin smile: 'Except your dad.
He came with the nose of Concorde

on worksheets reeking of grease and Swarfega,
bleating 'an inch is now a bloody centimetre'.

What's up with your schools? I'd say. Him – 'This is school'.
We squinnied blueprints as if they were braille.

Taught ourselves ground-up. A small conversion.
If your muck had stayed in family, if your gran

not gone nosing *gaujo* like they were the end-all.
Now you've had your end, fair do's. Get off pal,

you're not burnt up on fags or dodgy work.'

The ends, we want; the means are half the work:

something in his grip, under my sleeve like veins,
where hands lock together, become the same,

Arctic on Antarctica . . . *I need background.*
The uncle on my mother's side. 'Pulled from a pond.

The police were out for a man. Any taig or gyp.
Guns broke for a chicken-shoot. They found him face-up

and it fitted. They shot shite in a barrel.'
That B-road where Lancashire discharges its spoil.

Split mattresses. Paint tins. Grim stuff in carriers.
The sign No Dumping No Travellers.

I make my way back to the car, running
the hard keys from hand to hand then, turning,

pocket them. I do not move. It is not smart to show
(that plain car by the woods) how and where you go.

One uncle of mine went fishing. His name is snow.
Or thaw or mud. And you wouldn't know.

Anita Desai

DIAMOND DUST

'THAT DOG WILL kill me, kill me one day!' Mrs Das moaned, her hand pressed to her large, soft, deep bosom when Diamond leapt at the chop she had cooked and set on the table for Mr Das; or when Diamond dashed past her, bumping against her knees and making her collapse against the door when she was going to receive a parcel from the postman who stood there, shaking, as he fended off the black lightning hurled at him. 'Diamond! Why did you call him Diamond? He is Satan, a shaitan, a devil. Call him Devil instead,' Mrs Das cried as she washed and bandaged the ankle of a grandchild who had only run after a ball and had that shaitan snap his teeth over his small foot.

But to Mr Das he was Diamond, and had been Diamond ever since he had bought him, as a puppy of an indecipherable breed, blunt-faced, with his wet nose gleaming and paws flailing for action. Mr Das could not explain how he had come upon that name. Feebly, he would laugh when questioned by friends he met in the park at five o'clock in the morning when he took Diamond for a walk before leaving for the office, and say, 'Yes, yes, black diamond, you see, black diamond.' But when C.P. Biswas, baring his terribly stained yellow teeth in an unpleasant laugh, said, 'Ah, coal – then call him that, my dear fellow, coal, koyla – and we would all understand.'

Never. Never would Mr Das do such a thing to his Diamond. If his family and friends only knew what names he thought up for the puppy, for the dog, in secret, in private –

421

he did not exactly blush but he did laugh to himself, a little sheepishly. And yet his eyes shone when he saw how Diamond's coat gleamed as he streaked across the park after a chipmunk, or when he greeted the dog on his return from work before greeting Mrs Das, his grandchildren, or anyone at all, with the joyful cry, 'Diamond, my friend!'

Mrs Das had had a premonition – had she not known Mr Das since she had been a fourteen-year-old bride, he a nineteen-year-old bridegroom? – when she saw him bring that puppy home, cuddling it in his old brown jumper, lowering his voice to a whisper and his step to a tiptoe, as if afraid of alarming the sleeping creature. 'Get some warm milk – don't heat it too much – just warm it a little – and get some cottonwool.' She had stared at him. 'Not even about our own children – not even your first-born son – or your grandchildren, have you made so much of as of that dog,' she had told him then. She repeated it, not once, or twice, or thrice, but at regular intervals throughout that shining stretch of Mr Das's life when Diamond evolved from a round, glossy cocoon into a trembling, faltering fat puppy that bent its weak legs and left puddles all over Mrs Das's clean, fresh floors, and then into an awkwardly – so lovably awkwardly – lumbering young dog that Mr Das led around on a leash across the dusty maidan of Bharti Nagar, delighting in the children who came up to admire the creature but politely fearful of those who begged 'Uncle, let me hold him! Let me take him for a walk, Uncle!' Only in the Lodi Gardens did he dare slip Diamond off his leash for the joy of seeing him race across that lawn after chipmunks that scurried up into the trees, furiously chattering and whisking their tails in indignation while Diamond sat at the foot of the tree, whining, his eyes lustrous with desire. 'Diamond, Diamond,' Mr Das would call, and lumbering up to him, would fondle his head, his ears and murmur words of love to entice him away from the scolding creatures in the leaves.

But there were times when Mr Das went beyond that, times that his friends and colleagues whom he met daily on their morning walks, were astounded, if not scandalised, to witness, so much so that they could hardly speak of it to each other. Mr Das had so clearly taken leave of his senses, and it made them worry: how could a reputable government servant, a colleague, fall so low? They had caught him, as portly and stiff as any of them, romping ridiculously in a rose garden enclosed by crumbling, half-ruined walls that he had imagined hid him from view, chasing or letting himself be chased around the rose beds by a wild-with-excitement dog whose barks rent the peace of the morning park. They hardly knew how to tell him he was making a fool of himself. Instead, settling down on a bench in the shade of a neem tree and with a view of the Lodi tombs, watching parrots emerge from the alcoves and shoot up into the brilliant summer air, they discussed it between themselves gravely, and with distaste, as became their age and station – the decent elderly, civil servants with a life of service and sobriety behind them.

'There was that time Raman Kutty's grandchild was visiting him from Madras, and he would bring her to the park. He would even push the pram, like an ayah. During that visit, he couldn't speak of anything, or say anything but "Look, she has a new tooth" or "See her sucking her toe, so sweet." And that child, with its crossed eyes –'

'Tch, tch,' another reproved him for his ill-mannered outburst.

But the outburst was really occasioned by Mr Das, and the sight they had all had of him kicking up his heels like a frolicking goat in the rose garden, oblivious of the gardeners who sat on their haunches in the shade, smoking and keeping a vigilant eye on their rose beds.

'Look, here he comes with that wretched beast,' C.P. Biswas cried out. He was never in very good humour in the mornings; they all knew it had to do with his digestive system and its discomforts: they had often come upon him seated in the waiting room of the homeopath's clinic which was open to the marketplace and in full view of those who shopped there for their eggs and vegetables. 'I think he should be told. What do you say, should we tell him?'

'Tell him what, C.P.?' asked the mild-mannered A.P. Bose.

'That such behaviour is not at all becoming!' exclaimed C.P. Biswas. 'After all, a civil servant – serving in the Department of Mines and Minerals – what will people say?'

'Who?'

'Who? Look, there is the Under-Secretary walking over there with his wife. What if he sees? Or the retired Joint Secretary who is doing his yoga exercises over there by the tank. You think they don't know him? He has to be told – we are here to remind him.'

Unfortunately Mr Das chose not to join them that morning. He walked smartly past them, hanging onto Diamond's leash and allowing Diamond to drag him forward at a pace more suited to a youth of twenty, and an athletic one at that. He merely waved at his friends, seeing them arranged in a row on the bench, and clearly not intending to join their sedate company, disappeared behind a magnificent grove of bamboos, that twittered madly with mynah birds.

C.P. Biswas was beginning to rumble and threaten to explode but A.P. Bose drew out the morning newspaper from his pocket, unclasped the pen from his pocket, and tactfully asked for help in completing the day's crossword puzzle.

Of course their disapproval was as nothing compared to that of Mrs Das who did not merely observe Mr Das's passion from a distance but was obliged to live with it. It was she who had to mop up the puddles from her gleaming floors when Diamond was a puppy, she who had to put up with the reek of dog in a home that had so far been aired and cleaned and sunned and swept and dusted till one could actually see the walls and floors thinning from the treatment to which they had been subjected. Her groans and exclamations as she swept up (or, rather, had the little servant girl sweep up) tufts of dog's hair from her rugs – and sometimes even her sofas and armchairs – were loud and rang with lament. Of course she refused to go to the butcher's shop for buffalo meat for the dog – she would not go near that stinking hellhole on the outskirts of the marketplace, and Mr Das had to brave its bloody, reeking, fly-coated territory himself, clutching a striped plastic bag close to him with one hand and pressing a thickly-folded handkerchief to his nose with the other – but, still, she had to sacrifice one of her cooking pots to it, and tolerate the bubbling and frothing of the meat stew on the back burner of her stove. During the hour that it took, she would retreat to the veranda and sit there in a wicker chair, fanning herself with melodramatic flair.

'But do you want the dog to starve? Do you think a dog such as Diamond can be brought up on bread and milk?' Mr Das pleaded. 'How would he grow? How would he live?'

'Why not? I have heard even of tigers being fed on milk. It is true. Absolutely. Don't give me those looks, D.P. There was a yogi in Jubbulpore when I was a girl, he lived in a cave outside the city, with a pet tiger, and it was said he fed it only on milk. He brought it to town on festival days, I saw it with my own eyes. It was healthy, that milk-fed tiger, and as harmless as a kitten.'

'But I am not a yogi and Diamond is not a yogi's pet. What about that cat you had? Did it not kill sparrows and eat fish?'

'*My* cat was the cleanest creature this earth has ever known!' Mrs Das cried, holding the fan to her breast for a moment, in tribute to the deceased pet. 'Yes, she enjoyed a little fish from my plate – but she ate so neatly, so cleanly –'

'But fish, wasn't it? And sparrows? You see, an animal's nature cannot be changed simply because it is domesticated, Sheila. That tiger you speak of, it is quite possible that one day it turned upon the yogi and made a meal of him –'

'What are you saying?' Mrs Das cried, and began to flutter her fan again. 'That yogi lived to be a hundred years old!' and Mr Das went off, muttering disbelievingly, to dish out the meat stew for Diamond in an earthenware bowl in the courtyard and then carefully shut the kitchen door behind him so Diamond could not drag one of the bones into the house to chew on a rug as he very much liked to do and would do if not prevented.

The children of the neighbourhood were more appreciative, and properly admiring than his wife, Mr Das felt as he walked Diamond past the small stucco villas set in their gardens of mango trees and oleander hedges, attracting flocks of them as he went. But he was not so besotted or blinded as to ignore the need always to have Diamond firmly secured on his leash when children were around. He was not unaware that once he had turned his back, or if they had come upon Diamond when he was not around, they were quite capable of arousing the dog to a frenzy by teasing him. 'We were only playing, Uncle!' they would cry reproachfully after Diamond had broken loose and chased them until they fell sprawling in the dust, or even nipped at their heels as they ran. 'That is *not* how to play with a dog,' he reproved them severely. 'You must *not* wave a stick at him. You must *not* pick up a stone. You must *not* run –'

'If we don't run, he'll bite, Uncle! See, he bit Ranu on her heel –'

'Nonsense,' he retorted, 'that's only a scratch,' and Mrs Das walked quickly away, Diamond held closely, protectively at his side.

That was in the days of Diamond's innocent youth. Diamond was only in training then for what was to come – his career as a full-fledged badmash, the terror of the neighbourhood. There followed a period when Diamond became the subject of scandal: the postman made a complaint. He had only to appear and Diamond would rear up on his hind legs, bellowing for blood. Nor was it just an empty threat, that bellowing: he had chased the poor man right across the maidan, making him drop his bag filled with mail as he raced for shelter from Diamond's slavering jaws and snapping teeth. The dog had actually torn a strip off his trouser leg, the trousers the postal service had given him for a uniform. How was he to explain it? Who was going to replace it? he demanded furiously, standing on the Das's veranda and displaying the tattered garment as proof.

Mr Das paid up. But even so, their mail was no longer inserted in the mailbox nailed to the door but flung into their hedge from afar. 'The dog is locked up, what harm can he do you through the door?' Mr Das pleaded after Mrs Das complained that she had found a letter from her daughter lying in the road outside, and only by luck had her eye caught Chini's handwriting. It was the letter that informed them of their son-in-law's recent promotion and transfer, too; what if it had been lost? 'That dog of yours,' said the postman, 'his voice heard through the door alone is enough to finish off a man,' and continued to use the hedge as a mailbox. Who knew how many more of Chini's delightful and comforting letters to her mother were lost and abandoned because of this? 'Is he a man or a mouse?' Mr Das fumed.

It was not only the postman Diamond detested and chased off his territory: it was anyone at all in uniform – officials of the board of electricity come to check the meter, telephone lines repairmen come to restore the line after a duststorm had disrupted it; even the garbage could not be collected from the Das' compound because it drove Diamond absolutely insane with rage to see the men in their khaki uniforms leap down from the truck and reach through the back gate for the garbage can to carry its contents off to their truck; he behaved as if the men were bandits, as if the family treasure was being looted. Charging at the gate, he would hurl himself against it, then rear up on his hind legs so he could look over it and bark at them with such hysteria that the noise rang through the entire neighbourhood. It was small comfort that 'No thief dare approach our house,' as Mr Das said proudly when anyone remarked on his dog's temper; they looked at him as if to say 'Why talk of thieves, why not of innocent people doing their jobs who are being threatened by that beast?' Of course Mrs Das did say it.

Later, disgracefully, Diamond's phobia went so far as to cause him to chase children in their neat grey shorts and white shirts, their white frocks and red ties and white gym shoes as they made their way to school. That was the worst of all for Mr Das – the parents who climbed the steps to the Das's veranda, quivering with indignation, to report Diamond's attacks upon their young and tender offspring, so traumatised now by the dog that they feared to cross the maidan to the school bus stop without adult protection, and even had to be fetched from there in the afternoon when they returned.

'One day, Das, you will find the police following up on our complaints if you fail to pay attention to them. And then who can tell what they will do to your pet?' That was the large and intemperate Mr Singh, who could not tolerate even a mosquito to approach his curly-headed and darling baba.

Mr Das mopped his brow and sweated copiously in fear and shame. 'That will not happen,' he insisted. 'I can promise you Diamond will do nothing you can report to the police –'

'If he tears my child limb from limb, you think the police will not act, Das?' flared up the parent in a voice of doom.

The neighbours stopped short of actually making a report. It was – had been – a friendly, peaceful neighbourhood, after all, built for government officials of a certain cadre: all the men had their work in common, many were colleagues in the same ministries, and it would not do to have any enmity or public airings of personal quarrels. It was quite bad enough when their wives quarrelled or children or servants carried gossip from one household to another, but such things could not be allowed to get out of control. Propriety, decorum, standards of behaviour: these had to be maintained. If they failed, what would become of Bharti Nagar, of society?

Also, some of them were moved to a kind of pity. It was clear to them – as to Mr Das's friends in the Lodi Gardens – that he had taken leave of his senses where Diamond was concerned. When Diamond, in chase of a bitch on heat in the neighbouring locality, disappeared for five days one dreadful summer, and Mr Das was observed walking the dusty streets in the livid heat of June, hatless, abject, crying 'Diamond! Diamond! Diamond!' over garden walls and down empty alleys, in the filthy outskirts of the marketplace, and even along the reeking canal where disease lurked and no sensible person strayed, they could only feel sorry for him. Even the children who had earlier taken up against Diamond – for very good reason, it should be added – came up to Mr Das as he stumbled along on his search mission, and offered, 'We'll

help you, Uncle. We'll search for Diamond too, Uncle.'
Unfortunately, when this band of juvenile detectives caught
up with Diamond in the alley behind the Ambassador Hotel,
they caught him *in flagrante delicto* and witnessed to Mr
Das's strenuous exertions to separate his pet from its partner,
a poor, pale, pathetic creature who bore all the sorry marks
of a rape victim. The children went home and reported it all
to their families, in graphic detail. The parents' disapproval
was so thick, and so stormy, it was weeks before the air
cleared over Bharti Nagar. But it was nothing compared to
the drama of Mrs Das's reaction; sari corner held over her
nose, and over her mouth, she stood up holding a rolled
newspaper in her hand as weapon and refused to let the beast
into the house till Mr Das had taken him around to the tap in
the courtyard at the back, and washed, soaped, shampooed,
bathed, powdered, groomed and combed the creature into a
semblance of a domestic pet.

Mr Das bought stronger chains and collars for Diamond,
took greater care to tie him up in the courtyard and lock
every door, but when the season came – and only Diamond
could sniff it in the air, no one else could predict it – there
was no holding him back. His strength was as the strength of
a demon, and he broke free, ripping off his collar, wrenching
his chain, leaping over walls, and disappeared. In a way, the
neighbours were relieved – no longer was the night air rent by
that hideous howling as of wolves on the trail of their prey,
and also there was the secret hope that this time the brute
would not be found and not return. They hardened their
hearts against the pitiful sight of Mr Das limping through the
dust in search of his diamond, like some forlorn lover whose
beloved has scorned him and departed with another, but who
has not abandoned his bitter, desperate hope.

The Lodi Gardens clique, at the end of their brisk early
morning walks round the park, seated themselves in a row on
the bench in the shade of the big neem tree, and discussed
Mr Das's disintegration.

'The other day I had occasion to visit him at his office. I

intended to invite him to a meeting of the Bharti Nagar Durga Puja Association – and found him talking on the 'phone, and it was clear he was apologising, whether for the lateness of some work done, or for mistakes made, I could not make out, but it was a nasty scene.' Said C.P. Biswas.

'His superior is that nasty fellow, Krishnaswamy, and he is nasty to everyone in the department.'

'Maybe so, but when I questioned Das about it, he only held his head – and did not even answer my questions. He kept saying "Diamond is missing, I can't find Diamond." Now I did not say it, but the words that came to my mouth were: "Good riddance, Das, my congratulations."'

The apologist for Das clucked reprovingly, and commiseratingly, 'Tch, tch.'

But one day, at dawn, Mr Das reappeared, holding a thinner, sorrier Diamond at the end of a leash while his own face beamed as ruddily as the sun rising above the dome of the Lodi tomb. He waved at his colleagues sitting in the shade. Diamond slouched at his heels: his last escapade had clearly left him exhausted, even jaded.

'Ha!' remarked C.P. Biswas, crossing his arms over his chest. 'The prodigal has returned, I see. And is he repenting his misbehaviour?'

'Oh, he is so sorry, so sorry – he is making up for it in his own sweet way,' Mr Das beamed, bending to fondle the dog's drooping head. 'He cannot help himself, you know, but afterwards he feels so sorry, and then he is *so* good!'

'Yes, I see that,' C.P. Biswas said out of the corner of his mouth, 'and how long is that to last?'

But Mr Das preferred not to hear, instead busying himself by making the collar more comfortable around Diamond's neck. 'Now I must take him back and give him his bath before I go to work.'

'Good idea,' said C.P. Biswas, tucking his lips tightly over his yellow teeth.

Diamond, who had been badly bitten and probably thrashed or stoned in the course of his latest affair, seemed to have quietened down a bit; at least there was a fairly long spell of obedience, lethargy, comparative meekness. Mr Das felt somewhat concerned about his health, but seeing him slip vitamin pills down the dog's throat, Mrs Das grimaced 'Now what? He is *too* quiet for you? You need to give him strength to go back to his badmashi?'

That, sadly, was what happened. By the time the cool evenings and the early dark of November came around, Diamond was clearly champing at the bit: his howls echoed through sleepy Bharti Nagar, and neighbours pulled their quilts over their heads and huddled into their pillows, trying to block out the abominable noise. Mrs Das complained of the way he rattled his chain as he paced up and down the enclosed courtyard, and once again the garbage collectors, the postmen, the electric and telephone linesmen were menaced and threatened. Only Mr Das worried, 'He's gone off his food. Look, he's left his dinner uneaten again.'

Inevitably the day came when he returned from work and was faced by an angrily triumphant Mrs Das bursting to tell him the news. 'Didn't I tell you that dog was planning badmashi again? When the gate was opened to let the gas man bring in the cylinder, your beloved pet knocked him down, jumped over his head and vanished!'

The nights were chilly. With a woollen cap pulled down over his ears, and his tight short jacket buttoned up, Mr Das did his rounds in the dark, calling hoarsely till his throat rasped. He felt he was coming down with the flu, but he would not give up, he would not leave Diamond to the dire fate Mrs Das daily prophesied for him. A kind of mist enveloped the city streets – whether it was due to the dust, the exhaust of tired, snarled traffic or the cold, one could not tell, but the trees and hedges loomed like phantoms, the street-lamps were hazy, he imagined he saw Diamond when there was no dog there, and he was filled with a foreboding he would not confess to Mrs Das who waited for him at home with cough mixture, hot water and another muffler. 'Give him up,' she counselled grimly. 'Give him up before this search kills you.'

But when tragedy struck, it did so in broad daylight, in the bright sunshine of a winter Sunday, and so there were many witnesses, many who saw the horrific event clearly, so clearly it could not be brushed aside as a nightmare. Mr Das was on the road back from Khan Market where he had gone to buy vegetables for Mrs Das, when the dog catcher's van passed down the road with its howling, yelping catch of hounds peering out through the barred window. Of course Mr Das's head jerked back, his chin trembled with alertness, with apprehension, his eyes snapped with rage when he saw his pet enclosed there, wailing as he was being carried to his doom.

'Diamond! They will kill my Diamond!' passers-by heard him shriek in a voice unrecognisably high and sharp, and they saw the small man in his tight brown coat, his woollen cap and muffler, dash down his market bag into the dust, and chase the van with a speed no one would have thought possible. He sprang at its retreating back, hanging there from the bars for a horrid moment, and, as the van first braked, then jerked forward again, fell, fell backwards, onto his back, so that his head struck the stones in the street, and he lay there, entirely still, making no sound or movement at all.

Behind the bars of the window receding into the distance, Diamond glittered like a dead coal, or a black star, in daylight's blaze.

Peter Porter

NORTHERN LIGHTS

From the out-of-town train station on a wet
And graphite night, to walk in drenching shoes
Along a road where sheep and steers announce their deaths'
Anticipation from the half-lit market pens,
Then through the Christmas tangle of synthetic cheer
To eighteenth-century facades and tangy
Take-Aways – this is your Via Dolorosa to
A magical circumference where love and death are staged
And faces twice as large and keen as life are drawn.

Now you will know why at the final North
Where ghosts are consequent and sight analysed
As if by God unsure of what he's made,
A wasteful holiness is flecked against the sky,
Since here another scintillant abstraction,
Hosted by the town where Shakespeare's bones are laid,
Is made a codex of the natural, and peculiar Physics
Like a cruel experiment reveals to us and every
Creature of the shambles light's brief account of truth.

ORLANDO'S PARROT

Orlando's lighter-than-air sad parrot
Loiters out of breath, its head scarce held
Above the carpet, its gaze still heavenward.
The gods come down to this when their bright thrust
To weightlessness subsides and our attention
Is restored to our aspiring selves.
Yet, looking at its pained deflation, what
May human apprehension bring to mind

433

But pity at the subdivision of
Existence into rules and miracles,
The one subduing godhead to the floor,
The other drifting high defiantly.
Return O Helium God, defy all leaks,
Float the impossible beyond Nature's reach.

Michael Longley

PAPER BOATS

Homage to Ian Hamilton Finlay

fold paper boats
for the boy Odysseus
and launch them

ship-shape
happy-go-lucky
in the direction of Troy

SCRAP METAL

I

Helen Denerley made this raven out of old iron,
Belly and back the brake shoes from a lorry, nuts
And bolts for legs and feet, the wings ploughshares
('Ridgers', she elaborates, 'for tatties and neeps'),
The eyeballs cogs from a Morris Minor gearbox.

The bird poses on the circular brass tray my mother
(And now I) polished, swipes of creamy Brasso,
Then those actions, melting a frosty window pane,
Clearing leaves from a neglected well, her breath
Meeting her reflection in the ultimate burnish.

The beak I identified first as a harrow tooth
Is the finger from an old-fashioned finger-bar
Mower for dividing and cutting down the grass,
And, as he bends his head to drink, the raven points
To where the surface gives back my mother's features.

II

The head I pat is made out of brake calipers
With engine mountings from a Toyota for ears,
The spine a baler chain, the ruff and muscular neck
Sprockets, plough points, clutch plate, mower blades,

The legs a Morris Minor king pin or swingle tree.
Snow in Aberdeenshire and Helen's garden. A wolf
At the forest's edge where scrap metal multiplies
Waits on claw-hammer feet for the rest of the pack.

Eva Salzman

THERE'S A LOT OF ROOM

ART WAS A lot taller than Petra, and dark and handsome, so it seemed a privilege to be kissed by him, yes a privilege.

They'd walked down Bay Avenue, across Montiak Highway towards Vale Road and then doubled back to where they had started, the Town Dock. It was the circuit. There wasn't anything else to do but go around like this. Petra was too nervous to talk – her heart was hammering away and there was a tingling in her stomach – and Art didn't talk either.

Her deep crush had started at the Hamden Bays Square Dance. She couldn't believe her luck when he asked her out – by which was meant she was to sneak out of the house at night and meet him down at the town dock. There would be someone else for her sister June.

Back at the Town Dock, he kissed her.

His arms were wrapped around her shoulders and he wasn't moving much. In fact, he wasn't moving at all. He planted his large somewhat dry mouth over hers and there it stayed.

It's not that she minded that, of course, but, after a while, she found herself waiting for something else to happen, thinking he might tilt his head the other way for variation, or maybe suck or push a little with his lips or even introduce a tongue. But the activity, as Art apparently understood it, was completely stationary. Nor did his hands move down her back or try for her large breasts – which June had insisted would be Art's primary goal.

June was at this very moment stuck with Art's friend, a

puny little kid – a *kid*, the way that Art was not. Art was really into man territory with his height and girth, if not his kissing technique.

Petra had no idea what had happened to them right now. They had melted away into the dark night and now there was just this kiss.

Eventually, her heart began to slow down, until it reached its perfectly normal, unexcited, pedestrian pace.

At first, she'd kept her eyes shut, as you were meant to do. But after some time had passed she had a peek. Through her lashes Art's face loomed up, frighteningly close, so large and round it reminded her of a balloon, or a moon. She was shocked by her own realisation that it really wasn't all that attractive from this perspective.

So she closed her eyes again. Her face was probably also like a moon, but Art wasn't looking, or not while she was looking anyway.

All her concentration was on this large dry mouth like an 'o' fitted over her mouth. No biting (some boys did that, or they caught you with their dental braces), no sucking or gentle pursing to punctuate the activity. She began to wonder if it would ever end, what exactly would signal the end for him. What would make him stop?

She couldn't possibly end it herself, god no. It was his kiss after all – he had bestowed it and she was the taker. She'd feel stupid, ungrateful, embarrassed. So she just stood there.

It was so dark that at one point she slightly staggered, losing her balance. He just moved one leg slightly to improve the position and his open cave mouth enveloped hers again, so everything could return to normal.

She liked his smell. He smelled like wood. For a second she had a fantasy that he *was* wood, that they were both carved wood figures, locked in kissing position, posing for . . . posing for . . . what were they posing for? Maybe someone had artfully placed them there. Who? Why? *Artfully*. That was funny.

The smells of the beach came and went, little sharp draughts of salt and seaweed and crab. She could hear the light lapping of waves on the shore, the gentle creak of a moored boat, the occasional bumping sound of the hull against the dock. A light breeze brought the sharp tang of the nearby marsh – an intriguing rotten smell of mud and dank pond. Dank pond. That was vaguely unpleasant, not a word she should be dwelling on at this particular moment.

Eventually she drifted further and further away until she was home again, the very place she had escaped from that night, for these irresistible illicit purposes. Her mother and father were asleep in their bed. She entered their room and for the first time imagined them sleeping together.

Maybe her parents had kissed like this, or maybe they hadn't, maybe they'd kissed another way. Maybe her father was a lousy kisser. Was it possible for two people to stay together if one was a lousy kisser? Did he kiss other girls the same way he kissed her mother?

Now she felt like she was inside a coffin, the world had shrunk so much in the pitch black. She'd lost her perspective so utterly she might as well have been lying horizontally underground. She'd forgotten what she was doing, this activity so far from the subject of corpses and decay. Of course it didn't matter if she did forget – this kiss would just go on anyway, with or without her.

She'd lost all sense of direction and decided to occupy her time playing a little game with herself, to figure out her orientation. For this reason, she now positively wanted the kiss to end, to prove her calculations correct. Also, she was missing the considerably satisfying sight of June having a gloomy time with a pint-sized boyfriend.

But still it wasn't finished. Maybe this was the right way of it, kissing sort of like meditation, with your mind not necessarily on the matter at hand. After all, should one have to concentrate on the actual kiss? Then it might be more like work. Or maybe it was like an antechamber, or a large cathedral-like place itself. There was so much room in it, she'd never realised.

But why should the duration of this kiss also make it disappointing, make her feel robbed and deflated?

She knew now he had no intention of going any further. Besides which, if he did decide to progress in the usual manner, she might end up with this large, dry hand planted on her breast for an equally absurdly lengthy epoch, unmoving and spread out over her flesh, more like a brassiere than the curious, groping, desirous fingers of a hungry adolescent. And that might not prove to be much fun either.

So it was a considerable surprise when finally he closed his mouth and stepped back.

Then they walked back, arms wrapped around each other, and said goodnight. Once Petra and June had been dropped off, had softened the screen door's slam and made it safely up the stairs to bed, Petra found herself getting excited again at the thought of Art.

Of course she would have to tell her friends all about the kiss, about the way it was, as she remembered it, since it might never come again, or if it did, she might not have the patience for enough time to pass. How would she ever recapture the thrill which had waned so dramatically?

She wouldn't. It was the meanness of memory that left her forever locked into it, a ghostly statue of the two of them entwined on the beach, for as long as she could remember, something so wonderful only in remembering. And it's not that anyone would ever know they were there, would only step through them on their way to somewhere else.

Peter Benson

DOMINION

LONDON. THE NIGHT of spring. A man walked into a
Vietnamese restaurant, and stood by the door. He was with
his bought wife. She wore a red coat. There were no free
tables but they wanted to eat Vietnamese so they waited. He
made the decisions. She was only happy to be far from one
pain, and glad to be wearing a red coat. She smoothed her
eyebrows and thought about touching his cheek. He wore a
raincoat. She had the nervous smile of the fruitless. He had a
moustache and grey hair. She only talked when he asked a
question or made a remark.

They waited ten minutes and did not take off their coats.
The smell of a cooking flounder and ginger and lemon grass
came from the kitchen. The owner of the restaurant was
called Duckie. He sang while he worked and counted the
minutes until a table would be ready. He brought the couple
an aperitif.

The man had been married twice before, divorced twice,
swamped by alimony and final demands and reasonable
demands and the wings of lawyers, and he had been to his
office so many times and returned to an empty house so many
times and eaten how many TV dinners on his lap? Watched
how many re-runs of how many old shows? Wondered how
many times about his increasing weight and the dullness that
had crept into his eyes? Remembered how many times about
how the young man he had been had become the man who
stood alone at the bathroom door, a towel in one hand and a

toothbrush in the other, and a dry tear he could not weep in his right eye? Or was it his left? Did he know? He did not.

And the table didn't come. Duckie offered them another drink. The flounder was cooked perfectly, one and a half pounds of the healthiest white flesh ever caught, and it was swept from the kitchen in a cloud of steam and lemon grass, and the people who waited for it sat back and ran their tongues over their lips. They put their cigarettes out, pushed their wine glasses to one side and watched the waiter's face as he put the dish on the table.

'Perfect. It looks like the flounder from heaven.'

'It is. You enjoy.'

'We will.'

The man by the door looked at the flounder and then he looked at his wife. He was twice her size, big enough to split her and big enough not to care. The pound signs and neon signs and hopeless rhymes that tumbled and fell through his life were pooling at his polished feet. He looked at his shoes. They shone. 'What?' he said, suddenly. His wife said nothing. Her lips were still. Her lips were beautiful and her coat was red and there ... another couple finished their meal and stood to leave. Duckie took a deep, relieved breath. He offered to take the raincoat and the red coat but the man and his wife wanted to keep their coats. They crossed the restaurant and sat down.

The menu was good. Pork in a caramel sauce or scallops and shrimp baked however you want, or a chicken's breasts in cream, lemon and herbs. Or flounder or slivers of beef slowly cooked in wine and turned and cooked again. The man made the decisions. They would eat beef with steamed vegetables, and they'd drink more wine. Red wine now, something with fruit that dreamt in the glass, fruit that dreamt of the soil and sun of the south, the soil of a valley vineyard with views of the sea from its brim, and sun that could not stop shining.

Maybe the wife showed nothing in her eyes, but when Duckie came and stood by the table, and scribbled the table number on his pad and looked at the man's fingers as they traced across the menu, she looked at him and they swapped a glance. The man noticed. His face coloured and his blood waved in the restaurant. He said 'How's the beef?'

'Very good. Best beef in town. We cook it in wine, with herbs. It's very tender,' Duckie said, looking at the wife.

The man said 'I didn't ask how you cooked it. I can see how you do that,' and he pointed at the menu. '"Strips of beef, poached in a wine and oregano sauce, garnished with ginger." We'll have two of them, but go easy on the ginger. We don't like ginger, do we?'

The wife loved ginger but she said 'No.' This was the first word she'd said for half an hour, a word to deny desire and it did the job well, and when the man raised his eyebrows at the sound of her voice as if he expected her to say something else, she obliged with 'In England, you never see the same car twice.' She pointed out of the window. The street streamed light and bowled wheels. It split the north of the city like a knife, Duckie's knife, the man thought . . .

'What did you say?'

'In Thailand, there are not so many types of car.' She looked at the table cloth and picked its edge. Linen. That's a luxury item.

'What are you talking about?' He gave his voice splinters. She shook her head. Nothing.

In the kitchen, the beef was taken from the fridge, the pan was slapped on the stove, wine poured into the pan and heated gently.

The man smoothed his moustache and said 'What are you talking about? Are you going to tell me?'

She shook her head again. Some strands of hair slipped from the band that held it back. She was embarrassed by this. She wanted to look her best for her husband, a fat man who had saved her from poverty and a life without beef slowly cooked in wine with herbs and served on a bed of rice. 'Oh I love you,' she thought. 'Oh I do, with all my heart.'

The cook loved to cook beef. He loved to watch its quick flesh change. He kept the wine from flaming with a delicate flick of the stove's controls, and he didn't think about the woman he loved, his wife and their healthy conflicts. He concentrated on his work. Concentrate, sweep away all thoughts but one, and leave that thought to give itself a present every day. Perfect beef, wine making itself good through heat; it was easier to make a mistake with a flounder. Beef was so forgiving.

'Why the hell . . .' the man thought, and he studied his wife's face, and the light bruise he had given her the previous Sunday. God he hated Sundays. Sundays and Mondays; Tuesdays were better, Fridays were best, oh why the hell?

He'd visited Thailand as a divorce gift to himself. He'd never visited Asia before but he'd seen the movies, he'd tasted the food, he'd known what to expect, he'd known to avoid the water, only eat in the hotel, dream only his own dreams. The day he arrived he'd slept for twelve hours and taken a cab downtown; dream only his own dreams? He had been kidding himself, painting fakes in his own head and this was not something he was used to doing. Bangkok had raved his head, and as he strolled the bars and clubs he felt his head leak, and this was something else he was not used to. Was it possible that he was not the man he thought he was?

He met a man called Bob in a bar called The Cookie Crumble, and Bob had given him a tip. 'Do yourself a favour.'

'What?'

'While you're here, get yourself a wife.'

'Do I want to hear this?'

'Of course you do. You don't want to go home with nothing but memories. Some of this ass'll cream you forever.'

'Will it?'

'Sure.'

The man had stared at his drink. He'd refused ice for his stomach's sake, and the more he thought about his stomach the more his stomach thought about him. His stomach thanked him for refusing ice though the temperature was in the nineties, the humidity? at him like boxing gloves and The Cookie Crumble was only served by one slow fan.

The man had taken a slug and sat back on the stool. He

hadn't thought about home for twenty-four hours but now, suddenly, it came at him with a vengeance, and spread itself like a new plague in his head.

'Yeah,' said Bob. 'You can buy whatever you want here.'

'And I want to do that, do I?'

'Sure you do. Who wouldn't?'

The man thought about that. Who wouldn't? Two weeks later . . . two weeks later he returned to England with his third wife, and she was a woman who'd promised to cream him forever, cream him whatever sort of man he was, and whatever he did. She, of course, had no idea.

Does the steer know that it is beef? No idea, no more than the grape knows it's wine. But the cook knew exactly who and what and why he was. The priest of the kitchen, he was strong, not as strong as the beef or the bought wife who waited for a meal, but what is strength? He had no time for questions like these. He wiped his brow and cooked on.

And the man and his bought wife sat opposite each other. They sat in the lovers' style, and God, she wished he would reach out and take her hand just once, just once like he had done the day they met. The day they met had promised more than a breeze off the river or the sea or wherever a breeze was likely to come from. More than that, honey. Let me take you back with me. Sure, you can be my wife. Sure, I'll give you everything you've ever wanted, all the things you dream of. You can sleep in a bed that's wider than your wishes, you can feel silk against your skin. I'll give you all the chance you never had. I promise.

At this time, another couple walked into the restaurant. They were an old couple. She walked with a limp, he held her arm. There was a free table in smoking, and they were happy about that. They had those eyes you see sometimes; they reflected some grief, some happiness, mainly trust. Duckie knew them and greeted them by name.

'Ralph,' he said, 'and Connie. How are you doing? You having the pork today?'

'I don't know,' said Ralph. There was a shared joke about the pork but they didn't share it with the other customers.

These customers were kept in the dark. 'What do you want, Connie?'

Connie didn't know. She knew the menu but wanted to surprise herself. She really wanted to eat – maybe – duck. 'How's the duck?' she said.

'Very good today,' said Duckie, and he put his fingers to his lips and kissed them. 'Better than yesterday. You like a hot sauce? Something kamikaze?'

'You know we do.'

'Then have the duck, Connie. It'll be special for you.'

'Okay. Two duck. And a bottle of that Sauvignon we had last week.'

Duckie scribbled in his pad, whistled a vague tune through his lips and left Ralph to smile at Connie, take out a cigarette and light it. Connie didn't smoke but she liked the smell.

While the man stared at his bought wife, the beef arrived. The wine sauce breathed its promise and the oregano gave vague puffs, not like puffs of smoke, more a kind of hope. 'Yeah,' said the man to the waiter, and the waiter said 'Hope you enjoy your meal.'

'You'll know if I don't,' said the man, not thinking 'we' or any such thing. He had chased 'we' from his vocabulary, locked it in a weighted box and sunk it in a lake. 'We' sinking, leaving nothing but bubbles and a swirl where the word had been. Or 'we' where his world had been. It was all the same to him, lost and gone away, and never coming back.

How was that beef? Perfect. Tender as the bought wife's cheek could be, and it tasted like a good memory of childhood. She smiled at that memory and the man noticed, and wanted to know what was funny.

'Nothing's funny,' she said, quietly. 'I was thinking about my village.' It didn't seem so poor now, not so desperate or something she should have wished away.

'You don't want to do so much thinking. It's bad for you. It fools with your head.'

'I'm sorry,' she said.

'And you're sorry too much of the time,' he said, and he swilled a strip of meat in the sauce, and put it in his mouth.

'I know,' she thought, but she didn't say it. She thought on, on and into the fields that surrounded her village, past the road that wound four hundred miles to Bangkok and some old dream she wished had never bothered her head. Way back, way back before all this had begun, and she had sat at her mother's feet and listened to a story about a wild animal called The Rtufogn. It lived in mountain jungles, and had claws that tore in perfect strips, luminous whiskers and teeth that picked themselves clean. How do years betray life, and why? How do hours deny their minutes, and why? How does desperation fleece love, and why? How does the cook know when the meat is ready to serve? He knows because he tastes a bit.

'I'm not sorry about anything,' said the man. 'Never have been, never will be. You won't see me worrying over my food.' He pointed his fork at her plate. 'You want to eat up.'

'It's good,' she said.

'It should be, the price I'm paying.'

The price I'm paying. And this was the hinge and the hinge was getting rusty. Rusty with those little spots of rust you can't see but you know they're there. They squeak and they need a drop of oil. The man squinted at a curl of ginger and pushed it to the side of his plate, forked his last piece of meat, chewed and sat back. He patted his stomach and said 'Eat up.'

'At home,' she said, 'we used to chew our food. We used to treat it with more respect than you do.'

'Did you?' he said.

'Yes,' she said, and for the first time since she had become a wife, she looked at her husband and said 'I want to take my time.'

'Do you?' he said.

'Yes,' and now she said 'And I will,' and in the kitchen the cook clapped hands, Duckie smiled, and the other customers felt the dominion of the hour pass over the restaurant, stop for a moment, and laugh.

Louis de Bernières

LONDON VOICES

YOU GET USED TO YOUR NEIGHBOURS

I see you've got that black man moved in next door
He's alcoholic, that's what they're saying
I sold him two bottles of Scotch
A fiver each
I didn't want them
And bugger me if they weren't both in the bin
The morning after
But he's harmless.
And you've got them Albanian refugees
I know
I heard their dodgy music
Had the window open, didn't they.
I see Fagin's moved out
But he's only across the road, he ain't gone far
I'm glad about that
You get used to your neighbours, don't you.

REMEMBER WHEN BERT WAS ILL

Remember when Bert was ill
And he needed a lift to the doc?
And we asked Fagin, we said
Bert needs a lift to the doc
And Fagin says
Well, I would, but this car belongs to me bird
And she wouldn't like it
And we say 'Bert's ill'

And he says 'I would
But this car belongs to me bird'
So anyway, one day
Fagin's come back with his bird
And he's parking up by the kerb
And Dave's got a smoke bomb
And he slips it under the car
And the car's all filling with smoke
And Fagin leaps out and he's running
Waving his arms like a prat
Like he's leaving his bird there to burn
And she's just sitting there
And for all he knows
He's only left her to burn
Laugh?
Bloody Nora, mate
Me and Bert and Dave
We very nearly pissed ourselves.

PARKING MARKINGS, SOD THAT FOR A LARK

Well we come out one day
And there's this sodding great truck
With a jack and a crane and a sling
And they're moving our cars up the frog.
There's a couple of rozzers mooching
And we say
'Why are you moving our cars?'
And they say
'Sorry squire, it's parking markings,'
And we say
'Parking markings?'
And they say
'Yes, parking markings,'
And we say
'We don't want no parking markings
Parking's a pain as it is,'

And they say
'It's the council – silly sods –
Nothing better to do.
So don't blame us we're
Only doing our job,'
And we say
'Fancy a nice cuppa tea?'
And they say
'Can't say we mind if we do,'
And we sit in a row on the wall.
And then these blokes roll up, all right?
In them dayglo dungarees
All spotty and splattered with grime
Laying white lines here and white lines there
All pukka and careful and neat
And we say
'What are we going to do?
Parking's a pain as it is.'
And Dave's a roofer, right?
And he's got a gadget for tar
And that night Dave goes out
And I'm watching out for The Bill
And he burns up and blanks out the lines
And we park up our cars like before
The way we always did
And we say
'Sod the council, and
Sod the parking markings –
Parking's a pain as it is.'

Abdulrazak Gurnah

THE RETAINING WALL

HE TOOK OFFENCE easily. Perhaps it became something of a game in the end, for him and for his tormentors. Whatever he said, it was as if he expected to be misunderstood and misrepresented. Whatever it was, he said it with an air of wounded weariness, as if something else lay behind it, and his listeners obliged with mockery and disbelief. It was such feeble defence, no defence at all against assailants with so much time on their hands, and such an indulgent sense of what raillery permitted, such a callous sense of what lay beyond a joke. That should have been obvious, should not have required reflection, as should have been that there was no way of evading such attentions. That was how things were. Twice in his life he stood his ground, and on both occasions he was forced into humbling and wounding retreat. Except when he was overwhelmed by memories, he probably managed not to think about those times. No, I suspect he had no way of avoiding that either, but in any case, there is nothing to stop us doing so.

But first things first, and before we go any further (yes, you're coming) we need to sort some things out. His name was Iqbal. At the time I'm talking, he was exactly in his mid-thirties (thirty-five) and living with his mother in the hollowed-out shell of his father's old shop. The father had shuffled off several years before, the shop drying up as his own scope narrowed and his life flinched and shrivelled. In the last years he had opened the shutters every morning, and sat on the empty cash-box with his legs folded under him, his eyes absent in some burrowing retreat, but now and then darting cowering glances at people passing by, expecting and receiving their mockery for his abjectness before misfortune.

It had happened to everybody, the disappearance of trade and business, ever since the plunderers had slashed and brawled their way into government. They dignified their rapacity and their psychotic rage with high-sounding wounded phrases, and then filled themselves up with their paltry booty while everything went to hell. Here the same as everywhere, and not because any one of them needed an example to follow, but because that is what happened when the empire-makers found their grandiose ceremonials and their duplicitous rhetoric too expensive, and frugally returned home to run the world from there. Then the order they had punitively coerced the world into turned into a scramble and a frenzy to settle unforgotten business. It had happened to everybody, and people whispered and plotted, and saved what they could from the ruins, keeping their spirits up by believing and circulating the most scandalous rumours about the beastliness of the people who crouched over their lives with such unceasing malice.

Iqbal's father could not even manage that, could not manage the suppressed snigger and the manufactured rage which preserved hopeless hope and kept alive seething plans and desires. What had come to others as a sudden calamity on their thriving lives, had only hastened the accelerating depletion of his business, had turned him into a pauper. He had lost the desire for the business, had been listlessly going through the motions for months, lost in some speechless numbness which had overwhelmed something deep inside him. It was not that he was so old, he just gradually slid into this exhaustion. So when the new bullies stepped up with their bloodied cudgels and their hectoring words, Iqbal's father subsided into something cringing and still, as if history had chosen him as its special victim, and day after day sat in his emptying shop, waiting for the end. We knew all this about him because he was a shopkeeper, and so he lived out his decline in public. While other people bickered and wept behind closed shutters, then came out into the light with wrappers newly tightened and cuffs carefully straightened, he sat there in front of everybody, falling to pieces.

He had only been paying rent fitfully in recent times, and the end of the month had brought the angry landlord with his threats, to be placated somehow, with something: a down-payment, evasion, pleas, abject cringing pleas for mercy. *There's a crack in the wall*, he told the landlord, speaking at such moments with an eloquence and intensity that only appeared as he wheedled for clemency. *I can hear it growing bigger at night. This house could fall and crush all of us in our sleep. Why don't you fix the wall before we all die? God sees all this. Why do you persecute a poor man who is only looking to gather his small share?* When the landlord demanded to see the damage, Iqbal's father wept tears in sight of the street, pleading that the landlord should leave them in peace and not trample on their meagre privacy.

But now Iqbal's father paid no rent, and the landlord did not appear, because the government had expropriated all rented houses, and had not got round to making a register of what they had so carelessly acquired. The landlord was afraid that whatever he demanded now he would have to give back later, and it may not only be money that the beasts may require from him as recompense for his impudence. So nothing was demanded of Iqbal's father as he sat wasting away in his empty shop. His wife, with her high-pitched, wheedling, girlish voice, went from house to house in her ragged and garish sari, begging for washing, or failing that, for a plate of something left-over, and not everyone turned her away.

Where was our hero while all this drama was happening? He was there, the only thing that brought a spark of life and wrath in his father's eyes. Every morning (late) when Iqbal came through from the back of the shop where the family lived, smelling stale and unwashed, and with the dazed look in his eyes that he had worn most of his life, and then perched on the narrow step into the street, his father's eyes retreated from their wanderings and tightened on him. He was a small man, Iqbal's father, and then in his reduced state he seemed tiny. Sometimes they sat in this tense familiar, saying nothing until one of them moved, or someone walked past and jeered at them, or the mother came out from the back or returned from one of her endless foraging forays, then the father would begin to spit whining insults at his son, who sat silently a few feet away, not even turning round to glance at him.

'He doesn't even greet me. Doesn't he have a father, this one? Bastard of no nation. Does he ask about my health? There is work here in the shop, but do you see this filthy louse lift a finger to help? He just eats and shits and farts and sleeps. Like a goat or a snail, like a donkey without a name. He doesn't even give thanks to God. All he does is just wander the streets like a madman. Bastard without a brain. Hey you, at least go and wash your face, and brush your teeth. Water is free in the mosque, and while you're there you might as well wash those stinking clothes. You make me ashamed.'

Sometimes his insults came in Malayalam, to the delight of any casual listeners who might be strolling past. *Give it to him, bamkubwa, mtolee maneno kwa kihindi. Send him back to Bombay, the good for nothing*, they encouraged. I wouldn't have known it was Malayalam then. It was just Indian, *kihindi*, that was what we thought they all spoke.

'We don't come from Bombay,' Iqbal would protest, his surly stale mouth opening at last.

His father had fought the same battle for years. *I don't come from Bombay. I'm not one of those banias, I'm a Muslim. My family lives in Calicut. We have been Muslims since the time of the nabi, sala-llahu-alle.* But no one took any notice, or if they did it was only to laugh and to aggravate. It was not even so much as if they were disbelieved, but that anyone could see from the anguished note of their protests that this was something to yield a laugh or two. Aren't there Muslims in Bombay? So why can't you be from Bombay, you lying banian? It was even funnier that the son followed the father in this game, so that each session with the pathetic victims recalled earlier hilarities.

Iqbal once got into a fight over the matter. He was not a fighter, did everything he could to avoid getting into one, accepted any humiliation that had been asked of him so far ... except when he fought to refuse being described as coming from Bombay. And everyone acted with the sure knowledge that one day he would learn to accept that as well.

He was sitting with his tormentors on the benches outside the café near the airlines office when out of nowhere, as is usual with these things, someone began teasing him about booking him a ticket to go back home to Bombay. 'I'm not from Bombay,' he said, his voice lowered, the words spoken in an undertone to set off the ritual banter that would leave him speechless with defeat, or at times overwhelmed into a fixed grin which looked nothing so much as despair. Everyone knew how easily Iqbal took offence, and how swiftly he could be forced to submit to a humiliating retreat. Retreat? Yes, it was a kind of battle for most of us, when defeat would live forever in the stories of our lives. But Iqbal had been vanquished long ago, and the impact of stories about him lay only in the escalation of his humiliations, and the catalogue of his distracted absurdities, the steady decline of his portrayal as an eccentric tending towards derangement.

So, on this occasion, when he refused to submit and instead released a torrent of abuse and grievance which was first shocking for its unaccustomed lucidity, everyone laughed even harder. He was twenty then, as I was, and some of his listeners were grandfathers, yet no one saw anything remarkable in grown men – all of us – sitting outside a café in the middle of the day, loafing the hours away in this forgettable drama. Well, perhaps not forgettable to Iqbal, and probably not forgettable for the rest of us either, but it would be easy to overlook or even guess at its significance in the scheme of things. Then, out of nowhere, Iqbal rushed at one of his abusers and punched him in the face, on the forehead. It was obvious he had hurt himself, and as he clutched his fist in pain, everyone else fell about in frenzied glee. Iqbal fighting!

Everyone except the man who had been hit. Abudu. He used to be a fisherman until an injury to his foot kept him away from the sea, and now he lived on what he could, a little work, a little who knows what. Abudu grabbed Iqbal and forced him to his knees, then in front of everyone, there on the roadside, he pissed on him. *Bombay, Bombay,* Abudu chanted, as he sprayed Iqbal, running the jet all over him as if to reach all parts of a blaze . . . all over his long greasy hair, across his shoulders, down his neck. *Bombay, Bombay.*

Iqbal's father was still alive then, though it's unlikely that he would have heard this story. Very little reached him where he was at that time. It was soon after this that he died, so perhaps even if it had reached him he would not have attended to it. I was away for a few days in Mombasa, and I came back to hear that he had gone. I don't remember anyone saying how, and I certainly never thought to ask. When it's your time what does it matter anyway.

Even though no one spoke of how he had gone – or perhaps they had and I was inattentive, fever, suddenly in the night, severe diarrhoea, found dead in the morning, imprecisions in the telling that are overpowered by the impact of the erasure which is the cruel point of the story – there was enough talk of the event of his death. What an impressive number turned up at the mosque to say prayers for him before the burial. How enough people donated something to the family so that they could convey the body to God's mercy without disrespect. And jokes about where Iqbal managed to find the clean embroidered kanzu and the silver-threaded kofia he wore to the funeral. In his dead father's trunk, I'd have guessed, and as we probably all could have guessed, but men with time on their hands will talk about anything, and laugh and open wide their eyes in amazement as if the thought, the subject and its tantalising possibilities, had never occurred to them before. So: where could that empty-headed lofa, that pauper and son of a pauper, have found such fine clothes? Did you see him, holding his head up like a brave young man with an honourable name? Instead of? Instead of a beggar son of an impoverished Indian shopkeeper, may God have mercy on his soul, and a mother with a head full of fluff. And that's without the rest of all that other business about him.

In the first few days after the funeral, only one of the slats that ran across the front of the shop was opened, and Iqbal and his mother retreated to the courtyard that opened out behind the back hallway of their living quarters. A wall ran on one side of the yard, alongside the alleyway beside the shop. The other sides of the yard were the abutting houses around them and the wall and doorway into their own house, to which was attached a thatch awning on two slender mangrove posts. It was there under the awning that the two of them sat, their eyes browsing the cramped yard, and pausing idly over one or the other of their paltry possessions: a thick clay jar for cooling drinking water, a rusty sheet of corrugated iron rescued from somewhere and awaiting the hour of need to justify its awkward and menacing presence, a basket of charcoal, an aluminium bucket under the water-tap where Iqbal's mother used to do the washing she managed to persuade her neighbours to let her have. Beside them was a brazier where she cooked their meagre meals.

Her name was Fareida. At the time of her husband's death she was in her thirties, slim and a little round-shouldered after years of chores and never having quite enough to eat. Her hair, glistening with coconut oil, was parted in the middle and gathered in a knot at the back of her head. As she sat beside Iqbal in the aftermath of the loss which had befallen them, the beginnings of her habitual placating smile were already on her face. When the muadhin called out the afternoon prayers, his sweet hectoring call filled the yard, tremblingly rolling off the hot walls. Fareida looked guiltily at her son. After a while, her mouth swelled with words, and she made a small whining noise before she began to speak.

'I don't know what will happen now,' she said, her voice small and quivering to concede Iqbal's sudden ascendancy over their lives, and disarm something unpredictable and unresting which she sensed as she sat beside him. 'God will give us guidance.'

Iqbal said nothing to this, but a tiny rhythmic ripple ran through his body, making him rock back and forth almost imperceptibly. Then the moment passed and the silence returned between them, Iqbal's edgy and bristling while his mother's was pregnant with a kind of foreboding. Some days later, Iqbal said to her, 'I'm going to be a poet.' It brought tears to her eyes.

I imagine all this. I don't know if there was a courtyard at the back of the shop, or if Iqbal and his mother sat there on a hot afternoon in that desolate silence. I don't even know her name. I invented Fareida because it is a beautiful name, and it seemed sad that at a moment like that I should only be able to imagine her as the cowering woman in a bedraggled red sari that was my memory of her. I also imagined what people said about the funeral, for when I left just before Iqbal's father died, it was not to go away to Mombasa for a few days, but to leave and not return for fifteen years. I did not invent the *I'm going to be a poet* part. Though he may not have said it to his mother in quite the way I describe, he had said it to me several times.

Once, when I asked him to recite me one of his poems, he told me I did not understand what he meant. A poet did not just write poems, he said, but was someone who could see into things. If he wished, he – Iqbal – could recite a poem, or a story, or say nothing but merely stroll on the road to Maruhubi and back. That would not make him a poet nor prevent him being one. This was some of the portentous nonsense Iqbal was capable of, so to speed things up I said: 'Tell me a story, then, if you don't know a poem.'

This is the story he told me, as I remember it: 'There was a man who lived in a city by the sea. It was a rich city, with many beautiful houses and a large harbour which was busy in all the trading months of the year. One day this man left the city to trade with the outlying tribes of the human race. He was not himself rich, and this was the only way for him to make his fortune, to go to places other traders were fearful to risk and bring back valuable merchandise. He travelled south for twenty-nine days and arrived at a town deep in a valley surrounded by mountains. It was late when he arrived, but even in the gloom he could see it was not a large town, just a few large buildings with gaily decorated roofs. A river descended from the mountains and emptied in a lagoon on the edge of the town. By the time he entered the town it was dark, and everywhere was silent. The lagoon was a little brighter, from the light of the young moon reflecting in the water. He stood in the middle of the town not knowing what to do, and after a while he went to drink from the lagoon.'

That was the story, and despite all my pleadings Iqbal refused to add to it. At least tell me if the traveller got back to his city by the sea, I pleaded. I wanted so much for him to get back, before something happened to him. Iqbal only smiled slyly and refused to tell me. There was something familiar about the story, and for many years while I was away it came back to me, sometimes as evidence of Iqbal's eccentricity about being a poet, at other times as something profound which had survived the daily crushing of his spirit.

When I returned, I thought of him even before I saw him, for my family only lived a few houses down the street from the shop. There were too many other things happening to me for Iqbal to be at the forefront of my mind, but as soon as I caught sight of him in the street, I knew it was a moment I had already imagined. He was still as skinny as he used to be (whereas I had put on weight and disliked it) but his hair was long and grey, hanging all the way down to his shoulders. He wore a full beard, also bristling with grey, and was dressed in a large white shirt. At a distance he looked an image of sophisticated assurance, standing on the roadside outside the video shop near the intersection at the very top of the street.

He did not see me approaching, so I was able to get quite close before the attention of the two men who were sitting on a bench outside the video shop also made him turn to look. There was no hesitation in his greeting. He stepped towards me with hand outstretched, the familiar fragile grin evident through the hair that now gave his face a kind of strength.

'I heard you were back,' he said, touching my shoulder with a gesture of familiarity that suddenly took me back to earlier chafing intimacies that I thought I had erased from memory. We talked about predictable forgettable things mostly. I know I asked what he did now, and he said, pointing to the video shop behind him, that he helped run the shop. The two men sitting on the bench, whom I recognised but could not name, grinned at this. One of them said: *Yes, this shop would collapse without Iqbal,* then they both burst into that mocking street laughter which made me realise that Iqbal was still the butt of the frantic jeering I remembered from years ago. Unlike then, he now turned on the two men and abused them fully and handsomely, and they quailed in front of him and made placating noises . . . but I could see suppressed smiles behind their appeasing words. It was a depressing sight.

I had passed their old shop just a few moments before I saw Iqbal. Three or four of the boarding slats at the front were removed, so that the opening looked like the doorway of a house. I saw his mother sitting on a bench in the gloom just inside the shop, and thought I saw a child sitting on the floor beside her. For some reason I did not stop or greet her, and when I glanced back after I had walked on for a minute or two, I saw that she had got up and was standing at the doorway, looking after me. I asked my sister about her when I got back home. How had she managed to hang on to the house when Iqbal was not working? Because I had assumed when Iqbal said that he *helped* run the shop and the men laughed, that he was only putting the best meaning on something abject: that he hung around the shop and occasionally was given a hand-out. Or worse, that he was just a busy-body nuisance who was allowed to give himself airs for laughs or out of affectionately condescending tolerance. So how could she cling on in there when people were now clawing their houses back, or in any case the government had got much more organised about charging rent for property it had so casually sequestered those years ago?

My sister could be censorious about matters to do with men and women and what they did with each other. She was not unusual in this, it was a subject with its own righteous public language, and its own high-sounding meanness, here as much as anywhere else. A man moved in with her, a man much younger than her and as black as the devil, she said. He used to work as a porter in the docks until this government of robbers took over, then he became a person of influence and power. After the old man died, he moved in with her. They even have a daughter. I expected her to use a terrible name for the child, but she didn't. After glowering for a moment with eyes down-cast, she said: 'He's been looking after her. That's how she's still there. For all I know, they've even dispossessed the landlord.'

His name was Adnani, and when she told me that, I remembered him. He was a quiet man who, like all the other porters in the docks, went about his business bare-chested. I'd have gone bare-chested too if I had a body like his. (I wouldn't, but you know what I mean.) He was lean and bulging with supple glistening muscles, as if he was created to look just like that, as if his maker had paid detailed attention to every curve and poise of his powerful body. As children we played around the docks, and knew about all the personages who worked there, and he was certainly a personage. When merchants had work to offer, they first hired Adnani as the gang leader and let him find his own porters. I see Adnani striding unhurriedly between truck and cargo lighter as I write this, his body streaming with sweat in the sun, his face screwed up against the light. I said he was quiet, but really he was mostly silent, in a trade that was raucous and exhibition-ist, clownish. There was something scary about his silence and his scowling looks, something dangerous. I wouldn't have thought about it in this way when I was younger, but it looked like he felt a kind of grievance that he should be doing that work at all.

When I tried to imagine him courting Iqbal's mother, I couldn't. When I thought of her, I could only picture a bedraggled, thin woman of mature years with frightened airs and a grimy, garish sari. Timid and and intimidated, crushed by poverty and a lifetime of wheedling powerlessness, unstable. The next time I walked past the shop I slowed down and glanced into the darkened doorway to see if she was still sitting there. I waved to her and strolled by, but she got to her feet as she had done before and called after me by name, so I went back to greet her.

'Iqbal told me you were back,' she said, smiling with a kind of sympathy, as if she understood something I didn't. She looked younger than I expected, though I guessed she was about fifty. There was none of the twitching intensity I remembered of her. Had I misremembered? She had put on weight, and although her hair was pulled back as it used to be, it was now looser on her head, and it framed and softened her face with careless elegance. As we talked about the predictable things our circumstances obliged us to – how long, so far away, but at least you have good work, and the family, thank God – her air was mildly coquettish in that safe and familiar way of matronly flattery. Her voice was thin and whiny, but she looked happy, if that is not a stupid thing to say about another human being. Or maybe I just wanted to think she was. 'You must come and greet Bwana Adnani,' she said. 'He'll be very happy to see you.'

Perhaps because she had heard our voices, her daughter came out of the darkness of the shop. I knew it was her daughter even though she looked nothing like her. It was something about the way they acknowledged each other that made me think that, the mother's casual proprietary half-gesture towards the girl and her equally indifferent evasion of it. She was much darker than her mother, and at a quick glance had nothing of her features – perhaps the liquidly avid eyes. *She's nine years old*, her mother said, making her daughter smile with that vain glee that we all have as we count off the years of childhood bondage. *Her name is Jamila*. She looked at me as she said that, expecting a reaction, and I must have showed something because she smiled briefly and then smiled again more broadly.

As I walked away from them I expected that I would run into Iqbal outside the video shop near the intersection. Where else could he go? Jamila was the name of her other daughter, Iqbal's younger sister, who had died when she was nine. I was there when it happened. They were sitting on the retaining wall at the deep end of the dhow harbour, their legs dangling over the edge. Iqbal was not much older than Jamila, about twelve maybe, the same age as me. They were often together like that in the afternoons, from when they were very young, from when Jamila was a toddler. I think the parents expected Iqbal to take her out for a couple of hours in the afternoons, to get Jamila off their hands, and they just stuck at it like that. I was wandering the streets, looking for the gang of boys I hung around with in the neighbourhood, or anybody else I could sit and chat with or join in a game of football. I considered joining them on the wall, but Iqbal could be odd sometimes, intense and silent for long periods, which was bearable when you were in the mood but could be boring and scary when you were not, and Jamila was only a chatty little girl, either too eager to please or sulking.

The air was clear that day, and the late afternoon light reflected off the sea in blinding flashes, flattening their shapes into silhouette and then rounding them off again. I turned away before they could see me, and then after a moment looked back. The light flashed in my eyes, but even then I could see that only Iqbal was sitting on the wall. I looked around to see if Jamila had run off but there was no sign of her. Iqbal was sitting on the wall, palms pressed downwards, looking out to sea. I stood still, confused, heart pounding, tears suddenly in my eyes. I called out something, her name, his. I saw him shuffling back from the wall and rising to his feet.

Jamila, I shouted.

What happened? he asked, looking into that dark deep end by the wall.

I could see no sign . . . I got as near the edge as I dared, but it was deep there and we were warned to keep away, never swim there, sting rays and a giant octopus.

'Get help,' I screamed through tears and terror and a guilty and impotent pain, and because he did nothing, just stood in front of me heaving and beginning to blubber with strangled sobs, I ran away from him, calling out *She's fallen in, she's fallen in* for the whole world to hear.

He must have pushed her in. Of course he must've. I don't know what he said, but no one asked me about what had happened. When I told my mother about it, she made me promise to keep quiet. *Never volunteer yourself as a witness*, she told me. *Not when someone's died. You'll only make a lifetime of enemies.* And she never mentioned my presence there to me again. But he must've pushed her in, and whatever he said happened, that was what everyone believed. I never heard anybody mention it, but I'm sure that despite the silence everyone, including his parents, thought Iqbal had pushed her in. No, someone did mention it, perhaps. They found the body the next morning when the tide was out. The harbour police launch cruised slowly along the ribs of the wharf and found her body tangled in the beams and spars and the dark filth under there. And after they had pulled the body out with their boat-hooks, and laid it out on the launch and covered it with a length of canvas, Iqbal's father, who was watching among a whole crowd up on the wall, turned to his son and said something to him. He was a small man, dressed in a kind of finery, a clean white shirt and a waistcoat, and a brown embroidered cap. In the rising morning heat he shouted something at his son, frothing at the mouth with rage. Iqbal said something back, protested while tears ran down his face. His father shouted back at him, waving his arms with what looked like distracted anger. Iqbal stared at him and then walked away with his face turning from side to side, as if he was looking out for somebody.

This time he saw me coming. He was sitting on the bench outside the video shop, and when he caught sight of me he said something to the man beside him and came towards me with a wide grin, dressed in his large white shirt and cream linen trousers.

'I meant to ask you,' I said after we had exchanged greetings. 'Did you ever get to write the poems?'

He laughed, stroking his beard satirically, the affected intellectual. 'Oh yes, but they aren't any good. I'm still trying to produce at least one poem worth the name. Leave me your address when you go back. I'll send it to you when I've done it.'

'I met your sister Jamila,' I said. 'I was just talking to your mother a few minutes ago.'

'I told her that you were back, and she said she'd seen you,' he said, his grin beginning to tremble in that way he had when the men used to tease him when we were younger.

'It's a beautiful name,' I said.

'Now she's a poet, isn't she?' he said.

He stared back at me for a long moment. Sometimes I used to think I saw a shadow on the edge of that picture, a figure perhaps standing by the warehouse at the back of the wharf, someone late leaving work or a lone stroller. But that was only later, and I could have imagined that presence, wished for it. Iqbal looked back at me silently. A small familiar ripple ran across his face and his eyes retreated slowly. Then he said, *Fuck off* and walked away towards the main road, his shirt flapping in the breeze.

Paul Bailey

AN AFTERNOON IN MURANIA

WHEN I WAS twelve, my recently widowed mother took me
to the theatre for the first and only time. 'We're going to a
matinée up West,' she had announced the evening before.
'We'll be sitting with the toffs in the stalls for once.
Somebody very important gave me the tickets.'

'Who?'

'Never you mind who. You could learn a lot from him
when it comes to manners. He's very polite. He's a real
gentleman, unlike others I've met.'

'He must have a name.'

'Of course he has. If you don't disgrace me tomorrow, I
might tell you who he is.'

(The prospect of disgracing her loomed throughout my
childhood and adolescence. How was I to do it? 'You'll bring
disgrace on the family one of these days' was a prediction
reserved for me alone. Neither my brother nor my sister had
it in their power to be disgraceful, it seemed.)

'I shan't disgrace you.'

'We'll see about that.'

On that summer morning, she insisted that I scrubbed,
rather than merely washed, myself at the kitchen sink. I
would be mixing with people who noticed dirt. I was to use
the 'honest carbolic' all over my body, not just my hands and
face. She wanted me immaculate from head to foot.

We were a shining pair as we waited for the bus. Our shoes
gleamed in the sunlight. The Palace Theatre was our
destination, where a 'lovely show' – she had it on the best

466

authority – was playing. It was called *King's Rhapsody*, and if I didn't enjoy it then there was something wrong with her youngest son. She already knew the big tunes from hearing them on the wireless.

Although it was a hot day, the auditorium was packed with middle-aged women in bright dresses. I looked around for another boy, but couldn't find him.

'I'm the only boy here, Mum.'

'You should feel honoured, in that case.'

'And there aren't many men either.'

'Men work of an afternoon, especially those with pots of money.'

'Why have they got mauve hair?'

'You and your questions. Who?'

'These women.'

'Ladies to you. When a lady reaches a certain age, her hair loses some of its colour. That's when she dyes it. And it's not mauve, it's blue. They call it a blue rinse. They say it's fashionable to have a blue rinse.'

'It looks mauve to me.'

'Well, it isn't, Mr Clever Dick.'

'Why don't you have one?'

'One what?'

'A blue rinse. You're old enough.'

'I'm not a lady. Not like them, anyhow. You won't catch me tarting myself up. I'd be the laughing stock of the street. I'll stay as nature made me.'

She whispered 'Thank God' when the lights dimmed and the overture began.

At the start of *King's Rhapsody*, King Nikki of Murania is a contented bachelor living in Paris with his mistress – a woman of mature years and vast experience. The Queen Mother, however, is not happy with this arrangement and is soon reminding her feckless son of his regal responsibilities. The throne of Murania needs an heir, and quickly. Nikki is summoned back to his country, where a virginal young bride has been chosen for him. Princess Cristian (sic) is of Royal blood, but very distantly related to her husband-to-be. For a reason which I have forgotten, Cristian makes her first appearance disguised as a humble peasant. (In Ruritania and its surrounding states, the peasants are invariably humble, unless they are revolting.) In anticipation of her deflowering, perhaps, Cristian sings 'Some day my heart will awake' (to torrents of mauve applause that long-ago afternoon) and the marriage duly takes place, much to the delight of Countess Vera Leminken, a robust contralto with the kind of bosom that was once known as a 'shelf'. The wedding festivities involve a Tatar chieftain and his retinue, newly arrived from Central Asia; a band of gypsies, with fiddlers and dancing girls; the Muranian nobility and their offspring, and – this being a feudal society – a few privileged members of the peasantry.

Queen Cristian bears Nikki a son, and the Muranian throne seems safe for at least a generation. But Nikki is fretting. His wife is undoubtedly beautiful, but she doesn't excite him. She cannot compare with his lover in Paris, to whom he must return. Back in the French capital, he imagines he is a bachelor once more. Years pass. One night at the opera, he peers down from his box and catches sight of the Queen and Prince he has abandoned. Guilt seizes him, and – agreeing to abdicate in favour of his son – he travels to Murania to attend the coronation. He is in disguise, naturally – a lonely bystander amidst the throng in the great cathedral. The Prince is crowned King, while his father watches from behind a pillar. The congregation cheers. The new King walks solemnly from the cathedral, his proud mother behind him, his courtiers in attendance. The stage is deserted, except for Nikki. He moves towards the throne. He takes a white rose from his buttonhole, places it on the throne, and then kneels before it.

The curtain-calls went on and on – the actresses in crinolines, the actors in uniforms with Muranian medals and decorations, the Tatars, the Gypsies, the grinning peasants. Then it was King Nikki's turn to take a single call, and the blue-rinsed ladies who had been Ivor Novello's admirers when their collective hair was its natural colour stood up and loudly applauded him. He bowed deeply, and the curtain fell for the last time. My mother was dabbing at her eyes with a handkerchief, to wipe away happy tears.

'Wasn't it glamorous? Oh, it was so glamorous,' said my mother that evening. She had changed out of her posh frock, and was standing by the stove in a blouse and skirt, with a pinafore to cover them. 'Those wonderful clothes, and that beautiful music.'

'Who gave you the tickets, Mum? You said you'd tell me if I didn't disgrace you.'

'Do you really want to know?'

'Yes.'

'You won't believe me, I'm sure.'

'Who was it, then?'

'It was Ivor Novello,' she replied, with her back to me. 'Are you surprised?'

I answered that I was.

'Where did you meet him?'

Thanks to Aunt Bessie (she wasn't our aunt, but the family called her that), she had waited at table and helped with the cooking at a dinner party given by Lady Juliet Duff in her grand Chelsea home the previous Wednesday. The guests had included Somerset Maugham and Ivor Novello. When the meal was finished, Ivor Novello had come into the kitchen and thanked them warmly for the delicious food. He shook Aunt Bessie's hand (as he had done many times in the past, Aunt Bessie would later boast) and my mother's too. 'It was then that he gave me the tickets. Wasn't that kind of him?'

'Yes.'

'I'm no good at letter-writing, but you are. You can write for the both of us, thanking him for a lovely treat. You will, won't you?'

'Yes, Mum.'

'Aunt Bessie has his address.'

(My mother had met Bessie in service, and they had been close friends for almost thirty years. They had cleaned and cooked for the rich since they were young girls. Bessie was born into a working-class family in Wandsworth, but at some time in her life had acquired an impossibly cultivated accent, with the strangulated vowels of certain of her employers. My mother, who was not free of snobbishness, recognized that tendency in Bessie and affected to despise it. When she was exasperated with her friend, she would dismiss Bessie as a 'stuck-up cow' or a 'snooty bitch' and remark 'She thinks her shit is scented soap.' But Bessie had 'connections', like Lady Juliet, the society hostess, and had been a boon when money was scarce.)

I wrote the thank-you letter the following day, and Aunt Bessie posted it.

I kept my trip to Murania a secret when I returned to school in September. I was frightened of being considered a sissy, because only a sissy would admit to seeing *King's Rhapsody*. In the bar of the theatre, enjoying my promised ice cream, I had stared at a couple of men with lightly pancaked faces. In the days before the permanent sun tan, a few brave spirits could be sighted in London wearing discreetly applied make-up. Here were two of them, perfectly at ease among the blue rinses. I was on the verge of discovering my own sissiness, and continued to stare in wonder. I had guessed, that afternoon, that the man pretending to be King Nikki – the man who had invented the plot and composed the score – was what my relatives called a 'pansy'. How could I tell my mates that I was the only boy – *the only boy* – in the Palace Theatre? I couldn't, for fear of ridicule.

My mother would not have approved of King Nikki's morals, or lack of same, had she bothered to examine them. Adultery was a wicked sin, and a man who deserts his wife and child no better than a criminal. (I was to learn, after her death, that my father had ditched his first wife, but in circumstances my mother must have condoned.) She believed that those who were born and raised into wealth got up to things the poor would never contemplate. It was a fact that pansies came from the upper classes, and with this 'fact' she brought any discussion on the subject of homosexuality to a decisive close.

At thirteen, I was a sissy beyond doubt. I was in love with a boy who had a 'touch of the tar brush', and I remained in love with him until I was in my twenties. I kept this long infatuation – his surname was, appropriately, Long – a secret from my mother. I was desperate, for a while, to be open with her. I once left a copy of André Gide's *Corydon*, an apologia for men loving men, on the kitchen table, hoping that she might read one of his less opaque sentences and chance upon the truth about me. But the occasion to be honest finally seemed irrelevant, as the years passed and she befriended the man I lived with. Our scented afternoon together in Murania became a treasured memory for both of us. How glamorous it was, and how scented, how camp.

Was Ivor Novello thinking of Rumania (as the word was commonly spelled when he was alive) as he worked on *King's Rhapsody*? Rumania had been an ally during the First World War, owing to a considerable extent to the efforts of the English Queen Marie to maintain a close union between her adoptive country and Britain. Rumania's last king, Carol the Second, was a playboy, a dilettante, who – like Nikki – tried to fulfil his regal duty. Carol's mistress was Jewish, and although Carol's political views were Right-ish, they weren't Right enough for the Nazi sympathisers who deposed him. In the mid-1930s, it was still possible to imagine the Balkans and Austro-Hungary as places of romance and enchantment – those rosy-cheeked peasants; those dark-eyed gypsies. In reality, feudalism had long turned rotten, and when the Second World War was done, the terrible feudalism that is Soviet Communism replaced the older variety. 'Wasn't it glamorous? Oh, it was so glamorous' – yes, it was, Mum, for three mauve hours.

Edwin Morgan

THE POET AND THE ASSASSIN

*(one of Omar Khayyam's close friends became the
founder of the secret sect of Assassins)*

OMAR   Hassan, the wine-lodge doors are open wide.
Sundown beckons all good folk inside.
The swart vinemaster lets his donkey bray,
Bringing jorums for joy of groom and bride.

HASSAN Omar, go in. The flagon's lost its lure.
Men have a sickness and that's not the cure.
The braying beast is empty as the soul
That seeks eternity in Nishapur.

OMAR   What's empty in a wedding-feast, my friend?
When jars are full and hearts are full, we spend
An hour or two that old eternity
Must envy in its wastes – wastes without end.

HASSAN The face of the divine cannot be seen,
But what may be is never what has been.
The wind that sighs along the wastes has
     powers
To dry the seas, give us red grass for green.

OMAR   Who wants red grass, Hassan? Tulip and rose
Would lose their blaze, they'd disappear, they'd
     close.
Look how the tavern lights are winking now!
Now is the time to set the cups in rows!

HASSAN Who wants a tulip if he can get blood?
Clamp the throat of the unregenerate bud!
Enemies of the divine are everywhere.
They sprout, they flaunt, their roots are black as
mud.

OMAR   Hassan, Hassan, what has got into you?
We used to toast the sparkle of the dew,
Set up our friendly chessmen, or lie back
Till I had named you all the stars I knew.

HASSAN Astronomy to the dogs, with kings and rooks!
Yes and your verses, all your pagan books.
Join my band, sniff out the godless, snap
Their necks, garrotte their sin-gorged looks.

OMAR   Who are you? O listen to the wedding-guests!
The lute-player, how quick at their requests!
It is all as familiar as the moon.
Who are you to damn the dancing breasts?

HASSAN I am Hassan ibn al-Sabbah, first
Of the Assassins, but not yet the worst
When hashish-men and hatchet-men will hatch
Silent as shadows and strangle and be curst.

OMAR   I am no lush. I see as clear as day.
I love this battered caravanserai.
Unleash your hemp-soaked stalkers, but don't
think
The world will not have, trembling, the last say.

William Boyd

ADULT VIDEO

PLAY >

SPRINGTIME IN OXFORD is vulgar anyway, but something
about this particular spring in Oxford is having me on.
Really, these cherry trees are absurd. One wonders if just
quite so many flowers are necessary. It is almost as if the trees
on the Woodstock Road were trying to prove something –
some sort of floral brag, swanking to the other, less advanced
vegetation. Very Oxford. Could I work this observation into
the novel? 'Only in Oxford do the cherry trees try too hard.'
Good opening for the Oxford sequence?

REWIND «

My meeting with my new supervisor was not a success. Dr
Alexander Cardman. 'Call me Alex,' he invited almost
immediately. He referred to me as Edward without permission.

'How old are you?' he asked.

'Thirty-one. How old are you?'

'Thirty-three. And you've been writing this thesis for . . . ?'

'For, oh, six years. Seven. Seven and a bit. I left Oxford for
three to teach. Then came back.'

'Teach? Where was that?'

'Abbey Meade. It's a prep school in Wiltshire.'

'Ah.' I could hear the sneer forming in his brain.

'And you came back –'

'To finish my thesis.'

'I see . . .' I was disliking him quite intensely by now. He
looked like he had gel in his hair. The small trimmed goatee
was rebarbative and the faint West Country burr in his voice
struck me as an affectation.

PLAY >

Summertown. The Banbury Road. I push through the front
gate of See Breezes (sic) to meet my new student, Gianluca di
something or other. He is blind, so the language school has
told me, and he needs to be walked to my flat. Not every day,
I hope.

A cheery plump woman opens the door and leads me
through to a living room, where Gianluca sits. He is a tall boy
– eighteen or nineteen, I would say – with thick blond hair
and a weak-chinned, sad face. His eyes are open, and as I
introduce myself and shake his hand they seem to stare
directly at me, disconcertingly, with only a faint glaucous,
bloodshot hue to them.

We walk back to my flat on the Woodstock Road. His
right hand rests gently in the crook of my left elbow, his left
carries a briefcase and a folded white cane. We don't speak,
as he had said, in good English, that he needed to concentrate
and count.

We stroll through Summertown's shops and halt the traffic
at the beeping pedestrian crossing. Along Moreton Road to
Woodstock Road and then a hundred yards or so to the
house.

'Ring this doorbell,' I say, guiding his hand to the gleaming
brass knob, 'and I'll come down to get you.'

In the hall Gianluca stops and sniffs the air.

'What is this place?' he says.

'A dentist's,' I say, as breezily as I can. 'I live on the top
floor.'

PAUSE ||

Felicia, my girlfriend, has gone to Malaysia for a week to try
to sell Internet stocks in the Pacific Rim market, or something. Perhaps it's bonds, or fluctuations in other stock
markets, that she's selling; or she might even be selling other
people's hunches about fluctuations in stock markets in the
next decade. I don't even try to understand. She has given me
the key to her house so I can feed her tropical fish while she's
away. When she left at dawn yesterday, she kissed me

goodbye, told me she loved me, and said, ominously, apropos of nothing, that she thought I would make a wonderful father. I suppose it's as close as she'll ever get to issuing an ultimatum.

PLAY >

'"There is,"' I read, '"as every schoolboy knows in this scientific age, a very close chemical relation between coal and diamonds –"'

'Please,' Gianluca says, 'there is a preface by Conrad, no?'
'Yes.'

'Could you please begin with that.' He taps something into his little portable Braille typewriter, and I go back to the beginning. You would think that being paid fifteen pounds an hour to read Joseph Conrad's *Victory* to a blind Italian boy is, well, money for old rope, but I find my heart is curiously heavy with prospective fatigue.

In our first two-hour session we manage five pages. Gianluca listens with almost painful concentration and asks many, many questions, the answers to which he painstakingly types into his Braille notebook. I walk him down to the front door, where he unfolds his white cane and sets off back to See Breezes with an amazingly unfaltering step. As I turn back into the hall, Krissi, the actually not unattractive New Zealand dental nurse, leans out of the door of the surgery and says, 'Mr Prentice would like a word at end-of-business today.'

As I plod back upstairs to my little flat beneath the eaves I think that 'end-of-business' is a classic Prentissian trope and that I must add it to my collection.

MEMORY

I think, perhaps, that I was at my happiest in Nice. Nineteen years old. At the Centre Universitaire Méditerranéen. No family. No friends. No money. Just freedom. My frowsty room in Madame D'Amico's apartment. The young whores on the Rue de France. The French girls. The Tunisian boys. Ulrike and Anneliese. All those years ago. Jesus Christ.

REWIND «

Dr 'Alex' Cardman handed me back my chapter: 'Social Consequences of the 1842 Mines Act in South Yorkshire, 1843–50.'

'What do you think?' I asked. This guy did not frighten me, I had decided.

'There were fifteen errors of transcription in your first quoted passage,' he said. 'I didn't read on.'

'It's only a draft, for Christ's sake.'

'Even a second-rate examiner will refer you for that kind of carelessness,' he said, reasonably. 'You don't want to get into bad habits. Bring it back when you've checked everything.' He smiled. 'What made you so interested in mid-nineteenth-century mining legislation? Pretty arcane subject – even for an Oxford doctorate.'

Its very arcanity, you fool, I wanted to reply, but instead I chose a lie, hoping it might cancel the Abbey Meade blunder. 'My father was a miner,' I said.

'Good God, so was mine,' he said. 'Tin. Cornwall.'

'Coal. Lanarkshire.'

FAST FORWARD »

INTERVIEWER: You don't seem embittered, even bothered, by the attack in the *Times* by Sir Alexander Cardman.

ME: It's a matter of complete indifference. Wasn't it Nabokov who said the best response to hostile criticism is to yawn and forget? I yawned. I forgot.

INTERVIEWER: It seems unduly personal, especially when your book has been so widely acclaimed –

ME: I think people on the outside never fully realize the role envy plays in literary and cultural debate in this country.

PLAY >

Prentice is wearing his tracksuit and trainers: he likes to go jogging at the end of a day's dentistry. I offer him a glass of wine, which he, surprisingly, accepts.

'South African Chardonnay,' I tell him. 'Your neck of the

woods.' Prentice actually comes from Zimbabwe. He has had his gingery-blond hair closely cut, I notice, which makes him look burlier, even fitter, if that were possible. He is always very specific about not being identified as South African, is Mr Prentist the dentist . . .

'I prefer Californian,' he says.

'What can I do for you, Mr Prentist?'

'Prentice.'

'Sorry.'

He smiles, showing his small immaculate teeth. 'Bad news,' he says. 'I have to put the rent up. From next month.' He mentions a preposterous figure.

'That's a –' I calculate, trying to keep the rage out of my voice. 'A hundred-and-twenty-per-cent rise.'

'The going rate for two-bedroom flats on the Woodstock Road, so an estate agent informs me.'

'You cannot call that broom cupboard where I work a second bedroom.'

'Market forces,' he says, sipping, then nodding. 'This is actually an excellent wine.'

FUNCTION
Felicia is unnaturally blonde, has a tendency to plumpness, and is devoted to me. I taught her for a term when she was at Somerville. We had an affair, for some reason. She went to work for a bank in the City. She came back to Oxford three years ago. I think, now, that she returned to seek me out. She makes twenty times more money a year than I do.

DISPLAY
My as yet unfinished novel. Five years in the writing. Which today I have decided to retitle: *Morbid Anatomy*.

FAST FORWARD »
INTERVIEWER: Why did you resign the Trevelyan Chair of Modern History?

ME: I did not approve of the new syllabus.

INTERVIEWER: It had nothing to do with internecine strife within the history faculty, professional jealousies?

ME: As far as I was concerned, it was purely a matter of principle. It was my duty.

PLAY >

Gianluca looks at me – or at least his sightless eyes are turned in my direction. I read on, hastily: '"Meanwhile, Schomberg watched Heyst out of the corner of his eye" – ah, notice that glorious Conradian cliché –'

'Why is Heyst so passive?' Gianluca asks. 'He's like he's *stagnante*.'

'Same word,' I say, wondering why, indeed. 'Well, he's a bit of a drifter, Heyst, isn't he?'

Gianluca types – I suppose – 'Heyst = drifter' into his Braille notebook.

'Going with the flow,' I improvise. We have reached page 67. I don't think I have ever paid so much attention to a text, and yet I can remember almost nothing. Each day it's as if I'm starting on page 1 again.

REPEAT

'He meant to drift altogether and literally, body and soul, like a detached leaf drifting in the wind currents.'

PLAY >

Mrs Warmleigh has left her Hoover on the stairs. I go to look for her and ask her to move it, as Gianluca is due.

'The blind boy? He's amazing that one, the way he comes and goes. Fantastic, it is, bless him.'

I concur, wearily. Mrs Warmleigh has a warty, smiley face and, oddly for a dentist's cleaning lady, many pronounced gaps in her famous smile. 'Warmleigh by name, warmly by nature,' she says, at least two or three times a week.

'You look at him,' she goes on, 'and you'd swear he could see. Amazing.'

A nasty little sliver of suspicion enters my mind.

REWIND «

Felicia started talking about children on the day of her twenty-eighth birthday. We had been 'going out' for two years by then. I asked her why she chose to live in Oxford, with its tiresome, lengthy commute to London when, on her salary, she could have lived in town, conveniently and comfortably. 'I was always happy in Oxford,' she said. 'And besides, you're here.' The logic doesn't hold up. She came back to Oxford, bought her little house in Osney Mead, and then we met up again and, as these things will, resumed our affair. There is a character in *Morbid Anatomy* loosely, very loosely, based on Felicia. I think she dies in a plane crash.

PLAY >

This is vaguely shaming, but I know I have to do it. Gianluca leaves and thirty seconds later I am out the door following him. I watch him for a while, and, as he waits at the pedestrian crossing, I use a gap in the traffic to overtake him. I jog ahead up through the Summertown shops until I have a hundred-yard start on him and, hidden in a doorway, I watch his progress, steady and sure, toward me. It is true, as Mrs Warmleigh had observed, that without the white stick there would be nothing in Gianluca's stride to tell you he was blind. Is it a sad subterfuge, some mental problem, I find myself wondering – wondering with slowly stirring anger rather than commiseration, as I'm a significant victim of this subterfuge. Or is he merely partially sighted and playing it up for more sympathy?

I let him go by. 'Oi, mate,' I disguise my voice with a bit of Oxford demotic. 'You drop vis money.'

He turns. 'Excuse me?'

My empty palm proffers an invisible ten-pound note.

He steps toward me, his eyes moving. 'Some money?' He digs in his pocket, producing a wallet. He *is* blind, all right, blind as a stone, stone-blind, bat-blind, and a pelt of self-loathing covers me for an instant. 'I dropped money?' he says, fumbling with his wallet's zip.

'Gianluca?' a girl's voice calls. We both turn.

'Gianluca,' I say. 'Is everything all right?'

'Edward,' he says with relief. 'I thought someone talking to me.'

The girl has reached us now, and she takes his arm. She's small, with wiry brown hair and a mischievous look on her face, half laughing, half smirking. She wears black, and she's smoking.

'Is my sister, Claudia,' Gianluca says, introducing us. 'This is Edward. Claudia is coming to stay for a few days. She take me back home.'

I reach out to take her proffered hand.

'Gianluca has told me everything about you.'

'Not everything, I hope,' I say, looking into those thin brown sightful eyes. And I know.

PAUSE ||

It is a kind of watershed, I realize. When you know instantly. And when the other person knows you know. It is, in its own way, an infallible sign of adulthood – a threshold crossed. All your imagined, wistful, striven-for worldliness suddenly coalescing into a simple blunt adult recognition. The last shreds of adolescent insecurity finally gone. From now on there will never be any doubt or ambiguity. You can look into a person's eyes and, wordlessly, the question can be asked – if you want to ask it – and you will know the answer: yes or no. End of story.

FAST FORWARD »

INTERVIEWER: You didn't find that the Nobel/Booker/Pulitzer/Goncourt inhibited your creativity in any way?

ME: On the contrary. I found it liberating. And the cheque was very welcome, too. (*Laughter.*)

REWIND «

I left Cardman's rooms and wandered out into the quad holding my error-strewn chapter rolled up like a baton, like a truncheon, in my hand. The afternoon sun struck the venerable buildings obliquely, picking out the detailing of the stonework with admirable clarity. The razored lawn was immaculate, perfectly striped, unbadged by weed or daisy, almost indecently, absurdly green. I realized that I hated old buildings, hated honey-coloured crafted stone, hated scholarship, hated arrogant young dons with their superior ways. So much hate, I reflected, as I crossed Magdalen Bridge, can't be good for one. The leaves of my chapter helixed gently down onto the turbid brown waters of the Cherwell.

PLAY >

I walk through Felicia's neat, bright house trying to imagine myself here. Where would my things go? Where would my desk be? Everything is neat, neat, neat, everything is tidy and neat. Even the cuddly toys on her bedcover are neatly arranged in descending order of size. Predictably, I search her laundry basket for a pair of soiled knickers to masturbate into but find only tights, cutoff jeans, and a rugby shirt – and somehow the autoerotic moment is gone. Dutifully, I feed her dazzling, frondy fish, trying to analyse what I feel for Felicia, with her decency, her baffling, uncritical devotion, her compartmentalized mind, at once cutesy and clever, our fundamental incompatibility . . . I could just about fit in here, I suppose, but where would baby go?

REWIND «

I was watching *Blade Runner* for about the thirtieth time when Felicia called.

'Hi. What is it?' I said.
'Just to let you know I landed safely.'
'Oh. Great. Where are you?'
'Singapore. K.L. tomorrow.'
'K.L.?'
'Kuala Lumpur.'
'Why don't people refer to San Francisco as S.F.? Always wondered about that. "Hey, let's go to S.F."'
'Are you all right, Edward?'
'What? Yeah. I think I'm going to abandon my thesis. Concentrate on the novel.'

'That's wonderful news. Look, I must dash, the car's waiting. Love you.'

'Bye.' I put the phone down. 'Love you.'

PLAY >

Claudia lights my cigarette for me, a gesture that, for some reason, always generates in me a little gut spasm of lust, a little intestinal writhe.

'You must try some of our English beer,' I say. 'Old Fuddleston's Triple-Brewed Dog Piss.'

'Oh yeah. I think I stay with vodka.'

'Very wise, Claudia, very wise indeed.'

We are sitting in a dark booth in a low-beamed smoky pub off Broad Street, and I wonder whether I should kiss her now but decide to wait a bit – I'm quite enjoying the sexual sparring.

'So, Eduardo.' She plumes smoke at the ceiling, then leans forward far enough that I can see the swell of her small breasts in the scoop of her T-shirt. 'You write novels. Can I read them?'

'You bet, Claudia. One day.'

FAST FORWARD »

INTERVIEWER: So why settle in Big Sur/Sausalito/Arizona/Key West?

ME: Well, after the divorce, I needed to get out of Britain. I was with Cora-Lee by then and her father offered us the use of his villa/beach hut/ranch. I was in rough shape emotionally and needed peace. Peace of mind. The most valuable commodity on the planet.

INTERVIEWER: Cora-Lee is substantially younger than you?

ME: That's true. But her wisdom is ageless.

SLOW MOTION |>

Claudia's T-shirt comes off easily enough but I'm surprised to see her wearing a tough little sports-bra thing with no clasp or hook I tug at a strap I am pretty fucking pissed we're both pretty fucking pissed all that beer and vodka Jesus how much did we drink I kick off a shoe and hear the zip on Claudia's jeans zing open she weaves away to the bathroom I haul the rest of my clothes off and slide under the duvet bollock naked I think bollock naked she comes in damn still in the bra thing blue panties not matching she whips the duvet back laughing and shouting at me in Italian *preservativa preservativa*.

PLAY >

As luck would have it, as filthy pigging stinking luck would have it, Prentist the dentist comes through the front door just as Claudia and I are crossing the hall. What sort of dentist comes to work at 7:45 A.M.? And why should I feel guilty? I'm a grown man renting a flat from another grown man. I introduce Claudia. The fact that I'm only in this flat because Felicia knows Prentice from the squash club is something I prefer not to contemplate right now.

Claudia looks at me in that way she has. 'Goodbye, Edward, I see you later.' I imagine that we must reek of sex – a pongy, spermy, sweaty, tangled-sheets sort of exudation, filling the hallway like tear gas.

Claudia leaves.

Prentice turns to me. 'I don't know what she sees in you,' he says, his voice harsh.

'Claudia?'

'Felicia, you tragic bastard. I don't know why she wants to marry you.'

'Because she loves me, Prentist, that's why.'

'I want you out of here. End of the week.'

FAST FORWARD »

INTERVIEWER: Do you ever think of the future? Of death?

ME: Wasn't it Epicurus who said 'Death is not our business'?

PLAY >

'"Davidson, thoughtful, seemed to weigh the matter in his mind, and then murmured with placid sadness: 'Nothing!'"' I close the book. 'The end,' I say to Gianluca.

I walk down to the hall with him, and we make our farewells. Gianluca thanks me, with some sincerity. I find myself wondering if Claudia has described to him how I look. I will miss Gianluca, and endless, interminable *Victory* – or will I? I know one thing for sure: I will never read a book by Joseph Conrad again. The mood is one of ... of placid sadness. Saddish, but not unsettling, not unpleasant.

'Claudia say she will call you tonight.'

'I won't be here tonight,' I say. 'I'm moving out. I'll be staying with a friend. Tell Claudia ... Just say goodbye for me.'

PAUSE ||

'Let's get married,' I said to Felicia when she called to tell me when her plane was landing. It was strange to hear her crying all those thousands of miles away, her little choking noises, the sniffs.

'I mean, will you marry me?'

'I'm so happy, Edward,' she said. 'I'm so incredibly happy.'

PLAY >

I stand on the platform at Oxford station, a bunch of overpriced scarlet tulips in my hand, looking sympathetically across the rails at the commuters with their briefcases and newspapers. Felicia's train appears and slows to a halt, doors swinging open. I stand there waiting, not moving, and I see Felicia step down in her smart suit, lugging her suitcase (which contains, I know, a silk shirt for me), tucking her hair behind her ears, looking around for me, her future husband. I raise my bunch of overpriced scarlet tulips and wave.

FREEZE FRAME ◆

Ruth Padel

THE PHOENIX

Her once-red head locked
In a tank of steam,
    Her face foxing down into nothing
Saying 'All my beauty's gone',
Holding on

To your wrist, your bare arm,
Through a shock hedge of wiring, spliced
    Every which way to intestines
And rationing herself to Seven Up
(Plus morphine) on the rocks.

So cold, under the striplight
Night after night
    Through all the carry-ons:
The bubble-cloud of rosaries,
The small-hours foraging for ice

In the hospital kitchen. But so proud
Of this cuckoo she
    Brought into the world,
As you sang with her, day after glary day,
All the words of all the Jim Reeve songs

Or any you rustled up between you,
Anything anyone there could sing about –
    'Tipperary', 'Star of the Sea' –
To ease that inward
Journey, launch her out.

Lavinia Greenlaw

MEPHISTO

After a night in the cellar
where Goethe thought out Faust,
I am up in the air again,
cumulo-cirrus, thin ice, a voice
that is crushing and reasonable:
Your little life . . .

We fly over a river,
half frozen, half cracking up
at the end of a beautiful winter:
three months of blinding heaven
that will leave its smallprint
and otherwise nothing on earth.

Hamish Whyte

SWITCH ON THE WAVES

OSCILLATING WATER COLUMN sea clam bristol cylinder salter duck
bristol clam duck oscillating cylinder sea column salter water
sea duck water cylinder bristol column clam salter oscillating
bristol water oscillating duck cylinder salter sea clam column
sea cylinder oscillating clam duck salter column water bristol
cylinder sea salter clam oscillating bristol water duck column
water sea oscillating column duck clam cylinder salter bristol
column clam bristol salter cylinder duck oscillating sea water
clam column oscillating water salter sea cylinder bristol duck

BIOGRAPHICAL NOTES

Simon Armitage was born in 1963 and lives in West Yorkshire. He has published six poetry collections, including *Cloud Cuckooland* (1997) and a travel book, *Moon Country* (1996, with Glyn Maxwell). His prose memoir, *All Points North*, appeared in 1998. He has written extensively for radio and TV and was appointed Millennium Poet in 1999. His version of Euripides' *Heracles* was produced by the West Yorkshire Playhouse. He teaches at Manchester Metropolitan University and in the USA.

Trezza Azzopardi was born in Cardiff and lives in Norwich. She is a recent graduate of the Creative Writing MA at the University of East Anglia. Her first novel, *The Hiding Place*, will be published by Picador in July 2000.

Paul Bailey was a Literary Fellow at the Universities of Newcastle and Durham, and a recipient of the E. M. Forster Award. His novels include *At the Jerusalem* (Somerset Maugham Award and an Arts Council Award), *A Distant Likeness, Peter Smart's Confessions* (shortlisted for the Booker Prize), *Old Soldiers, Trespasses, Gabriel's Lament* (shortlisted for the Booker Prize) and *Sugar Cane*. His most recent novel, *Kitty and Virgil*, was published in 1998.

Peter Benson was born in 1956 in Broadstairs, Kent, and has published seven novels, including *The Levels, Odo's Hanging* and *The Shape of Clouds*. He has won a number of literary prizes including the Guardian Fiction Prize, the Encore Award and the Somerset Maugham Award. In addition to his work as a novelist, he has written a number of screenplays and short stories, and taught creative writing and contemporary British fiction at schools and universities, both in the UK and abroad.

Brooke Biaz won the NBC New Writer of the Year Award and the 1999/2000 EU writers and film-makers fellowship. Growing up in Britain and the South Pacific, Brooke graduated from the Universities of East Anglia and New England, has been shortlisted 3 times for the rich Vogel Award for fiction writers under 35, and is the inaugural holder of the Commonwealth Universities' scholarship for work in creative writing.

William Boyd was born in Accra, Ghana, in 1952. He is the author of two collections of short stories and seven novels, the latest of which is *Armadillo* (1998). His stories and novels have been published round the world and have been translated into over two dozen languages. He divides his time between London and southwest France.

John Burnside has published six books of poetry, of which the most recent are *A Normal Skin* and *Swimming in the Flood*, and two novels, *The Dumb House* and *The Mercy Boys*. His new collection of poems, *The Asylum Dance*, will be published in 2000, alongside a collection of stories entitled *Burning Elvis*. He lives in Fife, Scotland, in a small coastal town on the Firth of Forth, and is currently working on his third novel.

Harry Clifton was born and educated in Dublin, but has lived and travelled widely in Africa and Asia, as well as more recently in Europe. He has published five poetry collections, the most recent of which are *The Desert Route: Selected Poems 1973–1988* (Gallery/Bloodaxe) and *Night Train Through the Brenner* (Gallery). A travel memoir, *On the*

Spine of Italy, appeared in 1999 from Macmillan, and a prose collection, *Berkeley's Telephone and other fictions*, is due from Lilliput Press. He divides his time between France and Ireland.

Robert Crawford was born near Glasgow in 1959. His poetry collections include *A Scottish Assembly* (1990), *Masculinity* (1996) and *Spirit Machines* (1999). With Simon Armitage he co-edited *The Penguin Book of Poetry from Britain and Ireland since 1945* (1998), and he is co-editing with Mick Imlah *The New Penguin Book of Scottish Verse* for publication in the autumn of 2000. He is Professor of Modern Scottish Literature at the University of St Andrews.

Philip Davison was born in Dublin where he now lives. His published novels are *The Book-Thief's Heartbeat, Twist and Shout, The Illustrator, The Crooked Man* and *McKenzie's Friend*. His short stories have appeared in various literary journals. He has co-written two television dramas, *Exposure* and *Criminal Conversation*. His first play, *The Invisible Mending Company*, was performed on the Abbey Theatre's Peacock stage.

Louis de Bernières was born in 1954. He is the author of *The War of Don Emmanuel's Nether Parts, Señor Vivo and the Coca Lord* (Commonwealth Writers' Prize, Eurasia Region 1992), *The Troublesome Offspring of Cardinal Guzman* and *Captain Corelli's Mandolin* (Commonwealth Writers' Prize, 1995). His play, *Sunday Morning at the Centre of the World*, was first broadcast on BBC Radio 4 in March 1999.

Anita Desai was born in 1937; her father was Bengali and her mother German, and she was educated in Delhi. Her published work includes *Clear Light of Day* (shortlisted for the 1980 Booker Prize), *Fire on the Mountain* (Royal Society of Literature's Winifred Holtby Prize), *In Custody* (shortlisted for the 1984 Booker Prize) and filmed by Merchant Ivory Productions, *Baumgartner's Bombay, Fasting, Feasting* (shortlisted for the 1999 Booker Prize) and two volumes of short stories. She has also written books for children. She is a fellow of the Royal Society of Literature and a member of the American Academy of Arts and Letters.

Michael Donaghy has published two poetry collections, *Shibboleth* (1988) and *Errata* (1993). He has won the Whitbread Award for Poetry, the Geoffrey Faber Memorial Award, an Arts Council Writers' Award and a grant from the Ingram Merrill Foundation. His most recent publication is a Poetry Society monograph, *Wallflowers: a lecture on poetry with misplaced notes and additional heckling*. He is a Fellow of the Royal Society of Literature.

Vicki Feaver has published two collections of poetry, *Close Relatives* (1981) and *The Handless Maiden* (1994) which was awarded a Heinemann Prize and shortlisted for the Forward Prize. Her poem 'Judith' won the Forward Prize for the Best Single Poem. A selection of her work is included in *Penguin Modern Poets 2*. In 1993 she was awarded a Hawthornden Fellowship and in 1999 a Cholmondeley Award. She lives in West Sussex and teaches creative writing to undergraduates and MA students at University College, Chichester.

Neil Ferguson was born in 1947. He has published four books of fiction: *Bars of America* (1986), *Putting Out* (1988), *Double Helix Fall* (1990) and his most recent novel, *English Weather* (1997). He lives in southwest France and Notting Hill, London.

Carlo Gebler was born in 1954 and lives in Enniskillen, Co. Fermanagh. He is a graduate of the National Film and Television School and has directed documentaries for BBC and independent television. *Put to the Test* won the 1999 Royal Television Society award for the best regional documentary. His published work includes a volume of short stories, *W9 and Other Lives* and several novels, most recently *The Cure* and *How to Murder a Man*, as well as non-fiction,

The Glass Curtain and *Driving through Cuba,* and children's fiction. His version of Strindberg's *Dance of Death* was seen at the Tricycle Theatre in 1998. He is married with five children.

Alasdair Gray was born in Glasgow in 1934. He trained at the art school there and has lived mainly by painting, writing and, since 1981, book design, mostly of his own books. His novels include *Lanark, 1982 Janine, The Fall of Kelvin Walker, Something Leather, McGrotty and Ludmilla, Poor Things* and *A History Maker.* His other books are, *Unlikely Stories Mostly, Lean Tales* (with Agnes Owens and James Kelman), *Ten Tales Tall and True* and *Mavis Belfrage and Four Shorter Tales*; a poetry collection, *Old Negatives*; a play, *Working Legs (for People Without Them),* and *Why Scots should Rule Scotland 1992* and *1997*; and *The Anthology of Prefaces.*

Lavinia Greenlaw was born in 1962 in London where she still lives. She has published two collections, *Night Photograph* (1993) and *A World Where News Travelled Slowly* (1997), the title poem of which won a 1997 Forward Prize.

Niall Griffiths was born in Liverpool and is now living in Wales. His first novel, *Grits,* was published by Jonathan Cape and he is now working on a second.

Abdulrazak Gurnah was born in 1948 in Zanzibar, Tanzania. He is the author of *Memory of Departure* (1987), *Pilgrims Way* (1988), *Dottie* (1990), *Paradise* (1994), which was shortlisted for the 1994 Booker Prize, and *Admiring Silence* (1996). He teaches literature at the University of Kent at Canterbury.

Michiel Heyns was educated at Trinity College, Cambridge and at Stellenbosch University, South Africa, where he is now Professor of English Literature, and is the author of *Expulsion and the Nineteenth Century Novel* (1994) as well as numerous critical articles. He has also written stage and radio plays and his adaptations of novels by Henry James and Elizabeth Gaskell have been broadcast. *The Children's Day* is his first novel; he is working on his second, *The Reluctant Passenger*.

Richard Holmes is the author of *Shelley: The Pursuit* (1974) for which he won the Somerset Maugham Award, *Footsteps: Adventures of a Romantic Biographer* (1985), *Coleridge: Early Visions* (1989 Whitbread Book of the Year Prize), *Dr Johnson & Mr Savage* (1993, James Tait Black Memorial Prize) and *Coleridge: Darker Reflections* (1998, Duff Cooper Prize). *Sidetracks* will be published in Spring 2000. He is a Fellow of the British Academy and was appointed an OBE in 1992.

Robert Irwin was formerly lecturer in the Department of Mediaeval History in the University of St Andrews. He has written six novels, *The Arabian Nightmare, The Limits of Vision, The Mysteries of Algiers, Exquisite Corpse, Prayer-Cushions of the Flesh* and *Satan Wants Me*. He is also the author of *The Middle East in the Middle Ages, The Arabian Nights: A Companion* and *Islamic Art*. His most recent publication is *Night and Horses and the Desert: an Anthology of Classical Arabic Literature* (1999).

Rosie Jackson lives in Somerset where she writes, paints and runs writing workshops. She is the author of four books: *Fantasy: The Literature of Subversion* (1981), a critical exploration of the fantastic from Gothic fiction onwards, *The Eye of the Buddha and Other Therapeutic Tales* (1991), a collection of short stories about conflicts in the therapy world; *Mothers Who Leave* (1994), a study of women without their children, and *Frieda Lawrence* (1994), a reappraisal of D. H. Lawrence's wife. Her first novel, *Love and Damnation*, a rewrite of the Faust myth, awaits a publisher and she is currently working on her second.

James Lasdun is a British writer living in the United States. He has published two collections of short stories, *The Silver Age* and *Three Evenings*, and two books of poetry, *A Jump Start* and *The Revenant*. With Michael Hofmann he co-edited the anthology *After Ovid: New Metamorphoses*. A selection of his stories, *The Siege*, was published in 1999. The title story was adapted by Bernardo Bertolucci for his film *Besieged*. His awards include the Dylan Thomas Award for short fiction, a Guggenheim Fellowship in poetry, and first prize in the 1999 *TLS*/Blackwells Poetry Competition.

Toby Litt. 1968. UK. ISBNs: 0749386274, 0099268396, 0241140692.

John Logan was born in Glasgow in 1967 and lives in Inverness. His stories have appeared in *Scratchings*, *Secrets of a View* (Inverness Writers), *Northwords* and *Chapman*. 'Tortoises and Bats' is a chapter from *Belly Tugs*, an unpublished novel.

Michael Longley was born in Belfast in 1939 and educated at the Royal Belfast Academical Institution and Trinity College, Dublin, where he read Classics. In 1991 he took early retirement from the Arts Council of Northern Ireland. His collections include *Gorse Fires*, which won the Whitbread Prize for Poetry, and *The Ghost Orchid*, which was shortlisted for the T. S. Eliot Prize. *Selected Poems* was published in 1998. He is a Fellow of the Royal Society of Literature and a member of Aosdána. He and his wife, the critic Edna Longley, live and work in Belfast.

James McGonigal was born in Dumfries in 1947. Since *Unidentified Flying Poems* (1980), his work in Scots and English has appeared in various Scottish and London-Scottish reviews and anthologies. A second collection, *Driven Home*, appeared in 1998. His critical work includes *Sons of Ezra: British Poets and Ezra Pound* (1995) with Michael Alexander, and a forthcoming study of Basil Bunting and

British Modernism, with Richard Price. A teacher of English, he now works in the Faculty of Education of Glasgow University.

Jamie McKendrick was born in Liverpool in 1955. His last book, *The Marble Fly*, won the Forward Poetry Prize. A selected poems, *Sky Nails*, will be published by Faber & Faber in 2000.

Duncan McLean was born in Aberdeenshire in 1964. He is the author of *Bucket of Tongues* (Somerset Maugham Prize 1993), *Blackden* and *Bunker Man*. His collection *Plays: One* is published by Methuen and he has also written a travel book, *Lone Star Swing* (1997). He lives in Orkney.

David McVey was born in 1961. He has published over 40 short stories, including 'Jairzinho and my Dad' in *Flamingo New Scottish Writing 1998*. His articles and book reviews have appeared in *The Independent, The Scotsman, New Statesman* and many other magazines and papers. He lives near his home town of Kirkintilloch and works at the University of Paisley, writing open and distance learning texts.

Stuart Marlow was born in Yorkshire. He trained as a stage manager and has worked as a documentary film director and has written for TV and radio as an educational journalist as well as running various theatre groups. He now lectures in English at Essen University, Germany, specialising in contemporary literature, drama and media studies and practical stage production. He has collaborated in the writing and production of *Transactions* (1980), with Amnesty International in Rotterdam), *Game Set and Match* (1982) and *Interrogating the Crucible* (1998).

Adrian Mathews was born in London in 1957. He is the author of a critical history of 19th-century English literature,

Romantics and Victorians (Paris, 1992) and two novels, (Fourth Estate, 1996) and *Vienna Blood* (Jonathan Cape, 1998). He lives in Paris with his wife and daughter.

Sarah May was born in Northumberland in 1972. She studied English Literature at London and Lancaster Universities and currently lives in London. Her first novel, *The Nudist Colony*, was published by Chatto & Windus in 1999.

Edwin Morgan was born in Glasgow in 1920 and served in the war in Egypt, Palestine and Lebanon. He taught English Literature at Glasgow University, resigning as titular Professor in 1980. His books include *Collected Poems* (1990), *Collected Translations* (1996), *Sweeping Out the Dark* (1994), *Virtual and Other Realities* (1997), and a Scots translation of Rostand's *Cyrano de Bergerac* (1992). He has recently collaborated with the jazz musician Tommy Smith on *Beasts of Scotland* (1996), *Planet Wave* (1997) and *Monte Cristo* (1998). His most recent collection, *Demon*, was published by Mariscat Press last year.

David Morley directs the Warwick Writing Programme in the Department of English and Comparative Literary Studies at the University of Warwick and was recently a visiting lecturer for various universities in China. His collections include *Releasing Stone, Mandelstam Variations, A Static Ballroom* and *A Belfast Kiss*. He has received a Gregory Award, an Arts Council Writers' Award and an Arts Council Fellowship in Writing at Warwick University. He co-edited *The New Poetry* for Bloodaxe and is editing a new anthology of international poetry for publication by Arc in 2000.

Lawrence Norfolk was born in 1963. He is the author of two novels, *Lemprière's Dictionary* (1991) and *The Pope's Rhinoceros* (1996). He lives in London.

Julia O'Faolain has published six novels and three collections of short stories, worked as a translator, contributed to numerous anthologies and co-edited a documentary history of women. Her best-known novel is *No Country for Young Men*, and her seventh, *Ercoli e il Guardiano Notturno*, came out in Italian in October 1999.

Ruth Padel won the 1996 National Poetry Competition and has published four collections of poetry, of which *Rembrandt Would Have Loved You*, a Poetry Book Society Choice, was shortlisted for the T. S. Eliot Prize. She writes the *Independent on Sunday*'s popular 'Sunday Poem' discussion column and reviews for many papers including the *New York Times*. *I'm a Man*, her study of rock music, Greek myth and modern maleness, is published by Faber in April 2000. She is a Fellow of the Royal Society of Literature.

Tim Parks was born in Manchester in 1954 and grew up in Blackpool and later London. After studying in the USA, he moved to Italy in 1980 where he has written nine novels (all of which are characterised by a great dramatic intensity springing out of the dangerous combination of intimacy and mutual incomprehension in which his characters appear to live) and four works of non-fiction. His novel, *Europa*, was shortlisted for the Booker Prize. He has also translated such writers as Calvino and Moravia from Italian, and lectures on literary translation in Milan.

Don Paterson was born in Dundee in 1963. *Nil Nil* (1993) won the Forward Prize for the Best First Collection, and *God's Gift to Women* (1997) the T. S. Eliot Prize and Geoffrey Faber Award. He works as a musician and is poetry editor for Picador Books. He lives in Edinburgh.

Glenn Patterson was born in Belfast in 1961. He is the author of four novels, *Burning Your Own*, *Fat Lad*, *Black Night at Big Thunder Mountain* and, most recently, *The International*.

Peter Porter published his revised *Collected Poems* (2 vols) on his 70th birthday in 1999. This publication capped 40 years of writing poetry, the last 48 of them while living in Britain, where he came from Australia in 1951. He has also published four volumes of verse with illustrations by the late Arthur Boyd, and is a freelance journalist and broadcaster, specialising in poetry and music.

Robin Robertson is from the northeast coast of Scotland. His first collection, *A Painted Field*, won the 1997 Forward Prize for the Best First Collection, the Aldeburgh Poetry Festival Prize and the Saltire Society Scottish First Book of the Year Award. His poetry has appeared in a number of anthologies, including *The Penguin Book of Poetry from Britain and Ireland since 1945* and *Penguin Modern Poets 13*.

Neil Rollinson was born in Yorkshire in 1960 and studied fine art at Newcastle. His first collection of poetry, *A Spillage of Mercury*, was published in 1996 and was a Poetry Book Society Recommendation. He lives in London and is currently finishing his second collection of poems.

Eva Salzman was born in New York and has published two poetry collections, *The English Earthquake* (1992) and *Bargain with the Watchman* (1997). She has published features, poetry and reviews in *The Times*, *Observer*, *Independent*, *Times Literary Supplement*, *New Yorker*, *London Magazine* and *Poetry Review* and was Writer-in-Residence at H. M. Prison Springhill for two years. She is currently Royal Literary Fund Fellow at Ruskin College, Oxford, and is working on an opera Libretto.

Derek Sellen is Head of English at an international sixth-form college in Canterbury. His work has been published in various magazines and anthologies including *The Sunday Telegraph*, *Poetry Review*, *PEN New Poetry* and *Agenda*. His poems have won prizes in a number of competitions including the National Poetry Competition, the Cheltenham Festival Competition and Rhyme International. He also writes plays, short stories and books for foreign students. These poems are part of an unfinished sequence of sea poems which began with a reading on the beach at the Old Neptune, Whitstable.

Neil Stewart was born in 1978 and is reading for a degree in English Literature at the University of Glasgow. 'People We Want' is his first published work and is taken from a novel in progress, *There's Someone Close Behind You*.

Matthew Sweeney was born in Donegal, Ireland, in 1952. His poetry collections include *The Bridal Suite* (1997), and *A Smell of Fish*, published in 2000. A selection of his work is in *Penguin Modern Poets 12* (1997). He won an Arts Council of England Writers' Award in 1999.

Adam Thorpe was born in Paris in 1956 and lives in France. He has published three volumes of poetry, the most recent being *From the Neanderthal* (1999), and three novels, *Ulverton* (1992), *Still* (1995) and *Pieces of Light* (1998). His first volume of short stories, *Shifts*, appeared in January 2000. He has written several plays for BBC Radio and a stage play.

Jonathan Treitel's stories have appeared in *New Writing 4* and *New Writing 8* and in a number of other magazines and anthologies. He is putting together a book-length collection of his stories, and writing a novel and screenplay. He has lived in Japan and Wyoming, and is currently in Jerusalem, making fictions.

Rose Tremain's work has been shortlisted for the Booker Prize and she has won the James Tait Black Memorial Prize, the Prix Fémina Etranger, the *Sunday Express* Book of the Year, the Dylan Thomas Short Story Award, a Giles Cooper Award for a radio play and the Angel Literary Award. Her books have been translated into fourteen languages. Her most recent novel, *Music & Silence*, was published last year.

Vivienne Vermes is a writer, actress and broadcaster who has lived in Paris for 20 years. Her published work includes ten non-fiction volumes and numerous poems and short stories. In 1997 she won the Piccadilly Poets' competition. She spends most of her time travelling between England, France and elsewhere and is now working on her first novel.

Alan Warner grew up near Oban in Scotland and lives in Ireland. His first novel, *Morvern Callar* (1995) won a Somerset Maugham award. *These Demented Lands* (1997) won an Encore Award and *The Sopranos* (1998) won the Saltire Prize.

Marc Weinberg is 25 years old and was born in South Africa. He has a Master's degree in Renaissance Drama from Oxford and has just completed an MA in Creative Writing at Johns Hopkins University where he was a fellow in the Writing Seminars. He is working on a novel and a short story collection and lives currently in Baltimore.

Hamish Whyte was born in Renfrewshire in 1947 and lives in Glasgow. His latest volume of poetry is *Christmasses* (1998). He has edited several anthologies, including *The Scottish Cat* (1987), *Mungo's Tongues: Glasgow Poems 1630–1990* and *An Arran Anthology* (1997). He runs the Mariscat Press and is currently translating Martial XIII and XIV and is working with James McGonigal on a poetry project, *virtual memories*.

Jonathan Wilson was born in London in 1950 and studied at Essex University, St Catherine's College, Oxford, and the Hebrew University of Jerusalem. He has published a novel, *The Hiding Room*, a collection of short stories, *Schoom*, and two critical studies of Saul Bellow. His short fiction has appeared in numerous journals and magazines, including the *New Yorker*, for whom he also writes non-fiction, and has been anthologised in *Best Short Stories* and elsewhere. He has just completed a new collection of short stories, *Who Let the Dogs Out? Stories of Men in Trouble*, and is working on a novel and a memoir, *NW10*. He is chair of the English Department at Tufts University.